The Royal

1794 - 1994

The Royal

THE HISTORY OF THE GLASGOW ROYAL INFIRMARY
1794-1994

by

Jacqueline Jenkinson

Michael Moss

&

Iain Russell

Published by the Bicentenary Committee on behalf of
Glasgow Royal Infirmary NHS Trust

© Jacqueline Lucille Mary Jenkinson 1994
Michael Stanley Moss 1994
Iain Forbes Russell 1994

A catalogue record for this book is
available from the British Library

ISBN 08526 14 330

Printed and bound in Great Britain by HarperCollinsManufacturing, Glasgow

Designed by Medical Illustration Services,
Glasgow Royal Infirmary University NHS Trust

CONTENTS

AT THE GATE

The Royal Infirmary was founded on need. The need was for Glasgow to provide a hospital to care for its burgeoning population drawn to Glasgow by the expanding trade of the Industrial Revolution. Church, Town and University recognised the problem and worked closely together to find the solution. The generosity of public minded citizens of all backgrounds enabled the entire development of the infirmary to be funded by charitable donations.

Over the past 200 years the Royal Infirmary has had as its main function the care of the health needs of the citizens of Glasgow, mainly, but by no means exclusively, from the East End.

Other important functions have developed. These have occurred both on and off the main hospital site. The new geriatric assessment unit in the main hospital is an indication of how adaptation of an older building can be done successfully. Specialist services have become a feature of the hospital, offering expert advice to patients from West Central Scotland and elsewhere. Cardiology and cardiac surgery, nephrology, gastro-enterology, endocrinology are only a few examples of expanding departments and interests. The hospital has always had close links with the University in terms of teaching and research. Nowadays we have links with the University of Glasgow, University of Strathclyde and most recently the Caledonian University. Training of nurses, technicians and professions allied to medicine takes place alongside the teaching and training of the next generation of doctors.

The Royal Infirmary has always had a history of innovative research. Lister, Macewen and Macintyre are famous names from the past, but the Royal does not intend to rest on its laurels. The splendid facilities of the Queen Elizabeth building offer every opportunity for advance.

This book describes the ups and downs of the Royal Infirmary but progress has always been made.

We now face a new challenge. Trust status is upon us. The reorganisation of hospital services in Glasgow should soon move apace. We are ready for these challenges.

A Ross Lorimer
Consultant Physician and Cardiologist
Chairman Bicentennial Committee

PROLOGUE AND ACKNOWLEDGEMENTS

When we were invited to write the history of the Glasgow Royal Infirmary, we were asked to address a wide audience comprising 'everyone with an interest in the healing arts'. Clearly, in a group so diverse as to include doctors and nurses, administrators and auxiliary staff, and medical historians and former patients, there are many specialist interests and many different expectations from a hospital history. For this reason, we have attempted to include discussion only of those personalities, events and issues which we considered to be central to our story: the medical, social and administrative history of the infirmary. Readers who wish to discover more and in greater detail of some aspect of the hospital's history will, we hope, be able to find references in the footnotes which will help them in their own research. We are only too aware that there are many themes still to be explored in the hospital's extensive records held in the Greater Glasgow Health Board Archive.

During the course of our research we have received help from many people at the Royal, particularly the members of the bicentennial committee chaired by Professor Ross Lorimer, the Trust's Medical Executive. We thank William McIlvaney for permission to quote from *The Papers of Tony Veitch* in Chapter 7, Adam McNaughton for permission to quote from his 'Jelly Piece Song' on page 239, and the estate of the late Matt McGinn to reproduce 'Big Willie's Blues' on page 239. We owe special debts of gratitude to Bill Paterson, Jean MacDonald and Lindsay MacLeod of Medical Illustrations Services who have been responsible for designing the book and seeing it through the press. We would like to thank the staff of the Glasgow Room of the Mitchell Library and Glasgow University Library, especially its Special Collections Department, for their help. Throughout, Alistair Tough, the Archivist to the Greater Glasgow Health Board, has acted as physician, surgeon, nurse and porter to the project, advising on how to proceed, cheerfully moving records for us, counselling us in despair, and assiduously reading and correcting drafts. Last, but definitely not least, we thank Rita Hemphill of the University Archives, who has tirelessly reworked draft after draft of the manuscript.

Jacqueline Jenkinson
Michael Moss
Iain Russell   *Gilmorehill 1994*

1 BLESSING UPON
THE FOUNDATION, 1794–1815

This day being appointed for laying the foundation stone of the Glasgow Infirmary - at noon the Lord Provost, Magistrates, and council, preceded by their proper offices - the Principal and Professors of the University, in their Gowns, and with their Mace carried before them - the Faculty of Physicians and Surgeons [of Glasgow] - the Dean of Guild and Council of the Merchants House - the Deacon Convener and Trades House - the Mason Lodges of this city - assembled in St. Andrew's Church... Immediately after divine service they proceeded, three by three in a rank, along the Saltmarket and High Street, the Band of Music playing the King's Anthem.[1]

Glasgow Advertiser, 14-18 May 1792, p.326

ORIGINS OF THE INFIRMARY

In August 1791 the committee behind the infirmary project announced their intentions:

> That an Infirmary for the Relief of the Indigent Persons labouring under Poverty and Disease has long been wanted in the City of Glasgow and in the adjoining counties of Scotland, and it is become more necessary at present than at any former period on account of the prosperous state of Manufactures in Glasgow, and its neighbourhood, and the increased population of those Classes of Manufacture and labours of every kind, who are most likely to require charitable assistance.

This passage, which makes clear the need for public hospital provision in the city, appeared in the application for a Royal Charter to set the seal of prestige on the plans for the construction of an infirmary for Glasgow.

The impulse for the creation of the infirmary is identified with the name of George Jardine, lecturer, later Professor, of Logic at the University of Glasgow, who was elected Secretary of the original committee of subscribers, an office he held periodically for many years.[2] He,

11

and Alexander Stevenson, Professor of Medicine, were prime movers and among the first financial contributors to the scheme. The University of Glasgow as an institution was an early and strong advocate of the Royal. Six months after the first subscribers' meeting in June 1787, the University's support for the planned infirmary for the city was tangibly demonstrated by the vote of a subscription of £500 towards the project by the medical members of the University.[3]

Within the space of five years the initial suggestion for an infirmary had reached fruition. At the laying of the foundation stone in May 1792 two glass containers were inserted in the foundations to commemorate the occasion, in which were placed local newspapers from the day, coins of the period, a list of the prominent persons who attended the ceremony, a copy of the infirmary's Royal Charter, and samples of Glasgow's muslin manufactures. The Lord Provost laid the foundation stone itself, saying:

> May the Grand Architect of the Universe grant a blessing upon the foundation stone we have now laid and may he enable us to raise a superstructure upon it which, to the later ages shall prove a House of Refuge, and of consolation to the diseased poor of this City and their neighbourhood.

A little over two and half years later the building, financed by public and institutional subscription, was completed and partially furnished, and its water supply secured. The infirmary was formally opened on 8 December 1794 and had treated fifteen patients by the end of the year.

THE VOLUNTARY HOSPITAL MOVEMENT

But why build an infirmary in Glasgow at all? And why make it a voluntary institution? The first 'hospitals' in Britain were hostels for travellers and pilgrims in the Middle Ages rather than institutions for the sick. However, medieval medical treatment emphasised the benefits of rest, good diet and the dressing of sores, and these were in keeping with the idea of care in the hostels. The dual role of 'hospitals' as hostels and as institutions for the care of the sick evolved. After the Reformation and the closure of hospitals run by religious orders, charitable 'hospitals' reliant on endowments for financial support were established, but the main change in institutional medical provision in Britain occurred in the eighteenth century with the development of voluntary hospitals.

Voluntary hospitals were dependent, as the name suggests, on voluntary subscriptions for financial support; subscribers, in conjunction with permanent officials, took care of the administration; medical and surgical staff held honorary positions, receiving no salary, but usually having access to wealthy subscribers; and patients were not required to pay fees. The rationale behind this new attitude to health care provision lay in the growing concern in mercantilist circles that the prosperity of the nation was dependent upon the size and health of the population. This was linked to a reawakening of philanthropic tendencies and to a feeling that wealthy individuals seen to be giving in a public way (since lists of subscribers were invariably published) were salving their consciences by contributing to the welfare of the community. Associating one's name with local nobility also enhanced personal social prestige.[4]

Scotland was not slow to take up the idea of voluntary establishments for the care of the sick. In 1729 the first such, the Royal Infirmary of Edinburgh, was established. This was followed by Aberdeen Royal Infirmary in 1742. Dumfries and Galloway Royal Infirmary came next in 1778, followed by the Montrose Royal Infirmary and Dispensary in 1782, then Glasgow Royal Infirmary in 1794. The final Scottish infirmary to be founded in the eighteenth century was Dundee Royal Infirmary opened in 1798. Other Scottish infirmaries opened at a later date were the Northern Infirmary in Inverness in 1804, Paisley Infirmary (later renamed Royal Alexandra Infirmary) in 1805, Greenock Infirmary in 1809, the County and City of Perth Royal Infirmary in 1838 and Stirling Royal Infirmary in 1874.[5]

THE TOWN'S HOSPITAL INFIRMARY

Prior to the opening of Glasgow Royal Infirmary, institutional medical provision in the city lay chiefly in the form of the Town's Hospital. The Town's Hospital, situated close to the River Clyde, just off Stockwell Street, was opened in 1733, to provide indoor relief for the destitute poor under a workhouse system (whereby able-bodied paupers undertook unpaid labour in return for food and accommodation), with running costs provided by the parish authorities and through individual donations. Medical assistance was provided by an attending physician and surgeon, appointed in rotation from the ranks of the Faculty of Physicians and Surgeons of Glasgow[6] (which was founded in 1599 and was the licensing

13

authority for all medical practitioners in the west of Scotland). In 1738 the decision was taken by the directors to build an infirmary extension onto the hospital, funded by money raised by public subscription.[7] The infirmary was constructed to a design devised by the Faculty. The infirmary at the Town's Hospital was opened in 1740 and from the outset was accessible to students for clinical instruction as laid down in the rules approved by the Directors in August of that year:

> 6th. That all surgeons apprentices in the city and students of medicine in the City or University have access to the Infirmary and the Houses of Visiting and Dressing upon paying for the Benefit of the Hospital as follows. Viz the students of medicine who are strangers and whose parents do not reside in and are not freemen of the city half a guinea yearly and every surgeon's apprentice of the city half a guinea for his whole time and all students of medicine who are Freemens' sons and reside in the city half a guinea to be reckoned in the class of the apprentices.[8]

Clinical teaching was continued for at least two years in the infirmary. In 1742 the free admission of the infirmary surgeons' apprentices for clinical instruction caused consternation among other surgeons whose apprentices had to continue to pay for the privilege.

> The Directors upon a reference from the weekly committee do enact that the apprentices of the hospital surgeons are to pay for their admissions to operations in the same manner as the prentices of other surgeons pay who are not the hospital's surgeon.[9]

One reason suggested for the alleged absence of clinical instruction in the Town's Hospital[10] beyond the 1740s lay in the apparent lack of systematic medical teaching at the University of Glasgow and the subsequent small size of the medical school of the University for much of the eighteenth century.[11] On the contrary, there is no clear evidence on the nature of medical teaching at the University at this time, yet what is unequivocal is that medical teaching was offered at the Town's Hospital infirmary in the mid eighteenth century, both to medical students of the University and apprentices attached to surgeons in the city.

The close proximity of the Town's Hospital to the Clyde meant there was an ever-present fear of flooding in the vicinity. At the time of its extension in 1766 the Town's Hospital contained no more than twenty beds for the treatment of the sick 'deserving' poor, that is, individuals in poverty who were deemed of high moral standing, not homeless vagabonds. Eight of the beds were set aside for admissions by the physician and surgeon, possibly for emergencies, or to allow the opportunity of clinical teaching in the hospital. There is no further information on this matter in the surviving Director's minute books which contain little reference to the administration of the infirmary or to medical appointments in the years between 1756 and 1786. It is likely that such matters were discussed elsewhere, perhaps in the reports of the weekly committee of the Town's Hospital, but these have been lost. This assumption is supported by the reference in 1786, to the appointment of Robert Cleghorn as physician with leave to give a course of clinical lectures in the infirmary:

> The meeting [of Directors] having taken into consideration the recommendation of the weekly committee of Doctor Robert Cleghorn as physician in ordinary to the House, appoint him as such on the conditions mentioned in the minutes of said committee, (hereby referred to) with the liberty of lecturing in a room in the house as therein stated.[12]

Cleghorn was reappointed on the same terms as physician-lecturer at the Town's Hospital for a further three years.[13] Cleghorn graduated MD at the University of Edinburgh in 1783 and became a member of the Faculty of Physicians and Surgeons of Glasgow in 1786. He lectured on Materia Medica (that is, chemical and medical pharmacy, including sources, preparation and uses of drugs and potions) at the University of Glasgow from 1788 to 1791 and on Chemistry from 1791 to 1818. In 1794 Cleghorn became one of the first two physicians appointed to Glasgow Royal Infirmary.[14]

THE ROYAL INFIRMARY OF EDINBURGH

In the Royal Infirmary of Edinburgh, set up in 1729, the number of beds initially was no larger than the Glasgow's Town's Hospital infirmary. Only four to six patients could be admitted at any given time and thirty-five patients in total were treated in its first year of operation.[15] The infirmary gradually expanded the number of beds available after reconstruction on a new site, and in 1760, 840 patients were admitted to the infirmary.[16]

The infirmary immediately attracted medical students, on a scale exceeding that of Glasgow's Town's Hospital infirmary, drawing upon a large medical student community in the city. From the second half of the eighteenth century the expansion of the medical school in Edinburgh made the provision of clinical instruction through the sale of admission tickets to students and surgeons' apprentices one of the main sources of income for the expanding infirmary. By the final decade of the eighteenth century (when medical schools in continental Europe were closed to United Kingdom students due to the French Revolutionary Wars), such sales accounted for 25 per cent of the infirmary's total income.[17] With this figure, the link between the development of the infirmary in Edinburgh and the success of the University's medical school seems obvious, but the situation in Glasgow was somewhat different.

THE ORIGINS OF THE ROYAL

In 1787, when the initial plans were laid for the construction of an infirmary, Glasgow was a city on the brink of dramatic change. The city was about to witness a major expansion in its population. As late as 1712 the burgh had a population of only 14,000, rising to 43,000 in 1780. Thereafter numbers rose speedily—by the first national census in 1801 this had risen to 84,000 due in part to the development of trading links with the American colonies. The figure topped 100,000 for the first time in the 1811 census by which time Glasgow's population was over 110,000.

The attraction of the city to businessmen, industrialists and the working classes lay in the growth and development of new industries, the potential of which began to transform Glasgow. The economic structure of the city was gradually shifting as the wealth of Glasgow moved away from a concentration on the tobacco trade, (a consequence of British defeat in the American War of Independence, 1776–83), and towards new industries such as cotton production and iron smelting. Glasgow was also expanding its overseas trading links in this period with the project to deepen the Clyde basin to allow ships access to the heart of the city, and the subsequent development of the Broomielaw, just down the river from the Town's Hospital, as a thriving port area.[18] This combination of factors also made Glasgow attractive to investors and the city became a leading financial centre in this period.[19]

One consequence of the end of Glasgow's dominance as the tobacco trading centre of the world was an attempt to reinforce civic pride, and the plan to erect an infirmary for the city was an example of this. Many of the tobacco merchant families became subscribers to the new public institution. Of twenty leading importers of tobacco into Glasgow noted in 1783, eight were listed among the contributors to the funds of Glasgow Royal Infirmary in its first annual report. Two of these, Henry Glassford and Henry Riddell, served as managers of the infirmary.[20] Civic involvement in the plan to build an infirmary was demonstrated by a financial commitment in the shape of a £500 donation to the building costs and in the support of various city office-bearers, including representatives of the merchant and trade guilds. The University of Glasgow was permanently represented on the Board of Managers by the Principal of the University and the Professors of Anatomy and of Medicine. The President of the Faculty of Physicians and Surgeons of Glasgow was also a permanent member of the Board.

Late eighteenth-century Glasgow also played host to a substantial military garrison at a time when the nation was plunged into a period of warfare spanning twenty-two years in the French Revolutionary Wars. In 1794 the city raised four Volunteer Corps containing over 1,000 men. A further four corps were raised in 1797. In 1803, after the failure of the Peace of Amiens, signed the previous year, nine corps were raised in Glasgow, numbering 8,350 local volunteers. After 1808, when Volunteer Corps were replaced by local militia, five regiments amounting to 3,500 men were formed in the city. The militia regiments were not disbanded until the peace settlement achieved by the Second Treaty of Paris was signed in November 1815 after the defeat of the French at Waterloo. In 1795 the Glasgow barracks were opened in the Gallowgate in the east end of the city in response to the demands of quartering thousands of troops in the city. Designed to house troops of the line, the barracks contained accommodation for over 1,000 men plus additional accommodation for officers, numerous kitchens, a canteen and a magazine for arms.[21] The barracks later opened its own infirmary, but for many of these years of prolonged warfare a military garrison on its doorstep had a marked impact on the nature of admissions to the Royal.

THE CONSTRUCTION OF THE INFIRMARY

The first minuted meeting of subscribers in support of the scheme to build an infirmary in Glasgow took place on 5 June 1787. It was attended by twenty-two supporters of the plan and included representatives from the town council, business and the University, as well as members of local trades' organisations, among them the Journeymen Printers, the Tobacco Spinners and the Incorporation of Weavers.

> The meeting unanimously resolve to appoint a committee of their number to carry on with all expedition, the subscription for the Glasgow Infirmary and to make application to such persons and bodies of men as may be likely to take an interest in this humane and charitable scheme. It is also recommended to the said committee to turn their thoughts on a proper situation and plan for the building of said Infirmary, and upon such Regulations as may be necessary towards the establishment and administration of the said charity and to report to a General Meeting of the Subscribers to be called by them when they shall judge it necessary...

Given the range of local interests represented at the initial meeting, it is likely that this formal minuted entry was preceded by informal discussions among the leading figures of the city on the necessity of establishing an infirmary, and the degree of organisation of the subscribers is substantiated by the statement that the minutes of the first meeting should be published in the Glasgow press to attract attention and further subscriptions from the local community.

> Glasgow 5th June. At a meeting of the Subscribers for ERECTING an INFIRMARY at Glasgow, for the West of Scotland, held this day in the Tontine Tavern, the Lord Provost of Glasgow, was elected Preses, and Professor Jardine, Clerk.

> The meeting unanimously resolved to appoint a committee of their number to carry on, with all expedition, the Subscription for the Infirmary, and in their name, to make application to such persons and bodies of men as may be likely to take an interest in this humane and charitable scheme... The meeting order this Minute to be published in the Glasgow Newspapers. Signed, in the name of the Meeting and by their appointment, by JOHN RIDDELL.[22]

The next stage in the process of constructing an infirmary for the city was to select an appropriate location, and although several were considered, the committee appointed to purchase the land favoured the site of the former Archbishop's Castle adjacent to the city's cathedral and close to the original location of the University of Glasgow. The site chosen had been the property of the Crown since the Reformation, administered by the Earl of Dundonald. Although the land was readily released by the Earl, the process of investigating the suitability of the site in terms of water supply and of obtaining permission from the Exchequer for the land to be made over from the Earl to the subscribers took many months. It was not until June 1789 that the Archbishop's Castle site was finally approved of by a meeting of subscribers, when it was established that the location was sufficiently spacious to house an infirmary and that the site was well provided with water since there were two wells in the area, and it was near the Molendinar Burn and the Monklands Canal. It was also felt that the property could be obtained for a reasonable sum. There is no mention of a figure paid by the Royal's managers for the land, although in both minutes and early press reports there is reference to saving over £1,000 by building on the Crown site.

The next step was to select an architect. In October 1790 William Blackburn RA, a London architect, was approached by a sub-committee of the subscribers to design plans for an infirmary. Blackburn was a prominent architect of the period, who specialised in the construction of prisons, although he also designed private houses. He died in Preston in October 1790 shortly after he was commissioned by the Society of Friends of the Infirmary of Glasgow. Blackburn's death occurred as he was travelling to Glasgow for discussions with civic leaders on a planned gaol for the city.[23] After Blackburn's death and the refusal of his successor in practice to act in the planning of the building the managers looked elsewhere. Robert Adam, who was in Glasgow at the time overseeing the construction of the Trades House in Glassford Street, was approached in July 1791 and asked to design a three storey building with basement and space for 200 beds. Adam, born in Kirkcaldy in 1728 and educated at the University of Edinburgh, set up as an architect in London and served as Architect to the Queen during 1762–8, a post he resigned in order to stand successfully for Parliament for the seat of Kinross-shire. Robert and his brother James made their names as architects in the classic tradition.

Robert Adam designed stately homes including Luton House in Bedfordshire and Keddlestone in Derbyshire. He also built Register House in Edinburgh and the Admiralty in Whitehall.

Meanwhile negotiations for permission to build on the recently secured site continued with the Exchequer in London, and an approach was made to the Crown for a Royal Charter of perpetual succession for the infirmary when it was built. A Royal Charter converted the infirmary to corporate status and also enhanced the prestige of the institution, improving its public profile and attracting further financial support. The government of the institution, which was modelled on that of the Royal Infirmary of Edinburgh, was to be by a Board of Managers numbering twenty-five representatives of civic, political and institutional life in the city.[24] The petition for a Royal Charter stressed the need for a voluntary medical establishment in an expanding and rapidly industrialising city.

As the Charter was placed before the Lord Advocate for Scotland, Robert Adam's proposed design was considered by the committee of subscribers. His original proposals were rejected on the grounds of the great expense involved in their construction, £8,726, but his amended plan for a 'plain building' at a cost of £7,185 was accepted by the committee. By the end of December 1791 estimates from tradespeople were invited for the construction of the building and renewed efforts were made to attract additional funds to meet the building costs by appealing for subscriptions from magistrates and prominent people of all the towns in the West of Scotland.

In February 1792 the infirmary received its Royal Charter, and the plans for the construction of the building continued, despite the death of Robert Adam in March of that year. James Adam, although declining the building contract, agreed to oversee the construction of the infirmary according to his brother's plans with an employee of his firm permanently on site during the period of construction, the building work to be under-taken by the firm of Morrison and Burns at an estimated cost of £7,900. The ceremony to lay the foundation stone of the Royal in May 1792 following a procession of city notables, included a high profile presence of the city's Masonic lodges, who it is safe to assume were prominent early supporters of the infirmary.

> The Lord Provost, assisted by the Masters and Wardens of the several lodges, who left their places for that purpose, together

20

with James Adam Esquire, Architect, and Messrs Morrison and Burns, the contractors, proceeded to place the Inscription, coins, writings etc in the stone, according to the ceremonies of Masonry. When this was finished, the Masters and Wardens of the several Lodges returned to their places, and the Band of Music struck up 'On, on my dear Brethren' ... The whole company were dressed in black, and made a very fine appearance.

The greatest concourse of people assembled to witness the procession ever remembered upon any occasion whatever in this city.

After this impressive beginning the construction proceeded apace, and the infirmary was formally opened for the treatment of patients on 8 December 1794.

The Royal Infirmary in this city, a building much admired both for the excellence of its situation and the taste discovered in the plan and execution, was opened on Wednesday last for the reception of patients.[25]

THE FIRST SUBSCRIBERS

The social background of the early supporters of the plans for an infirmary consisted of a cross-section of the Glasgow elite (although lower-income citizens were represented in terms of their subscriptions and subsequent votes for managers at the annual meeting of the General Court of Contributors). Among the contributors to the Royal were gentry, merchants and industrialists, civic leaders, the medical profession and university representatives. The Duke of Argyll, a powerful figure in local and national politics, was one of the earliest subscribers to recommend a patient to the infirmary. Apart from the City of Glasgow itself, which gave £500 towards construction costs, leading businessmen were also closely involved, including David Dale,[26] merchant, banker, cotton manufacturer and philanthropist, and Archibald Speirs, tobacco merchant, industrialist and landowner.[27] Dale, one of the original managers, contributed £200 and Speirs £100 to the costs of the infirmary. A further £50 was contributed by the 'work people of the Cotton Mills near Lanark, under the name of the Benevolent Society there'. Such provision for illness and injury in the workplace through subscription to the infir-

21

mary was increasingly in evidence in the nineteenth century. The mills at New Lanark owned by David Dale were some of the largest and most advanced of their kind in the world. In 1800 Robert Owen, the social reformer, assumed the management of the New Lanark mills from Dale, and he too became a manager of the infirmary in 1803 and again in 1806.

From such early involvement the number of merchants and manufacturers who supported the Royal financially rose in the early part of the nineteenth century. The 1804 annual report listed 327 subscribers. Of those named, 137 (42 per cent) were listed with occupation or professional title. Although not a comprehensive list, this sample indicates the range of subscribers making donations to the infirmary at this time. Of the 137 subscribers whose title or occupation was listed in the annual report, thirty-nine (28 per cent) were given as merchants; twenty-six (19 per cent) were involved in trades of some description (for example brewing and watchmaking); and sixteen (12 per cent) were given as manufacturers. Only eight subscribers (6 per cent) were medical men, while fifteen (11 per cent) were employed in the legal profession as 'writers' (solicitors). Eight subscriptions (6 per cent) were received from religious sources: five from individual ministers and three from congregations or their representatives; the managers of the Gaelic Chapel, Glasgow; the Gorbals Kirk Session; and the Methodist Congregation, Glasgow, each donating five guineas.

Glasgow, 10th. May, 1794.

We, the Subscribers, hereby promise to pay to Mr. Archibald Grahame, Cashier of the Thistle Bank in Glasgow, the Sums annexed to our respective Names, for the purpose of establishing an Annual Fund for the support of the Glasgow Royal Infirmary. The Annual Subscriptions to commence from the 1st. of January, 1795.

The first subscribers' pledge made to the Royal, 1794

John Riddell, the Lord Provost of Glasgow at the time the infirmary was first proposed in 1787, and a prominent merchant in the tobacco trade,[28] presided over the initial meetings of subscribers, and under the terms of

the Royal Charter subsequent Lord Provosts became permanent repre-
sentatives on the governing Board of Management of the infirmary.
Other civic leaders permanently represented were the Dean of Guild, as
head of the Merchants' House, and the Deacon Convener of the Trades'
House, along with the Member of Parliament for Glasgow district of
Burghs, as the Glasgow seat was known in the late eighteenth century.

Medical professional involvement in the plans for erecting an infirmary to serve the needs of the local community came in the shape of
members of the Faculty of Physicians and Surgeons of Glasgow and of the
University's medical school. Aside from the permanent presence of
the President of the Faculty of Physicians and Surgeons of Glasgow, and
the Professors of Anatomy and Medicine in the University, there were
seventeen other members of the Board. Ten of the members were elected
annually by the General Court which was open to all individual subscribers who made donations of two guineas or more, and representatives
of institutions who donated five guineas or more. Three other Board
members were nominees of the Faculty, and one member each was
nominated by the Merchants' House, the Trades' House of Glasgow and
the Church of Scotland ministers in the city. In addition, the Principal of
the University was a perpetual member on the Board of Managers.

The University's decision to support the construction of an infirmary
by the donation of £500 in December 1794[29] came at a time when the
medical professors were anxious to increase its standing as a centre of
medical education. Of 112 medical doctorate degrees awarded by the
medical school in the last two decades of the eighteenth century, fifty-
seven, (51 per cent) were awarded in the years 1783–7. Support among
the teaching staff of the University for the building of a hospital in
Glasgow also reflected the success of the Edinburgh medical school which
coincided with access to the wards of the Royal Infirmary of Edinburgh
for clinical teaching purposes.[30]

Representatives of local church parishes were among the original subscribers to Glasgow Royal Infirmary and there were a number of
subsequent subscriptions from individual parishes, both established and
non-established, in the first years of the infirmary's existence. There were
also general appeals to the Glasgow and West of Scotland synods to hold
collections periodically to boost the infirmary's funds: for example, in
1802 arrangements were made to take up collections in parishes of 'the

different churches and religious congregations in the city' in return for the rights of recommendation of patients to the infirmary. The degree of funding received from individual Kirk Sessions was formally recognised in 1806 when the Board of Managers decided to allow each of the ministers of the Church of Scotland in Glasgow to nominate two patients per year for admission to the infirmary. In 1808 it was recommended that the general church collection in aid of infirmary funds which had been taken up in 1802 become a regular occurrence. This step once taken resulted in a substantial increase in the level of subscriptions to the infirmary. The income immediately rose from £2,723 in 1808 to £4,228 in 1809, £926.17s.10d. of which came from collections from parishes and individual congregations. Subsequently annual collections were discontinued and the practice became one of the infirmary managers approaching the local Kirk Sessions for collections to boost hospital funds in times of special need, for example during epidemics in the city.

ADMINISTRATION OF THE INFIRMARY

The infirmary was administered by the twenty-five-strong Board of Managers which met quarterly, and by the general court which convened at the annual meeting, but which as a body had the power to make policy, even if it ran counter to the proposals of the Board. The Board of Managers was sub-divided into numerous committees, chosen by ballot. These included a weekly committee which met to consider day-to-day matters in the running of the infirmary such as patient admissions, and which incorporated the medical staff. Other committees were the accounts, subscriptions, provisions, and medical (supplies) committees.

The Faculty of Physicians and Surgeons of Glasgow controlled medical appointments to the infirmary for almost a century, and although staff members were sometimes chosen from the ranks of the medical school at the University of Glasgow, the responsibility for clinical teaching in the infirmary lay with the Faculty.

THE PATIENTS

From the first, patients relied on a subscriber's line for admission except in cases of emergency.

1. No patient, excepting in cases which do not admit of delay,

24

shall be admitted into the Infirmary without the consent of a committee to be appointed for that purpose, of which committee the attending Physicians and Surgeons shall always be members.

2. That Patients are to be admitted by the recommendation of contributors...

A minimum single contribution of £10 or an annual subscription of one guinea was required before the donor was allowed to recommend one patient a year to the infirmary. Higher levels of contributions enabled the subscriber or contributing institution to recommend more patients, up to a maximum of four a year, with no more than two patients to be recommended for admission at the same time.

The system of subscribers' recommendation placed an immediate hurdle in the path of those seeking admission to the infirmary. Further regulations excluded those deemed incurable, and women with young children were not admitted to the infirmary unless prior provision for the children's removal was made in the event of the mother's death. No infants were to be admitted as patients.

Fifteen patients were admitted to the Royal in December 1794. In contrast to the future intake of the infirmary, twice as many female as male patients were admitted in this first month of operation (ten females to five males). This imbalance was soon reversed. Of the first 100 admissions sixty-four were male and thirty-six female. The occupations of half of the female patients in December 1794 were listed in the admissions register; four were servants, and the other was listed as a 'widow'. Of the five male patients, two were labourers, two soldiers, and one was a servant. The range of occupations among the first 100 patients admitted to the infirmary confirms labourers (seven), soldiers (eight), weavers (fourteen) and servants (fifteen), as among the common occupations held by those first individuals admitted to the infirmary. No occupations were given for twenty-four patients.

The subscribers who recommended patients to the infirmary were listed in the records, presumably to prevent subscribers recommending more patients than they were entitled to by size of donation. Among the earliest recommenders were Professor Jardine, James Jeffray, Professor of Anatomy at the University, and John Stirling, son of William Stirling, one of the original managers of the infirmary, and owner of the large cloth printing and bleaching firm William Stirling and Sons, whose original financial success lay in the Atlantic tobacco trade.[31] One patient, John Hamilton, a soldier, was recommended by a female subscriber, Miss Aitchison, the only case of a female subscriber recommending a patient in the first 100 admissions.

The illnesses suffered by the first patients admitted to the infirmary ranged from leg and hand ulcers, to rheumatism (two cases), palsy, breast cancer and diabetes. Of the first 100 admissions, ulcers, commonly a result of poor diet, accounted for twenty-nine cases, there were seven cases of 'consumption' (tuberculosis), six of cancer, six of 'fever', six fractures, five cases of palsy and five of venereal diseases, categorised as 'pox' in the admissions register. Among these patients, fifty-eight were dismissed as 'cured', eighteen were released at their own request, thirteen were 'relieved', two others were released for 'irregular behaviour', and nine patients died. Two of the deaths occurred among the first fifteen admissions, caused by cancerous sores in one case, and a pneumonic complaint in the other.

The parish of birth was also often listed in the admission register of patients. Not surprisingly, forty-eight of the first one hundred patients admitted listed Glasgow as their home parish. More specifically, ten others were listed for the Barony parish of Glasgow, the parish in which the infirmary was located. Six patients gave Paisley as their parish, while twenty-four others gave parishes from across Scotland, including Inverness and Callander. No parishes were given for fourteen patients.

After the slow start in December 1794 numbers of patients admitted rose gradually in the first year and by the end of 1795, 276 patients had been admitted to the hospital. Also during this period over 3,000 outpatients were seen by the medical staff. The numbers of patients admitted to the infirmary rose steadily in the first decade of the nineteenth century, averaging 753 patients per year. By the end of 1811, almost 12,000 patients had been admitted and over 30,000 out-patients had been treated. In 1812 the numbers of patients admitted rose from 872 the previous year to 1,030, causing great problems of overcrowding and increasing the risk of infection among the patients.

> ...the Wards of the Infirmary are from necessity too much crowded and in order to prevent infectious diseases, which are apt to arise when this is the case, and with which in fact the

Infirmary was lately threatened – the Directors have in con-
templation to enlarge the present buildings, by completing the
original plan...

The great rise in the number of patients admitted forced the Board of
Managers to consider increasing the size of the building to accommodate
them and in November 1813 a committee was set up to consider the
extension of the infirmary building. Meantime, the pressure of numbers
had caused an outbreak of contagious fever (undefined), in the summer
and autumn of 1813 and there was a recurrence of contagion in 1815,
when the overcrowding had reached the stage where patients were sleeping on the floor in some wards, and 'nervous fever' (again not defined)
was rife. In the annual report for 1813, 14 patients were diagnosed as suffering from nervous fever, representing less than 1.4 per cent of the 1,022
cases admitted that year. In 1814 the figure rose to 84 cases (7.4 per cent)
of the 1,135 admissions. By 1815, the figure was 185 cases of nervous
fever, 12.4 per cent of the 1,492 cases admitted.

The possibility of closing the hospital to new admissions for a time was
raised, in order to contain the disease, and also by dismissing as many of
the present patients as possible to allow for a complete cleaning of the
wards. This drastic action was not taken. Instead, the weekly committee
was instructed to admit only urgent cases, and to convert the Managers'
Room and another auxiliary room into temporary wards until the existing wards could be thoroughly cleaned. Within three months the planned
extension, to be built at a cost of £5,000 with the money to be raised by
public subscription, was approved by the medical committee. The number of beds available to patients in the Royal remained around 150 (in
theory 136 beds in eight wards of seventeen beds each) from the infirmary's opening, and did not rise to 226 until 1816, with the opening of
the extension leading from the centre of the existing Adam building.

The nature of patient admissions came to reflect the rapid industrialisation of the city. Patient entry was increasingly sponsored by merchants,
manufacturers and other employers in the city. The number of accident
cases treated (who did not need subscribers' lines) also rose steadily from
a low initial level. In 1813, twenty-seven patients were admitted with
bruising, twelve with burns, twenty-nine with simple and compound
fractures, and twenty-five with accidental wounds, from a total of 1,030
admissions. Although no details of how such injuries occurred are given

in the ward books of the period, the fact that 9 per cent of all admissions to the infirmary in that year were apparently due to accidental injury is indicative of the city's growing industrial base.

> The great increase of manufactures in this part of the country, while it has afforded to many the means of bettering their fortune has also necessarily increased the number of indigent poor. The great public works in the neighbourhood, and the numerous buildings which have been for some time carrying on in this city, have greatly increased the number of patients suffering by accidents, to whom the Infirmary is at all times open.

PATIENT CARE: DISEASE

Varicose leg ulcers were the most common ailment treated in the infirmary in the period from 1794 to 1815 although the numbers varied over time: 90 patients were treated for ulcers from 402 admissions in 1796, (22 per cent); forty-six were so treated from 765 patients in 1804 (6 per cent), and 114 from 1492 in 1815 (8 per cent). The number of patients admitted suffering from consumption and various fevers was also substantial. Fever figures fluctuated from year to year, but did not in these years reach the epidemic proportions witnessed later in the nineteenth century, despite the outbreak of nervous fever in the period 1813–15. There were few patients in this period admitted diagnosed as suffering from smallpox, and there were only three patients diagnosed as having cholera in the years up to 1815.

A noticeable feature of the early years of the infirmary is the very few surgical operations which were carried out in comparison to the number of patients treated; twenty-five operations out of 276 patients (9 per cent) in 1795, fifty-two operations carried out from 820 admissions in 1802 (6 per eent), fifty-six operations out of 1492 admissions in 1815 (4 per cent). These figures compare favourably with the early years of Edinburgh Royal Infirmary, where in the three decades between 1770 and 1800 only nineteen surgical operations were conducted from a total of 3,047 admissions (0.62 per cent). Of these fourteen were amputations, and there were three lithotomies ('cutting for the stone' from the bladder).[32] In the Royal, the most common operation carried out in these years was amputation, although there was also trephining (or 'trepanning', that is reducing pressure on the brain by removing a small section of the cranium), tapping (draining fluid from body cavities) and hydrocele (removing fluid from the testicles or spermatic cord). The restricted range and number of operations reflects the wider picture of hospital care at this time, when surgical practice was limited by a high mortality rate for 'capital' (major) operations before the introduction of anaesthetics and antiseptics in the middle decades of the nineteenth century.[33] Early operational mortality figures are not available since the first annual infirmary reports did not provide a separate figure given for deaths after operations; all deaths were added together in a single total.

Patient care: venereal disease

After varicose ulcers the next most common complaint treated in the early years of the Glasgow Royal Infirmary was venereal diseases, including syphilis and gonorrhea.

> The Managers find that the demand for admission of patients having venereal complaints is constantly increasing - they recommend to the committee not to receive, or have in the Infirmary at any time more than eight persons exclusive of those in the soldiers' ward...

The implication is that soldiers accounted for many of such cases. In 1795 a specific ward was set aside for the treatment of soldiers stationed at Glasgow barracks and special arrangements were made for their admission to the infirmary, with the expense of their treatment to be met by their regiment, (the Second Fencibles were among those stationed at the Gallowgate barracks who had dealings with the infirmary in this period). In 1804 a hospital was opened for soldiers at the barracks, and although soldiers continued to be admitted to the infirmary, it reduced the overall number of patients in the infirmary from 895 in 1803 to 765 in 1804. The number of patients admitted suffering from venereal diseases also fell from 100 in 1803 to 41 in 1804.

The conclusion that most of the soldiers admitted to the hospital were suffering from venereal diseases is also supported by the level of 'fines' exacted from soldiers admitted with these diseases. From early 1798 'fines' (in reality, additional payments for the upkeep of the venereal disease ward) of five shillings were levied by the infirmary for patients admitted suffering from venereal diseases. This figure was in addition to the flat rate of eight pence per day charged for the cost of all soldiers admitted to the infirmary. In 1809 these fees generated £31 13s 10d in daily expenses from soldiers admitted and a further £5 in 'venereal fines' for twenty soldiers treated for venereal diseases, (from a total of sixty-seven such cases admitted to the infirmary in that year).

The special arrangements for the admission of soldiers into the Royal should be seen in the context of the protracted French Wars, 1793 to 1815, when the health of the nation's armed forces was of great importance.

> While the Directors, in common with their fellow citizens deplore the calamities thereof [the War], as Managers of this Institution they have peculiarly to regret, that, in their consequences they not only dry up the sources of that charity on which their Institution depends; but tend also, in various ways, to increase its necessities and expense.

Certainly, the admission of soldiers suffering from venereal diseases appears to have been regarded as a special case. Civilian patients suffering from the disease were looked upon as an inconvenience, and in 1787 it was decided that no female patients suffering from the disease be admitted to the infirmary without a recommendation as to decency of character.

The link between the infirmary and the military garrison in the city was strengthened by the donation in 1806 of £1,200 by the First Regiment of Glasgow Volunteers to the infirmary representing the whole of their regimental fund remaining at the end of their period of muster in the Napoleonic Wars. In recognition of the regiment's generosity a plaque thanking them for their donation and recognising their great service in the war was placed on a wall in the infirmary, and the regiment's commanding officer, Lieutenant Colonel James Corbett, was elected to serve on the Board of Managers.

PATIENT CARE: TREATMENT

Early ward day books reveal that the treatment of patients was limited. Often case notes read as little more than observations of the patient's outward signs and a description of his or her sleeping and dietary patterns. On 27 December 1794 James Sinclair, a servant, aged seventeen, was admitted to the infirmary, diagnosed as suffering from pneumonia:

> Complains of frequent cough... very bloody expectorate... Has also pain in his head and slight vertigo on sitting in the erect position.
>
> *December 28th.* Slept ill during the night from the frequency of the cough... bled a little at the house this morning—the Headache is less violent. His tongue is moist but he complains of thirst... Was somewhat delirious in the night.
>
> *Dec. 30th.* Passed a good night being little troubled with the cough. Pain in side and back gone. Cough much less urgent...
>
> *Jan. 1st 1795.* Only complaint is the cough. Expectorate is of yellowish colour but no tinge of blood. Has now a desire for food.
>
> *Jan. 3rd.* Cough nearly gone. Appetite is good.
>
> *Jan. 4th.* Dismissed cured.

Also noted in December 1794 was James Hamilton, a soldier aged thirty-two, who had been struck by lightning while out walking eleven months earlier. He went into a stupor and when he recovered was left blinded. He recovered his sight the following day, but over the next eight days he felt worse and a fever developed. It took three months for the fever to pass, and when it had his eyesight had deteriorated so much that he could do nothing more than tell night from day. On admission his eyes were observed to be inflamed and the lenses milky. He was in no pain and otherwise enjoyed good health. His case notes go on to say:

> *December 13.* Blisters applied.
>
> *Dec. 14.* Both blisters rose well and have discharged freely. Feels sight improving.
>
> *Dec. 15.* Blisters continue to run. Sight as yesterday.
>
> *Dec. 16.* Can distinguish lights with both eyes and objects with right eye.
>
> *Dec. 17.* Vision as yesterday. Bad taste in mouth.

[This treatment by blistering was continued with the same general observations and steady improvement in vision, until 21 February when his eyesight improved to the extent that he could distinguish facial features. Blisters continued to be applied for a further few weeks, with no other improvement to his sight.]

Mar. 27. Goes out by desire.

PATIENT CARE: HOSPITAL DIET

The patients' diet was divided into three categories: low, middle and full. The low diet (usually prescribed in all conditions deemed to be inflammatory) consisted of bread, milk, oat or barley porridge, sago rice and milk, potatoes and water gruel, served as appropriate at breakfast, dinner and supper. Drinks included barley or rice water, and cows' milk whey. No alcoholic beverages were allowed in the low diet, although wine was prescribed in some cases as a stimulant. In the middle diet (given to most patients admitted to the infirmary) breakfast was the same bread, milk and porridge as in the low diet. Dinner consisted of beef or mutton broth with bread, followed by rice or bread pudding. Supper was porridge or bread and small beer. The full diet (prescribed to convalescing fever patients or those with chronic, non-digestive complaints) allowed small beer to be taken at breakfast along with porridge and bread. Dinner consisted of broth, boiled beef or mutton, or fresh fish, followed by pudding. Supper in the full diet was the same as in the middle diet, although a larger allowance of small beer was available. Fresh fruit in season was also part of the hospital diet.

The appearance of alcoholic drinks in hospital diets was not uncommon at this time (they were also featured in Edinburgh Royal Infirmary's published diet lists).[34] Although often administered as medicines, alcohol was viewed as a permissible stimulant to be administered in clinical situations of debility, that is in the case of fevers, particularly typhus, and in all convalescent states where recovery was dependent on proper sustenance. Small beer of a low alcohol content was available in ready supply in all but the low diet. Wine, however, was generally given as a tonic or diuretic. Spirits, in dilute form, were administered for stronger stimulation.

MEDICAL STAFF

As the infirmary building reached completion in the second part of 1794 the managers decided on staffing levels. Two physicians and four surgeons, a resident apothecary, a physician's and a surgeon's clerk, were

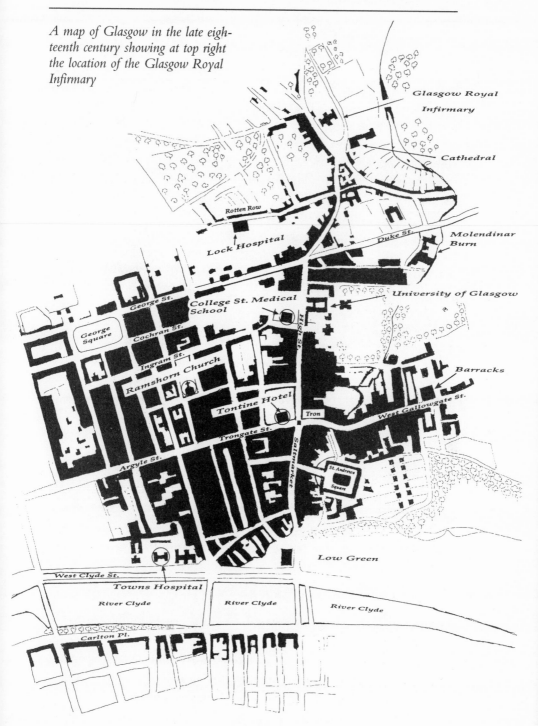

A map of Glasgow in the late eighteenth century showing at top right the location of the Glasgow Royal Infirmary

appointed to treat patients. The physicians and surgeons visited patients at one o'clock each day and together acted as a committee to decide on the admission of new patients. No cases deemed incurable were to be admitted to the infirmary although this regulation was never fully implemented. It was also the responsibility of the medical staff to ensure that no dissections were undertaken on deceased patients without a written authorisation signed by at least two of the infirmary's managers and to ensure that bodies were decently sewn up and dressed before their return to relatives for burial. In addition, the physicians and surgeons examined the case notes of the patients as entered by their respective clerks and corrected them as required. The apothecary's role was to make up and dispense prescriptions to patients as per the instructions of the physicians and surgeons, and to order and oversee the pharmaceutical supplies of the infirmary. The apothecary also registered patient numbers and maintained records, from which he composed an abstract of patient admissions, diseases treated and results of treatments for inclusion in each annual report.

Clerks employed by the infirmary were junior medical men, and there was a frequent turnover in these fixed-term appointments as those employed found positions elsewhere. Surgeons' dressers were also appointed to hospital service, from the ranks of students enrolled for clinical instruction at the infirmary. Dressers were guided by the clerks and by the surgeons when present. A further duty of the surgeons was to advertise the time of forthcoming major operations which were open to the public, although medical students studying in Glasgow would be chief among those interested observers:

> All greater operations are to be performed in the theatre, and to be advertised by a placard put up in the consulting room, at the ordinary time of visiting the day before they are to be performed, unless in such cases as cannot admit of a days delay.

Nursing and orderlies

The non-medical staff appointed to the infirmary in this early period consisted of a housekeeper, a porter, a cook and six nurses. Of these the position of housekeeper carried most responsibility. Her duties as matron were to inspect the wards, carry out inventories of all furniture and instruments, buy in provisions, keep accounts of daily expenditure and of all donations of food and other provisions, to oversee food preparation and to admit '... any patient severely hurt by accident when the Physician, Surgeon or Clerks are not at hand'.

The porter's duties were to keep the court, staircases and managers' room clean and tidy, to act as doorkeeper to the managers and medical staff, and to refuse admittance to visitors when the medical staff were on their rounds. The porter was to refuse 'drink-money' from interested strangers wishing to view the infirmary but 'to gratify their desire' and admit them free of charge. It was not unusual for individuals to view the workings of hospitals by way of public spectacle, surgical operations were open to the public, and there was a feeling that potential or actual subscribers should be allowed to visit the institution.

The nurses appointed at the infirmary were hired servants, whose duties included washing and dusting the wards every morning, serving the patients their meals and prescribed medicines daily, and changing and airing beds between admissions. The sole medical aspect to their duties was that of observation of patients in order to report any unusual symptoms to the medical staff. The absence of specialised training for nurses in the late eighteenth and early nineteenth centuries is shown by the fact that in the Royal female relatives of patients admitted to the infirmary could be taken on as 'supernumerary nurses' with the consent of the medical staff to attend to their relatives' needs.

Onerous cleaning duties and low wage levels did not attract the better servants to nursing positions in the Royal in its early years and in late 1795 a decision was taken to increase the wage levels as a result of poor nursing service.

> Upon a representation from the attending Physicians and Surgeons that the patients in the Infirmary are ill-attended by nurses, on account of their wages being too small, the meeting empowers the matron under the Direction of the medical gentlemen, to make such addition to the wages of the nurses as they shall find necessary to get proper nurses.

Individual nurses could rise above their expected level of service. In 1797 Agnes McKenzie was recognised as having performed '... her duty with great diligence and fidelity for the space of a year', by the attending physicians and surgeons, who proposed that she be made a small gift, not exceeding seven shillings and sixpence, to be presented to her in front of the other 'servants'. Five years later the servile nature of nursing in the infirmary was highlighted in the decision to publicly humiliate any nurses dismissed for bad behaviour:

> In consequence of some complaints that had been made against some of the nurses that attended patients in the Infirmary, the meeting resolve that in future when any Nurse is dismissed from the House for improper conduct that it shall be intimated to the public in such a way as the managers shall appoint and that intimation... [shall] be published in the News papers or by placard.

No chaplain was appointed at the infirmary until 1801 due to lack of funds. In this year the apothecary, John Allan, who was also an ordained minister of the Church of Scotland, agreed to act as chaplain without addition to his salary of £40. He continued in this way until his chaplaincy work was formally recognised by the Board of Managers in 1806 and an additional sum of £10 was awarded him. Allan worked in this dual capacity until he left the hospital in 1814 to serve as a chaplain in India.

FINANCING THE ROYAL

Although the infirmary relied on donations from the public and institutions to maintain its functions, the managers used other methods to enhance the income they had available. Appeals for donations were published in the press, in particular in conjunction with the infirmary's annual reports which made much of the duties of the more fortunate members of society to aid the ailing poor.

> The Directors... in the most earnest manner, and under the deep impression of the miserable state of those who must eventually remain victims to disease and poverty, renew their solicitations to the Public, and particularly to the opulent in this City, and in the West of Scotland, on whom the poor and miserable have, at all times, just and pressing claims.

The infirmary's finance committee also arranged for personal applications to be made to wealthy members of the local community to appeal for support.

> The Clerk reported that he had made up a list of persons in

easy or affluent circumstances in Glasgow who had not yet contributed to the funds of the Infirmary with the view of the Managers making applications to them for subscriptions...

In addition the infirmary became a lending facility to the local public authority (by 1802 the infirmary had made loans of £3,000 to the City of Glasgow). The infirmary's directors also invested in Government stock. 'The meeting [of managers] resolve to purchase £2,000 of 3 per cent consols, at the lowest rate [price] they can be got and appoint the Dean of Guild and the Secretary to invest the same without loss of time'.

EARLY MEDICAL TEACHING AT THE ROYAL

From its inception the infirmary was planned as a teaching hospital.

> That the students of Medicine and apprentices of Surgeons should be permitted to attend the Infirmary on paying for the behoof of the hospital the sum of five guineas, or two guineas per annum. That a certain number of these should be appointed dressers to the surgeons.

In 1794, prior to the hospital's opening, Robert Cleghorn and Thomas Charles Hope, appointed as the first physicians to the infirmary, obtained permission from the Board of Managers to deliver clinical lectures on their patients to students on the grounds that it '... would induce a greater number of students of medicine to attend the house and would form an important addition to the Medical School of Glasgow...' In 1791 Hope had become Professor of Medicine at the University of Glasgow, a chair which he held until 1795, when he was appointed to the chair in Chemistry at Edinburgh, succeeding Joseph Black.

In May 1797, John Burns, one of the first surgeons appointed to the infirmary, obtained the managers' permission to deliver a series of clinical surgical lectures:

> Gentlemen – In the Edinburgh and many of the English hospitals, lectures are read on Surgery, but as yet nothing of the kind has been attempted in this Infirmary – it is evident however that such a course of lectures if properly conducted, would not only be beneficial to the students, but also to the medical school established here and particularly to the Infirmary, as every additional means of improvement provided here must increase the number of students, and

consequently augment the fees of the hospital.

John Burns, educated at Glasgow and then Edinburgh University, was first appointed to the infirmary in July 1795 when he was given the dual post of apothecary and surgeon's clerk, a position he held until May 1796. After his service as surgeon/lecturer in 1797–8, Burns was not reappointed until 1808–9, due to his association with grave-robbing in order to obtain subjects for anatomical dissection. In 1797 he set up his own private medical school in College Street close to the University of Glasgow. (The medical school had no formal links to the University, but students often attended courses at both, although this was not compulsory at this time when no formal qualification was required to practise medicine. College Street Medical School continued to offer medical instruction until the mid 1830s.) Burns taught anatomy, surgery and midwifery at his school and later lectured in these subjects at Anderson's College. Anderson's College was opened in 1796 as a result of a grandiose plan for a new university to rival the University of Glasgow in the will of former Professor of Natural Philosophy, Dr John Anderson, who had vainly sought to reform the University during his lifetime. In fact, his will realised insufficient funds to create more than a solitary joint-lectureship in anatomy and surgery which Burns filled. However, the College began to grow steadily in the years after 1815, providing a whole range of extramural courses.[35] Burns was ultimately appointed first Professor of Surgery at the University of Glasgow in 1815. He later served as physician to the Royal Infirmary from 1833 to 1836.[36] He died in 1850.

Burns came from a notable family in Glasgow religious, medical and business life. His father, John Burns DD, served as Minister of Barony parish, close to the infirmary site, for more than sixty years,[37] and two brothers were heavily involved in shipping companies including Hutcheson's (later MacBrayne's) and Cunard. Another brother, Allan, was a talented anatomist and medical author. Allan Burns also served as physician to Catherine the Great for six months in 1805, during a period when Catherine sought to establish a hospital in St Petersburg along the lines of the Scottish voluntary system. He returned to Glasgow to undertake some of John Burns' lecturing work. Allan Burns, in fact, took over his brother's anatomy practice in 1806 when John Burns was forced to give up anatomical instruction in the face of impending public prosecution alongside his anatomy students for alleged resurrectionist practices to obtain subjects for dissection.[38] Allan Burns published two works on anatomy and died in 1813.[39]

Despite the early start made by Cleghorn and Hope in 1794, and by John Burns in 1797, the provision of clinical teaching at the infirmary was irregular and surgical instruction in particular was offered only periodically. After Burns' departure in 1798 the next offer of clinical instruction in surgery was made by William Dunlop, one of the attending surgeons, in 1801, and was given for a period of less than a year. In 1810 a letter from the 'medical students of the town' was addressed to the managers asking that a University course in clinical surgery be given at the infirmary, to supplement the medical clinical instruction provided at the hospital. Students training with a view to enroling in the army as surgeons at this time of war would require experience of, for example, amputations.

In August 1810 the medical committee of the Board of Managers responded to the students' appeal, by supporting the principle of clinical surgical teaching, but by disputing the popularity of such a course. The committee felt that a course in clinical surgery would not attract enough students to offset the cost of paying a permanent lecturer in surgery which they believed would be necessary to deliver such a course. The committee's judgement was apparently based on information on clinical courses in Edinburgh and London, where the clinical surgical courses were not so well attended as the clinical medical ones. The wider debate was whether practical surgery would achieve the same status as clinical medical teaching and whether the Royal should make special provision for such teaching. The committee recommended that existing surgeons appointed at the infirmary should be encouraged to give clinical lectures on any of their cases they considered appropriate.

PROFESSIONAL CONFLICT IN THE INFIRMARY

The provision of clinical teaching at the infirmary was an area where the conflicting interests of the Faculty of Physicians and Surgeons of Glasgow and the medical school of the University of Glasgow came into direct confrontation. The struggle over the selection of clinical lecturers towards the end of this period was a precursor of the greater conflict which was to occur between 1816 and 1840 as the two bodies resorted to protracted court action in order to assert their rights to examine and grant the right to practise to students in surgery.

The dispute also spilled over into the selection of medical staff in the infirmary, as in the controversy in 1809 over the Board of Managers' selection of a surgeon, J. McDougall MD who was not a licensed member of the Faculty of Physicians and Surgeons of Glasgow, but a graduate of the University of Glasgow, and also nephew to James Jeffray, Professor of Anatomy.[40] This selection was challenged by John Nimmo, elected physician to the infirmary at the same time as McDougall. Nimmo, backed by two other members of the medical staff, put forward a resolution that in future no one who was not licensed by the Faculty of Physicians and Surgeons of Glasgow be elected for a post on the medical staff of the infirmary. Four months later and after the annual meeting at which the Board of Managers was newly elected, a decision was taken on Nimmo's resolution.

> The meeting... refuse to enact the law proposed by that motion which would have the effect to prevent the Hospital from having the benefit at any time of medical or surgical assistance, however eminent, unless the Practitioner was previously enrolled as a member of the Faculty of Physicians and Surgeons of Glasgow. The meeting at the same time expressed their gratitude for the aid the Infirmary had received from the Faculty, and the very high sense the Managers entertain of the liberal and able support and assistance received from many individuals of that Faculty ever since the house was opened and upon the continuation of which the usefulness of the Institution depends.

Despite this decision, McDougall was not re-elected as surgeon to the infirmary, and the Faculty's dominance over medical posts in the infirmary remained.

In 1811 attempts were made to introduce more regular clinical teaching by the physicians at the infirmary by changing the date of their election to office, and that of the surgeons, from January of each year to August, with a starting date in November, at the time the beginning of the University year. After appointment the physicians were to offer one clinical course in either the period from 1 November to 1 February or from 1 February to 1 May, the end of the University session. This was clearly an attempt to offer clinical teaching in a form more compatible with the instruction offered at the medical school at the University of Glasgow. The Board of Managers also assumed the right of appointing outside medical instructors to offer these courses should any of the physicians not accept the new teaching responsibilities.

This measure produced only a temporary answer to the problem of clinical teaching at the infirmary. In May 1812 Richard Millar, house physician, and Robert Freer, Professor of Medicine at the University of Glasgow and a manager at the Royal, put forward a motion to allow managers to appoint physicians of their choice to deliver clinical lectures at the infirmary, and not to be restricted to the physicians who were on the hospital staff. The motion was referred to the next quarterly meeting of the managers, at which a deputation from the medical school of the University stated that for the previous two winters only one three-month clinical medical course had been offered at the infirmary, instead of the six months of instruction intended by the Board, which had induced many of the more advanced students to go to another university, presumably Edinburgh, where a course of clinical lectures was given regularly for six months to tie in with the University winter session. At this time the medical school at Edinburgh had clinical courses which ran for six months in rotation in the winter and summer sessions to allow students to see a variety of diseases prevalent in different seasons of the year.[41] The deputation to the University proposed that members of the medical faculty of the University take over the clinical instruction, to be given in two three-month cycles, with the staff appointed to have access to patients in the infirmary for treatment as well as teaching purposes. In return for direct access to the wards the medical faculty of the University proposed to make clinical instruction an integral part of their medical degree.

> The [Medical] Faculty propose to make it necessary for every person, before he can become a candidate for a degree in medicine to produce evidence that he had attended at least one such clinical course as above mentioned either in this or some other University, and no student can be allowed to attend a course for clinical lectures here, who has not at the time a ticket for the Glasgow Royal Infirmary.

The Faculty of Physicians and Surgeons of Glasgow strongly opposed this plan, and insisted that only elected medical staff of the infirmary (a process over which the Faculty had direct influence), should be eligible to fulfil clinical instruction duties in the hospital. Under this pressure, the managers rejected the University's proposals and retained their power of appointing clinical lecturers to the infirmary.

The managers' action in upholding their right to make medical appointments in no way diminished the resentment felt by members of the University medical school at their lack of influence over clinical teaching in the infirmary. The dispute between the University medical members and the Faculty factions on the Board reached such a level of intensity in May 1813 that a retrospective decision was taken to destroy the minute book in which the row had been noted, and to begin afresh with all reference to the two meetings at which the disagreements had occurred completely removed.

Conflict among professional medical interests in the infirmary was also apparent in this period in the area of payment of medical staff. As early as 1796 a number of physicians and surgeons declined to accept posts for which they had been nominated due to the fact that the infirmary made them no salary payment. In the early years of the infirmary this was explained by the Board of Managers on the grounds that the finances of the infirmary were not sufficient to allow for payments to be made. 'The managers are sorry but they have nothing but acknowledgements to make [to the medical staff] for such faithful and useful labours.'

Honoraria were a common feature of the voluntary hospital system throughout Britain. Medical appointments were regarded as prestigious positions which guaranteed the holder an introduction to the hospital's board and subscribers, and could offer opportunities to act as medical attendants to this wealthy clientele.[42] Indeed, many of the first medical attendants were well-established practitioners with a high profile in Glasgow medical circles, including former and future Presidents of the Faculty such as Robert Freer, who was also Professor of Medicine at the University of Glasgow. Salaries were, however, introduced to the Royal in 1807 as the steady increase in patient numbers meant that case loads became more demanding and the honorary staff were committed to spending more of their time at the infirmary. Initially this was an annual payment of £30 for physicians on completion of two years free service, and £10 for surgeons on the same conditions. There was also a reference to a possible linkage between the medical staff's salaries and the income the infirmary received from student tickets. At this time such income averaged £80 per annum, and it was suggested by the Board of Managers that should this figure reach an average of £100, part of the additional income would be made over to the medical staff. Despite a great increase in the income generated by student fees, which by 1810 reached a figure of over £267, representing 7 per cent of the total income of £3,667 for that year, the medical staff did not begin to receive a proportion of this money until changes in medical staff regulations in 1828. However, in 1810 salaries were raised to £50 and £20 respectively for physicians and surgeons as a reflection of the increasing income from student payments.

MEDICAL STUDENTS

Although students had access to the infirmary from its opening, their behaviour in the hospital was, not surprisingly, strictly regulated. No students were to visit patients other than when the medical staff were making their rounds, they were not to speak with or examine patients in the waiting rooms or to visit the apothecary's shop. In addition,

> Students who attend the Physicians or Surgeons during their prescriptions, are to study a composed and decent carriage, and are not then to stroll about the wards, converse together, stand upon the benches, beds, or do anything that may be disturbing to the Physician, Clerk, or patients.

The provision of facilities for student instruction at Glasgow Royal Infirmary served to boost the status of the medical teaching offered in the city. The link between the rise in stature and increase in student numbers of a medical school and the opening of a hospital with provision for clinical instruction had previously been demonstrated at Edinburgh.

> The success of the Edinburgh School, whose reputation depended in no small measure on the parallel emergence and growth of the Royal Infirmary of Edinburgh after 1729, rendered such an institution vital to the anticipated development of medical education in Glasgow.[43]

At the time of the Royal's opening the number of students enrolling in medicine at the University of Glasgow was relatively few, but this number began to rise substantially, (the number of students enrolled in the medical faculty rose from 54 in 1790 to 387 by 1831)[44] and the opportunity for clinical education was an added incentive to students who came to the University. Throughout the early years of its existence a growing group of medical students came to use the clinical instruction opportunities provided at the infirmary. Tickets for admission to the wards were sold in increasing numbers and mounting emphasis was placed by the student body on the provision of clinical lectures in medicine and surgery at the infirmary.

Student fees were levied in respect of tickets of admission to walk the wards, which allowed the observation of patients and access to the ward book to note down case histories. Additional income was generated from payments by students, including surgeons' apprentices, to assist in the apothecary's shop, and also in payment for diplomas confirming good service as surgeons' dressers. The demand for such positions was so intense among the students that the period each dresser served was cut from six months to three in 1809 to increase the number of students who could take up these posts. By this time there were ninety-eight students attending the wards, generating £205 16s in fees for the infirmary, with an additional six students attending the apothecary's shop at a total cost of £31. The sale of eleven dispenser's diplomas added a further £2 15s to the infirmary's income from student attendance.

It is no coincidence that at the same period as students were pressing for an increase in clinical instruction at the Royal Infirmary, the numbers of students enrolled at the University medical school was on the increase. This was in part due to the heightened demand for medical attendants in the army and navy in the course of the Napoleonic Wars. The rise in student numbers is clear from figures enrolled in the anatomy class. From ninety-one students in 1803, the figure rose to 352 in 1813.[45] The actual numbers of students studying medicine was even greater, when those attending medical classes offered by extra-mural lecturers in the city (such as College Street Medical School) and at Anderson's College are taken into account.

STUDENTS AND DISSECTION

The increasing number of students attending the infirmary led to additional pressure to provide bodies suitable for dissection. The problem of obtaining sufficient corpses for anatomical teaching was one which was shared by medical schools and other institutions of medical instruction for much of the late eighteenth and early nineteenth centuries, and while body-snatching by hired 'resurrectionists' and the murderous activities of Burke and Hare in Edinburgh in the late 1820s have attracted much attention,[46] it is also clear that medical students were not averse to providing their anatomy lecturers with bodies for dissection or undertaking their own dissection work on any corpses which may have fallen into their hands by one means or another.[47]

Although such behaviour by Glasgow medical students was tolerated by the authorities of the medical schools in default of any Government legislation in this period (the Anatomy Act governing dissection was not passed until 1832), they were not openly protected in their body-snatching activities. The nearest approach to official recognition was the provision of free tickets to the dissection rooms for those who took part in the exhumations.[48] At the College Street Medical School, Granville Sharp Pattison, an eighteen-year-old surgeon who studied medicine at the University of Glasgow between 1806 and 1812 (but like many students of his period did not graduate), became Allan Burns' anatomy assistant and demonstrator in 1809. He also became leader of the student resurrectionist group. In 1813 parts of a female body, allegedly that of recently deceased Janet McAllister, were discovered in Pattison's dissection rooms after a police search had been triggered on discovery of her disturbed grave in nearby Ramshorn Churchyard by her relatives. At the succeeding trial before Edinburgh High Court, Pattison, his partner Russell and two students, Munro and McLeod, were found not guilty and not proven of felonious abstraction of Janet McAllister's body due to some doubts being raised by the defence as to whether all the body parts identified as McAllister's were, in fact, hers.[49] The stigma of a court case did not linger long for Pattison: within a year he had secured appointment as a junior surgeon at the Royal.

At the Royal, on several occasions, circumstances had led the managers to tighten their regulations on the dissection of bodies of patients who had died in the infirmary. In 1805 new regulations governing access to the 'Dead Room' were drawn up, the main thrust of which was to ensure that the apothecary, the only medical member of staff in constant attendance at the infirmary, held the key to the mortuary to control access, and remained with bodies taken from the 'Dead Room' for dissection purposes. In addition,

> ...if he shall discover either during the dissection or afterwards
> that any part of it has been abstracted, he shall give informa-
> tion thereof to the Physician or Surgeon by whom permission
> to obtain it had been planned.

After 1809, students appointed as surgeons' and physicians' clerks signed a declaration regulating their duties. Among the regulations it was stated that any dissection undertaken should proceed no further than was necessary to discover the cause of death and that clerks on no pretext whatsoever were to be directly or indirectly concerned 'with the lifting of dead bodies'. In 1812 the procedures for obtaining permission to conduct dissections were reviewed and again made more stringent.

Anatomical lecturers in the city had similar problems of supply which again could lead to serious consequences for those involved in procuring subjects through illegal means, as the case of John Burns has already demonstrated. The University of Glasgow also had problems with students involved in resurrectionism. Such practices angered the local population and placed the University buildings under threat from crowds eager to express their distaste for acts of grave robbing, as in 1813 when the University Medical Professor Robert Freer's teaching rooms were attacked by a crowd which broke all of the windows in the wake of the discovery of the removal of Janet McAllister's body from its grave. In response the University voted to expel any student found guilty of resurrectionist activity.[50]

TWENTY-ONE YEARS ON

The early years of the Royal were characterised by concerns regarding the financing and smooth running of the new institution. The financial side had been placed on a solid footing by an aggressive campaign for subscriptions and by drawing upon periodic special church donations. On the administrative front there was some readjustment as the level and duties of staff were altered to come to terms with the thousands of patients which the infirmary now treated. Within the space of twenty-one years the Royal had become an essential part of the city's existence, so much so that the attention of the infirmary's management, staff and patients was focused on the expansion of the hospital planned for 1816, to cope with the great rise in demand for its services generated in the two decades since it was first opened for patients.

2 FEVERISH TIMES, 1816–60

...the number of Fevers amounts now to more than one-third of the whole number of Patients...the Directors observe, that, in the difficulties presented to them as to the admission of Patients, they have refused as few Fever cases as possible, though they have been obliged to refuse a great number of Ordinary cases

[Extract from the Royal's Annual Report for 1825]

PRESSURES ON THE INFIRMARY

If the early history of the infirmary was mostly concerned with the building, financing and organisation of the new institution, the next period in
the history of the hospital, from 1816 to 1860, can be characterised by the
attempts to accommodate the ever increasing numbers of patients admitted suffering from epidemic disease. In the years after 1815 the hospital
became the major treatment centre for thousands of the city's inhabitants
who succumbed to a variety of epidemic diseases, particularly typhus, but
including those which were previously little heard of, such as cholera.
The pressures on the infirmary were supplemented by the startling rise in
the city's population which almost doubled in the space of twenty years.
The 1811 census figure of 110,460 rose to 202,495 by 1831. By 1851 the
figure was 357,000.

Other issues too occupied the attentions of the managers of the infirmary, but often these were related to the overriding concerns of the
continued threat of epidemic disease and the demands this placed on the
resources of the infirmary. The pressure to provide beds for those most in
need through the ravages of epidemic illness, and at the same time to
continue to offer beds to the regular intake of cases of the hospital, was a
perennial concern in this period. Increased numbers of patients added to
the running costs, so the financial position of the hospital was a prevailing
consideration throughout these years. Growing demands placed on the

infirmary during epidemics led the managers to decide upon a programme of expansion to augment the number of beds available. New
buildings called for additional finance, and the problem for the Royal's
managers was to find new sources of funding.

One increasingly significant financial resource for the infirmary was
the money received from employees' contributions from local factories
and businesses. For example, of a total income of £3,137 in 1822 £2,244
was raised in annual contributions, while only £21 came from employee
contributions. By 1841, out of a total of £8,331, the respective figures
were £3,082 and £632 and in 1858, out of a total income of £10,914
the gap had closed further, with £3,418 in annual subscriptions and
£1,851 in money from 'public works'. These contributions were made
to provide access to the infirmary for those employees who needed attention either through accident or illness. That this area of funding should
become important to the infirmary during these years reflects the rapidly
changing face of Glasgow, as large public works and factories with mass
workforces became common. The effects of the growth in industry in
Glasgow on the Royal Infirmary were not simply shown in increasing
revenue for the hospital from this source, but by a corresponding rise in
the number of accident admissions. These rose to such an extent that a
separate record of all accident admissions began to be kept by the infirmary, detailing how each accident had come about, with the vast
majority occurring at the individual's place of work.

The other dominant feature of this period in the infirmary's history
was the struggle between the Faculty of Physicians and Surgeons of
Glasgow and the medical school of the University of Glasgow for control
over the appointment of clinical lecturers to the infirmary. In fact this area
of dispute came to be overshadowed by the major court actions between
the two parties between 1815 and 1840, over the right to grant surgical
qualifications and regulate medical practice in the city, which in the end
was referred to the House of Lords for final judgement. However, the
continuing struggle over infirmary appointments and teaching opportunities between the two rival bodies played a major part in sustaining the
atmosphere of animosity and retarded the development of clinical
instruction in the Royal Infirmary for many years.

FEVER

In 1818 a great change occurred in the way one category of patients was admitted to the Royal. An alteration in infirmary regulations was made to allow patients suffering from fever to be admitted to the hospital on the recommendation, not of a subscriber or contributor, but of a specially-formed sub-committee of the infirmary's managers, the 'Fever Committee'. The reason behind this decision, taken by a large majority at a general meeting of subscribers in July 1818, was a practical one: the number of fever sufferers requiring admission far exceeded the number of subscribers willing to recommend such cases to the Royal.

Admission on the basis of need for fever patients was introduced in a bid to control the spread of epidemic disease in the city. The general term 'fever' was used to describe all febrile illness in annual reports and other infirmary records until the 1820s, when precise numbers for a variety of fevers began to be recorded. Even after this period there was little attempt to define the various types of 'continued fever' (typhus, typhoid and relapsing fevers) admitted to the infirmary.[1] This is hardly surprising since the differentiation of these diseases was not medically recognised until the pioneering work of Robert Perry, physician at the Royal from 1834 to 1848. In a paper of 1836 he correctly described many of the distinctions between typhus and typhoid (enteric fever). The complete separation of these diseases was a gradual process of investigation, and Perry's work was followed by Dr W W Gerhard of Philadelphia in 1837 and more completely defined by Dr A P Stewart of Glasgow in 1840.[2] Robert Perry was not the only medical attendant at the Royal to assume a prominent place in medical scientific research in this period. Andrew Buchanan, who served as surgeon at the Royal periodically from 1835 to 1862, was one of the first to investigate the subject of coagulation of the blood.[3]

Typhus aside, other fever admissions to the infirmary in this period included intermittent fever, cholera (which reached epidemic proportions in the 1830s, 40s, and 50s), and the eruptive continued fevers: scarlet fever, smallpox and measles. Typhus was by far the most prevalent fever in terms of epidemic occurrence. Later, more detailed, infirmary records demonstrate that it was also the most common cause of fever admissions.

Transmitted by lice or fleas, typhus is of sudden onset and lasts about fourteen days. It is characterised by an intense headache, delirium and an

upper body rash. The delirium increases in the second week of the illness.
Gangrene can develop in severe cases. In fatal cases, death occurs around
the fourteenth day, usually from heart failure. The death-rate for the disease is in the range of 10–100 per cent, reaching the higher levels in times
of severe epidemic.[4]

The admission of fever patients on request, space permitting, dramatically altered the nature of the Royal. The infirmary thus became a chief
source of public health provision for the city of Glasgow in one of the
most trying times in its history (the city's Poor Law institution and infirmary, the Town's Hospital, also admitted fever patients). The change was
not immediately recognised, and the annual report for 1819 stressed that
fever patients were only to be admitted without recommendation so long
as it did not interfere with the regular admission of patients with a subscriber's line. This intention, to put recommended patients first, was soon
to be overtaken by circumstance, as the numbers of fever patients admitted to the Royal during epidemics grew in number to the extent that the
hospital was on many occasions forced to turn fever victims away, due to
lack of available beds.[5] In this context, the admission of individual patients
supplied with subscriber's lines, however great their need, was overwhelmed by the mass of fever victims requiring treatment.

In 1819 two wards of the Royal were set aside for fever patients. A
third ward was left empty to house patients from other wards who were
decanted in rotation to allow their wards to be thoroughly cleaned. This
was to reduce the chance of infectious fevers spreading to other patients.
As a period of national trade depression hit the city causing increased
deprivation, the number of fever patients continued to rise. In 1823 the
fever wards and then the remaining hospital wards were filled with fever
sufferers, and the less serious medical and surgical cases were sent home.
The annual report for 1824 drew attention to the severe problems of
overcrowding caused by the rising number of fever victims, from 310
(269 with typhus) in 1823 to 572 (523 typhus patients) in 1824. In 1825
fever patients amounted to one third of all admissions to the Royal.

The mounting pressure on the infirmary to accommodate as many
patients suffering from fever as possible led to discussions in 1825 on
building a fever hospital next to the infirmary, and to requests for special
assistance from the Royal's subscribers to meet the costs of the construction. Despite further recommendation to this effect every year thereafter,

GRI DISEASE LIST 1822-52	1822	1823	1824	1825	1826	1827	1828	1829	1830	1831	1832	1833	1834	1835	1836	1837	1838	1839	1840	1841	1842	1843	1844	1845	1846	1847	1848	1849	1850	1851	1852
BRONCHITIS/INFLAMM OF BRONCHIA	0	0	0	22	24	27	19	14	5	2	6	45	2	0	52	67	92	167	103	153	85	75	40	84	92	101	92	110	88	105	101
BURN	0	15	17	17	23	20	27	22	28	34	39	34	63	66	62	54	84	79	68	81	62	81	60	76	72	132	75	64	63	63	62
CHOLERA	1	1	4	9	3	5	2	7	6	0	9	0	1	10	4	9	6	6	7	8	10	5	2	20	3	4	3	190	10	6	2
CONCUSSION	7	0	0	3	5	5	2	7	6	0	4	9	5	10	4	9	6	7	7	8	10	5	30	20	27	0	3	6	10	6	7
CONTUSION/BRUISE	17	34	40	12	18	50	20	29	38	30	48	100	71	51	53	45	87	145	110	92	85	82	66	151	187	132	88	89	109	133	82
DROPSY, GENERAL	21	21	19	23	11	11	28	29	29	34	18	37	5	12	35	15	8	14	25	10	17	18	41	29	26	58	20	18	15	12	14
DYSENTERY	1	2	5	5	14	110	104	23	13	43	23	37	5	12	15	5	8	3	7	3	18	3	11	12	23	21	25	32	11	19	18
DYSPEPSIA, INDIGESTION	70	30	61	55	51	35	49	47	25	50	37	57	31	53	45	67	32	2	72	59	70	14	55	78	67	19	24	20	33	27	21
ERYSIPELAS	59	37	26	68	656	35	15	11	14	39	22	34	53	64	45	67	57	79	101	55	40	33	39	46	42	35	62	65	38	33	27
EYE, DISEASE OF	39	47	52	48	28	17	26	26	16	14	15	14	53	0	45	0	57	7	101	8	12	1	2	0	0	0	0	0	0	0	0
FEVER, CONTINUED	229	269	523	895	922	1078	1500	758	729	1657	1509	1288	536	1258	3125	5408	2173	1464	2396	2533	1146	405	703	182	1071	2390	528	228	215	422	296
FEVER, INTERMITTENT	6	12	2	4	4	6	11	7	7	2	3	4	11	3	4	0	4	3	3	29	48	28	28	10	43	81	33	17	29	36	13
FRACTURE, (COMPOUND)	7	16	7	12	16	13	21	18	16	26	19	64	59	85	64	35	33	26	58	29	65	29	38	44	32	44	18	45	43	34	67
FRACTURE (SIMPLE)	53	48	61	102	110	107	101	109	94	121	119	79	102	105	137	132	114	170	217	179	138	136	176	198	180	161	176	133	165	185	172
GONORRHEA	6	20	10	15	10	10	6	4	1	1	8	7	11	7	17	0	12	4	10	4	4	2	2	9	12	3	66	10	10	4	3
HEART, DISEASE OF	10	20	21	21	10	16	6	11	12	24	18	18	53	41	17	17	12	59	26	40	36	35	39	48	48	28	28	31	9	9	27
INFLAMMATION, LUNGS	24	43	30	33	35	28	22	11	12	17	17	26	14	12	42	44	64	45	46	27	33	14	27	29	43	31	29	38	31	70	58
JOINTS, DISEASED	55	62	70	47	33	33	10	10	29	0	42	92	66	25	49	53	94	73	68	101	109	77	87	79	130	94	58	64	64	68	—
LIVER, DISEASE OF	0	6	10	9	9	5	8	1	0	12	0	0	10	8	12	11	7	27	22	17	17	25	13	14	5	2	4	23	16	11	7
MANIA / HYSTERIA	2	1	9	3	6	5	1	6	1	8	8	15	16	8	12	11	7	7	3	8	16	19	17	14	20	9	16	23	8	7	9
MEASLES	0	8	11	0	0	0	3	0	0	0	0	0	11	6	0	0	6	6	8	0	0	1	2	4	0	0	3	0	9	15	3
OVARY, DISEASE OF	0	0	2	5	1	0	0	2	0	0	0	3	6	6	0	1	2	0	8	0	0	1	2	4	4	6	25	9	1	1	0
PARALYSIS	23	0	0	38	31	41	0	0	0	0	0	32	21	23	31	11	26	26	43	26	29	33	22	25	27	33	25	22	39	40	40
PHTHISIS, PULM./CONSUMPTION	50	61	53	37	48	42	29	43	46	69	46	47	54	74	57	65	74	80	80	69	64	48	63	72	120	83	101	70	77	95	90
RHEUMATISM	74	96	80	58	60	69	91	112	71	99	70	124	114	80	71	69	160	164	102	101	112	104	86	111	147	77	74	138	119	154	100
SCARLETINA/SCARLET FEVER	3	20	6	4	0	0	1	0	1	0	0	4	0	23	0	0	0	0	0	19	16	18	21	12	0	0	18	15	8	8	20
SCIRRHUS/CANCER	20	30	18	22	18	30	24	24	20	26	18	17	33	33	29	24	10	37	36	21	23	18	21	26	19	18	22	19	13	4	14
SKIN, DISEASE/CUTANEOUS APPLIC.	50	50	55	49	41	54	55	55	37	37	25	54	73	62	77	69	73	95	87	92	82	81	57	71	72	57	84	62	98	97	74
SMALLPOX	0	0	37	0	0	0	4	8	10	12	3	14	62	72	0	0	59	59	61	26	32	0	0	0	2	0	48	43	0	163	117
SYPHILIS	65	105	96	85	88	69	72	70	45	76	69	96	92	83	91	60	111	135	126	133	116	101	112	139	135	89	101	98	88	87	49
ULCER, COMMOM	144	109	129	87	94	125	122	127	120	125	130	188	192	141	155	10	154	311	211	217	273	160	162	72	255	110	91	98	165	161	139
WOUND, COMMON	10	27	59	33	39	30	27	16	23	35	54	34	64	66	70	53	43	69	65	56	20	22	39	72	58	70	78	78	67	89	90
TYPHUS													1400										711	266	500	2399	807	342	382	919	1297
TYPHOID FEVER																												1	1	49	134
STARVATION																														6	10

Figure 1

the fever hospital was not completed until 1829. Meanwhile, the number of patients admitted suffering from typhus alone continued to rise: to 922 in 1826, and to 1,078 in 1827. In 1827 the number of fever cases caused such overcrowding that erysipelas (a contagious, often fatal, inflammatory skin disease, attended by fever, caused by streptococcus pyogenes, also known as 'hospital fever', sometimes a complication of certain forms of exhausting disease such as typhoid and tuberculosis)[6] spread among the wards, causing fatalities among some recuperating fever patients. Such consequences of overcrowded wards led the managers in June 1827, to rent two wards of the newly constructed, but as yet unoccupied, Blind Institute at Spring Gardens in the city centre to provide further accommodation for fever patients. This move was initiated by the local Relief Committee for Unemployed Operatives (workers) in the city, which recommended more typhus patients to the infirmary than could be found beds, and which then offered to pay the infirmary £100 in order to open the Spring Gardens building as a temporary fever hospital. Over 250 patients were accommodated at the Blind Institute in the space of five months, and the Relief Committee made over a payment of £200 to the infirmary for costs incurred. The Committee also paid the Royal an additional £500 for the treatment of fever patients admitted on its recommendation in the course of the year to the infirmary itself. In July 1828 additional accommodation was provided when a temporary fever 'shed' was put up in the infirmary grounds in order to increase the number of fever beds available by eighty.

The Royal's annual report for 1827 contained a very full medical and surgical report. The medical section of the report included information on the background of the fever sufferers, 'the bulk of them Irish labourers'. An analysis of the places of residence of male fever patients for part of the year indicated that the great majority resided in the overcrowded, rented accommodation in the centre and east end of Glasgow (High Street, Bridgeton, Gallowgate) and also in the outlying villages of Gorbals and Anderston. The medical report also noted from the Ward Books that five cases of fever from the same family had been admitted to the infirmary, as had eight cases from the same lodging house. The insanitary, cramped conditions of the poorer working class communities in the city were identified as the root cause of such epidemic outbreaks of fever:

In our now large and overgrown, City of Glasgow, there must constantly spring up, more especially among our crowded lanes and alleys, and confined dwellings of the suburbs, numerous cases of Typhus, ready at particular seasons, to break out, and contaminate the whole town.

While the conditions which brought about epidemics such as typhus, and dysentery (which was also prevalent in Glasgow in this period), were recognised by the medical staff of the infirmary there was no attempt by the infirmary's managers to press the local authorities to ameliorate the conditions which allowed fever to spread unchecked among the poorer communities in the city. Preventive health provision lay some time in the future, and an understanding of the nature of the disease itself was a long way off. Treatment in general, was palliative:

> ...[a] warm bath..., with shaving of the head, invariably, on admission, a routine long followed in our Infirmary; afterwards, cathartics, so as to preserve a regularly open belly; evaporating lotions, blisters applied to the head and other parts, when requisite; diaphoretics, anodynes, rubefacients, and, finally, the usual stimulants, wines, spirits and sulphuric ether.

The building of the fever hospital continued during 1828, although the plan initially sanctioned by the managers for a 220 bed hospital at a cost of £2,900 was modified due to rising costs of materials, and accommodation for only 120 fever patients was planned. The building was opened in 1829, but due to a temporary lull in the number of fever patients admitted to the Royal, was only partly commissioned.

> But the partial truce which the epidemic now observes, cannot, if we judge from the past, be expected to last long; and when the victims of contagion shall again become numerous, the Fever House will serve a double purpose - it will afford the means of cure to the destitute sufferers, and will also contribute to the public safety, by insulating many sources of morbific influence, to which persons of every rank are exposed.

Fever patients accounted for the largest number of admissions to the Royal Infirmary suffering from any one disorder throughout the period 1816–60. There was some annual variation in the figures for fever admissions, peaking in the years 1818, 1832, 1837, 1847 and 1851–2 when typhus reached epidemic proportions in the city. Even outside these years, 'continued fever', principally typhus, maintained the highest occurrence of all disease admissions for the whole period (See Figure 1, which lists the number of patients admitted to the Royal in the thirty years between 1822 and 1852 suffering from a range of illnesses). Within the decade from 1822 to 1832, the number of 'continued fever' patients rose from 229 to 1,509, and was never less than a thousand in the years between 1827 and 1843.

The peak year for 'continued fever' admissions to the Royal was 1837, when 5,408 patients were admitted suffering from such fevers. The severe typhus epidemic, which resulted in a death-rate of 41 for every 1,000 of the city's population, led to further temporary measures by the infirmary's managers to augment the number of beds available. On this occasion the Board of Managers obtained the permission of the Glasgow Police Board to set up a temporary auxiliary fever hospital in the former police office.

Between the years 1836 and 1838, over 10,700 fever patients were admitted to the Royal and its temporary accommodation. Such high levels of fever admissions and the impossible burden they put on the resources of the infirmary led to two alternative proposals for increased permanent fever accommodation in the city. In 1838 the Glasgow 'Board of Health', which had been set up in 1831 by the city's magistrates,[7] with representatives of the police, medical and religious authorities, and funded from the rates, proposed that a chain of three fever hospitals be built in the overcrowded suburbs of Calton, Gorbals and Anderston, where most of the fever sufferers lived. The Board of Health already pursued a policy of tending to fever sufferers within their locality in an attempt to prevent the fever spreading to other parts of the city. In November 1831 a disused cotton mill in King Street in the east end of Glasgow was taken over by the Board of Health and fitted up with 135 beds for fever patients. After a meeting between the Board, the city magistrates and the managers of the infirmary, it was decided that this temporary fever 'asylum' should be run by the infirmary, so long as no cost would be incurred. In the course of 1832 1,145 patients were admitted to this temporary fever hospital. In 1838 the Board of Health asked that the Royal give up its own proposal to build an auxiliary fever hospital in the city centre, at Charlotte Street, and invest in the planned suburban fever hospitals. The managers firmly rejected this overture on the grounds that it would be a misuse of the infirmary's subscriptions.

> ...They cannot apply the funds of the Infirmary to the erecting of Hospitals in the suburbs under the application before them. But trust that the Infirmary Auxiliary Hospital they are about to erect, will be sufficient to meet any exigency which may occur hereafter.

In the event neither scheme went ahead, and the infirmary continued to rely on the expanded fever hospital in its grounds, and ad hoc measures for additional accommodation as the need arose, such as the temporary use of the abandoned Lock Hospital, the venereal disease hospital, for the first six months in 1847. The Board of Health proposal, which was itself an indication of a growing awareness of the need for a unified public health policy, came to nothing as the immediate need for increased fever hospital accommodation was lessened by the temporary remission in the number of fever cases in the city.

There were later concerted attempts to increase public provision for fever patients in Glasgow. In 1847, during the worst typhus epidemic in the city over the whole period 1816–60 (coinciding with a time of unparalleled agricultural distress), when the death rate reached 56 per 1,000 of the population,[8] the infirmary erected another temporary fever shed in Anderston, which was partially financed by Barony Parochial Board. A change in organisation of parish relief in Scotland had occurred as a result of the Poor Law Amendment (Scotland) Act of 1845.[9] Poor relief was now placed in the hands of lay parochial boards (later known as parish councils), which had powers to raise funds necessary to provide relief for their parish, replacing previous local kirk session provision. Later in 1847, which witnessed the highest number of fever admissions to the infirmary since the peak in 1837, a committee of the managers of the infirmary approached the Police Board (another new local authority occasioned by municipal government reform) '...to impress upon them the necessity of aiding the Directors in taking vigorous measures for arresting the progress of fever in the city'.

By the time of the 1847 epidemic the figures for typhus admissions had been separated from those of other forms of fever. Typhus accounted for 2,399 from a total of over 4,700 'continued fever' admissions. The last great typhus epidemic in the city occurred in 1852 (the final year of the period covered in Figure 1). In that year 1,297 typhus admissions were recorded, and 297 other 'continued fever' patients were admitted.

Despite the growing municipal involvement in public health provision demonstrated by the schemes to secure temporary fever accommodation epidemic outbreaks remained the concern of the voluntary hospitals and not yet local government. The Royal, which relied on private subscriptions for its funding, remained the chief source of treatment for citizens of Glasgow who succumbed to epidemic disease. Yet the involvement of the city's Police Board and particularly, local parochial boards, is suggestive of a changing emphasis in health provision. By the mid nineteenth century the problem of epidemic disease, and public health generally, was too great to be solved by calls for increased individual subscriptions to the city's infirmary. Indeed, the financial co-operation sought for and obtained by the infirmary's managers in 1847, for assistance from the Barony Parochial Board, in providing temporary fever accommodation, highlights a change in municipal provision for public health needs. Money was diverted from parochial poor relief funds to the infirmary to pay for this short-term measure. More generally, parish poor rates came to be used to pay for the admission of poor patients to the infirmary, in the wake of the reform of the Scottish Poor Law. For example, during the typhus epidemic of 1847, the city's Parochial Board acted to secure the disused former Town's Hospital buildings (The Town's Hospital had moved in 1842 to premises formerly occupied by Glasgow Asylum in Parliamentary Road in the city's east end), which were fitted up to serve as a temporary fever house.

CHOLERA

In contrast to the great numbers of typhus patients admitted to the infirmary, the number of patients admitted suffering from cholera was never of the same magnitude, despite the outbreak of epidemics in the city in 1832, 1848–9 and 1853–4. This had much to do with the virulent nature of the disease, where sudden death, sometimes in a matter of hours, occurred, limiting the number of sufferers who could be conveyed to hospital. Cholera originated in Asia, where epidemics had occurred for many centuries, before it first came to the attention of European doctors after an epidemic in India in 1817. The first epidemic in Britain occurred in 1831–2 and there were further epidemics in 1841 (the most severe), 1853, and in 1865–6. Cholera is transmitted through infected water, or carried by flies which contaminate food. The disease is characterised by the sudden onset of painless diarrhoea and vomiting. This is followed by cramps in limbs and then the abdomen. The patient has a dreadful thirst and becomes exhausted. The next stage is one of collapse, where the patient becomes cold and the voice is reduced to a whisper. Death frequently occurs within twenty-four hours at this stage. The death-rate can reach over 50 per cent in epidemics. It is a disease which is more virulent among the very young and old.[10]

The impact of the first cholera epidemic in 1832 on the infirmary was not measured by the number of admissions of those suffering from the disease, but on the immediate effect the epidemic had on the finances of the hospital. There were no recorded cases specified as cholera in the infirmary reports for 1832. A total of 1,509 cases of 'continued fever' (100 less than in 1831) were admitted in that year. Yet the recorded death-rate for the epidemic in the city reached 2,842 (an average of 46 per 1,000).[11] Meanwhile, in November 1832, the level of subscriptions made to the infirmary for the planned addition to the fever hospital was so adversely affected by the calls on public charity by the prevailing cholera outbreak that the treasurer was given permission to overdraw on the infirmary's bank funds by £1,000 to help pay for the fever hospital expansion.

The next cholera epidemic in Glasgow occurred in 1848–9. Arrangements for meeting the threat of the epidemic were drawn up by the Board of Managers on 6 October 1848, the day news of a cholera outbreak in Edinburgh reached the Royal. The infirmary's fever hospital was set aside for cholera patients, and other fever sufferers were sent to the fever sheds. Temporary wooden fever accommodation had been put up on the infirmary site as the situation demanded, for twenty years. The first fever shed had been erected in 1828, the latest in 1847. After the cholera epidemic of 1853–4 the sheds, which accommodated 150 beds, were used to house ordinary medical and surgical cases, until they had ceased to be used after falling into a state of disrepair. They were finally pulled down in 1860 as building work began on the infirmary's new surgical block.

In November 1848 the latest cholera epidemic reached Glasgow. The number of patients admitted to the Royal was not great due to the high mortality rates of the disease. Of 73 recorded cholera admissions to the infirmary in the last two months of 1848, 37 died.

> ...during the last few weeks, the Epidemic has become very general over the city, and has been attended with an appalling amount of mortality, commonly singling out its victims from among the haunts of poverty and wretchedness, but in no small number of instances attacking persons in higher walks of life.

On 8 October 1848, two days after reports of the cholera outbreak in Edinburgh, a letter was received from Barony Parish asking if the infirmary would be willing to receive cholera patients from the parish. The managers replied that the Royal was willing to accept cholera patients, on condition that a separate account was kept to monitor the cost of their treatment, and that the parish agreed to meet the cost of each patient treated. Within two days a general arrangement had been reached with all the local parishes, Barony, City, Gorbals and Govan, agreeing to accept up to 220 cholera patients into the infirmary's fever hospital, and to keep a separate account of each parochial board's financial liability.

The epidemic continued into 1849, but as in the previous year, the number of cholera admissions to the infirmary was limited. Of the 139 cholera patients treated in the infirmary, 68 died. The infirmary's annual report for 1849, commenting on the epidemic, explained the limited number of patients treated for cholera in terms of the fearful rapidity of the disease, the unwillingness of sufferers to be taken from their homes, and the success of the precautionary measures adopted by the parochial boards to deal with the outbreak.

There was a similar story in the next cholera epidemic in 1853–4, when a combination of the virulence of the disease and growing basic parochial provision limited the number of cholera admissions to the infirmary.

> The rapidity with which the fatal symptoms of the disease attacked its victims precluded the possibility of many being sent to the Hospital. Besides, preparations were made for a greater number of patients being promptly attended and treated in their own houses than on former occasions, and more accommodation was prepared by the Parochial Authorities of the city than was occupied at any period in the epidemic. A limited number of cases was received in the Infirmary.

The first years of the period 1816 to 1860 mark a transitional stage in both the infirmary's and the city's history, as the consequences of large scale industrialisation took their toll on the social conditions and the health of the working community. Also in this period there was an increase in the local authority health provision, as magistrates and parochial boards came to play a direct part in the financing and erection of temporary fever accommodation for the city. Throughout these years however, the infirmary retained its pivotal role as the chief public health institution in Glasgow. It is no coincidence that local authority temporary arrangements were administered by the infirmary's managers, or that application was made to the Royal before any temporary measures were enacted.

THE IMPACT OF URBANISATION & INDUSTRIALISATION ON GLASGOW ROYAL INFIRMARY

The urbanisation of Glasgow in the nineteenth century left a familiar legacy of overcrowding, deficient sanitation and poor nutrition on the city's labouring population.

> Although the population increased 5-fold between 1801 and 1861, the whole of the Glasgow of 1775 remained geographically intact. There was in the centre of this rapidly expanding conurbation a medieval city covering about 100 acres with narrow winding ill-paved streets which were quite unsuited to the requirements of an industrial city. The central business district, including the new City Chambers, had moved west, and much of the new industry had fanned out along both sides of the Clyde and to the north. The middle classes had moved west, leaving the declining areas to the poorest classes. Virtually no demolition took place, and indeed, the demand for cheap dwellings was so great that former middle-class gardens were filled with jerry-built back tenements.[12]

Even without the ravages of epidemic fever, the health of Glasgow's expanding population deteriorated in the first half of the nineteenth century, as the lack of fresh water supply, malnutrition and cyclical unemployment combined with overcrowded living conditions, to make Glasgow a classic example of the worst consequences of rapid industrialisation.

It was a combination of these factors which made the working-class inhabitants of the suburbs and east end of the city particularly susceptible to epidemic disease. Fever patients were different from the Royal's usual clientele of 'respectable poor'. Reference to the Royal's records has already demonstrated that the vast majority of fever patients admitted in the period 1816-60 were from the city's overcrowded working-class centre and suburbs. Within this community the newest, lowest paid, arrivals to the city were even more at risk. The Royal Infirmary annual report for 1827 identified the majority of fever patients admitted to the infirmary as Irish labourers. The Irish community in Glasgow expanded during the nineteenth century as increased employment opportunities in a growing city combined with the starvation level subsistence in Ireland to make the city a magnet for those wishing to improve their standard of living. By 1851 18.17 per cent of the population of Glasgow gave Ireland as their place of birth.[13] The Royal's 1858 annual report listed for the first time the place of birth of patients admitted in the course of the year. From a total of 2,717 admissions, 1,677 were Scottish. Of the non-Scottish patients 918 were Irish, with the next highest figure of foreign-born patients numbering seventy-nine who were born in England. Among fever admissions (which of course, did not require a subscriber's admission line) the proportion of Irish-born patients was even greater. From a total of 510 fever admissions, 343 were Scottish, 148 were Irish and nineteen hailed from elsewhere.

Great numbers of people from the Highlands also moved to the city seeking to improve their prospects. They too suffered from the side-effects of poor housing, overcrowding and malnutrition. In the 1840s, special arrangements were made to provide infirmary care for Highland migrants in the city. Highland society was deeply affected by the potato blight which destroyed this staple food. The blight of 1845–6 left over 100,000 people in the Highlands destitute and dependent on charity relief funds to avoid starvation.[14] Many subsequently left the region in search of improved living standards. In May 1845 Reverend Dr MacLeod of the Highland Destitution Fund (and minister of Barony Church, the Royal's local parish), appeared before the managers of the infirmary to offer to apportion part of the Fund to the infirmary in return for the treatment of '... such Strangers coming to Glasgow and requiring medical aid as they had no parochial or other claim'. Later that month the managers of the infirmary agreed to accept a payment of £500 in return for the

Destitution Fund securing the right to recommend no more than twenty 'poor sick or maimed persons from the Highlands and Islands' per year. There is no specific mention of accepting fever patients but the admission of this category of patients was on a separate basis of need and pressure on accommodation decided by the Fever Committee.

In 1851 a smallpox epidemic broke out in the city. Of 163 patients admitted to the Royal, thirty died. The annual report for that year identified the majority of the victims as Highland people recently arrived in the city.

> The mortality which occurred among this class of patients, was chiefly confined to individuals who had not received the benefit of vaccination, a neglect of this important remedial agent being still observable among our Highland population, and seen to be fraught with the most injurious results.

A renewed outbreak of smallpox in 1857 led the infirmary to begin a free vaccination service at its dispensary. Most of the recipients were children. In addition to initiating this service the infirmary's managers sent a memorial to the Lord Advocate for Scotland asking that a law be introduced to make vaccination compulsory in Scotland, as it was in England. Support for the introduction of this measure was sought from the members of Parliament for the city. By the end of 1858, 1,063 free vaccinations had been carried out in the infirmary dispensary. Smallpox was not, however, eradicated, leading the annual report for 1859 to conclude:

> It has been long observed that persons coming from the Highlands to large cities are especially liable to be attacked by this disease [smallpox]. Many female servants, labourers and mechanics in this city come from the Highlands, and when small pox appears they are among its first victims, and are the means of propagating it among the families, and in the houses and factories in which they are employed. It would be very desirable that the rule which prevails in some countries, that no person will receive employment, and that no child will be admitted into the schools, who does not produce satisfactory evidence of his having been vaccinated, should be adopted in this country.

ACCIDENT ADMISSIONS

The increased propensity to fall victim to epidemic disease among the new arrivals to Glasgow was one aspect of the urbanisation and industrialisation of the city which had an impact on the Royal. Another was the growing number of accident admissions. From its outset the infirmary had opened its doors to accident cases without recommendation. The cost of treatment was therefore supported by the infirmary's own funds. By the mid nineteenth century the number of accident admissions had considerably increased, creating an extra burden on the running costs of the infirmary.

In 1845 the annual report included a table of the number of accidents treated in the infirmary. The table included all accident admissions to the infirmary; some, such as gunshot wounds and dog bites, were not a result of the expanding industrial base of the city. Many, however, can be directly attributed to factory and works accidents (see Figure 2), such as machinery, railway and coal pit accidents, which accounted for ninety of the 576 accident admissions in 1845. Other types of accidents such as burns, falls from height, and being hit by weights, which account for 222 of the accident admissions for the year, may well have occurred in the workplace, but there is not sufficient information given in the infirmary's accident table to prove this conclusively since place of work is not given. Almost 10 per cent (fifty-five) of the accident patients admitted in this year died.

Although the number of accident admissions was not listed in the infirmary's reports in the years before 1845, the figures for numbers of operations performed were given, revealing a steady rise. In 1827, 2,930 patients were admitted to the infirmary, of these only ninety-one had operations. Amputations accounted for thirty-five of the operations performed that year. Twelve of the ninety-one patients died. By 1845, when 2,635 in-patients were treated at the infirmary, the number of operations performed had risen to 175, of which sixty-seven were amputations. No separate mortality figures were given for operations, although it is likely that they accounted for some of the fifty-five accident mortalities for this year.

The growing number of accident admissions by the 1840s was a cause for concern among the infirmary's managers.

Accident Admissions to the Royal in 1845

	Total Cases	Dismissed		Died	
		M	F	M	F
Assaults	22	4	18	0	0
Burns	76	43	27	2	4
Bites (dog)	2	1	0	1	0
Coal pit accidents	23	19	0	4	0
Cut-throat	3	2	0	1	0
Crushes between walls, vehicles, etc	7	6	0	1	0
Falls on ground	70	46	21	1	2
Falls from a height	59	25	33	1	0
Gunshot accidents	72	51	10	6	5
Kicks (horse)	6	5	0	1	0
Machinery accidents	61	43	12	5	1
Railway accidents	6	4	0	2	0
Run over by carts/carriages/horses	28	20	7	1	0
Thrown from carts/carriages/horses	15	13	1	1	0
Thrust arm through window	1	0	1	0	0
Trod on piece of glass	2	1	1	0	0
Weights and heavy articles falling on	74	62	4	7	1
Unknown	45	31	6	8	0
Total	572	376	141	42	13

Figure 2

The urgency of accident and operation cases, renders it necessary to give to these a preference over cases of a lingering and chronic character... During the last year, a very large number of casualties of this kind have occurred, and have been attended with a proportionate increase of mortality. The most prolific sources of these have been the Public Works in and around Glasgow, the various Railroads leading in to the city, and the numerous Collieries of the mining districts.

The increasing mortality rates caused by such admissions added to the apprehension caused by the mounting cost of treating non-subscribed accident admissions. The pattern continued in the following decade. In

1853, 3,311 patients were admitted to the infirmary, 244 operations were undertaken resulting in thirty deaths. Of the operations carried out 104 were amputations, nineteen of which ended fatally. Other operations included the excision of lip cancers, reduction of humerus, and anal fistulas. In 1859 it was noted that accident admissions were '... as usual the chief cause of mortality in the Surgical department of the House'.

By the 1850s the increased local authority provision for fever patients by the parochial boards in the city, and the various temporary arrangements made for the treatment of fever patients outside the infirmary, had removed some of the pressure on beds in the hospital, and allowed more space to be provided for accident admissions. In 1852 three fever wards were made over for the treatment of additional surgical cases. The measure was a short-term one, since these wards could at any time be required to house fever patients in the event of a new epidemic outbreak. In 1853, therefore, the general court of the infirmary approved plans for a new surgical hospital to be built. Nothing further was done until 1857, when land adjoining the infirmary property was purchased and plans were drawn up for a 200-bed surgical hospital.

FINANCES OF THE INFIRMARY 1816-60

The financial position of the infirmary fluctuated during this period. The infirmary attempted on various occasions to force the local parochial boards to pay for the number of patients which they recommended to the infirmary, in excess of those to which they were entitled by their level of subscription. In 1829 various local parishes and representatives of the magistrates and of the Town's Hospital met with the Board of Managers, to object to this proposal, stressing that the majority of patients recommended by these institutions were fever patients, who under the infirmary's regulations were admitted to the hospital free of charge. In 1840 the Board of Managers again proposed that the various public bodies: Glasgow City, Barony and Gorbals parishes, the Police Board and the Town's Hospital, make up the considerable shortfall between their subscriptions and the number of patients they recommended annually to the infirmary.

Between January and August of 1840 it was noted that 1,379 patients were admitted without recommendation to the Royal. Of this number 206 were accident admissions, which by their pressing nature had always been, and continued to be, exempt from the usual rigours of obtaining a note of recommendation from an infirmary subscriber. The admission of the unrecommended patients had cost the infirmary £2,068. The infirmary sub-committee set up to investigate this anomaly suggested that the parishes in question be asked to contribute twenty-one shillings (although the actual cost of each patient was estimated at thirty shillings), for each additional patient they sent to the infirmary, beyond those for which they were entitled to recommend through their annual contributions, with the money to be taken from the local parish poor rates. The proposal was not put into operation at this stage, and it was not until after the change in the Scottish Poor Law in 1845 that the scheme was implemented. The appeal for increased parochial contributions towards the running costs of the infirmary was revived in 1847, with a renewed outbreak of typhus fever. The contribution of Barony Parish to the erection of a temporary fever house has been mentioned, and in addition the infirmary met the local parishes to press for an increase in the charges for fever admissions to the infirmary. A charge of twenty shillings per patient recommended by parochial boards was introduced on 10 June 1847 as an experiment dependent upon the subsequent state of funds of the infirmary. In August 1847 it was decided that the twenty shillings charge be continued until further notice, which suggests that the infirmary's financial position remained insecure faced with the increased demands placed upon it during this latest fever epidemic. In 1848 £923 was received from the various parochial boards in this way to meet the cost of fever patients. This income, plus the erection of their own temporary fever accommodation by the City and Barony boards lessened the pressures on the Royal.

An additional source of funds was sought by the infirmary in 1840 by the introduction of pay-beds to allow medical students and other 'respectable persons' to be treated on payment of fees, at a cost of twenty shillings per week for day and night attendance, and ten shillings for more limited care. The plan for pay-beds was first mooted in 1838, when it was envisioned that paying patients could be admitted to a separate fever ward, in order to avoid the embarrassment of admission to common fever wards. In 1843 the scheme of pay beds was extended to provide individual, private care for the more wealthy fever patients. The former Superintendent's accommodation, a two-storey house on infirmary grounds, was fitted up with beds for '... fever patients of the better class who are willing to pay one guinea per week...'

In view of the uncertain financial state of the infirmary in this period it is not surprising to discover that requests for general church collections, first begun in the early nineteenth century, were revived. This was notably successful in 1818, when £2,000 was raised for the infirmary. The response was less generous in 1828, when the infirmary's managers approached the Church of Scotland Synod of Glasgow and Ayr and the Synod of Argyll to request that a collection be held in all churches in order to help offset the construction costs of the planned fever house. A circular letter was similarly sent to the various dissenting churches asking for collections to be taken up at services. On this occasion, less than £600 was raised. The continued pressure to provide accommodation for typhus sufferers on request, led to a deficit in the infirmary's finances in 1831, and again a request was made to the Established and Dissenting Churches to hold a collection to make up the shortfall. A further collection was granted the Royal by the Presbytery in Glasgow in 1837, during the severe typhus epidemic. In 1847 the outbreak of a further epidemic of typhus again stretched the finances of the infirmary to the extent that another church collection was requested from 'clergy of all denominations', to help finance the cost of the emergency fever accommodation provided by the Royal.

A new and increasingly significant source of income for the infirmary in this period came from contributions and subscriptions received from a growing number of factories, collieries and public works in the area. In 1841 subscriptions from 'operatives and seamen' to the infirmary accounted for £632 of the £8,331 of the annual income of the infirmary. By 1849 the collections from these workers had risen to £1,014, compared to £2,521 received in annual subscriptions for that year. Among the firms whose employees contributed to the Royal were:

Clyde Iron Works	£29.13.0
Edinburgh and Glasgow Railway, Cowlairs Station	9.09.0
Kelvin Haugh Weaving Factory	3.11.5
Neilson Quarry	2.08.0

An analysis of the 103 works and factories which contributed to the infirmary in 1849, includes fifty-one firms whose trade was listed in the annual report: twenty were foundries, nine were mills, four were collieries, three were colliery/iron works, two were railway companies, two were distilleries, one was a shipping firm, and ten were spread among various single trades.

By 1858 the contributions received from employees in public works had risen to £1,850. A further £110 was contributed by steamship crews and captains. Annual subscriptions amounted to £3,417 in the same year. Among the 225 firms contributing to the infirmary in this year were fifty-two foundries and iron works; twenty-three mills; twenty-one collieries; five shipping lines, four railway companies and three engineering firms. Eighty companies did not list their trade, and thirty-seven were from a variety of single trades. Given the great number of various companies' employees contributing towards the upkeep of the Royal it is beyond the scope of this history to discover which firms in fact sent patients to the infirmary. However, annual reports of the managers frequently referred to subscribers exceeding the number of patients they could recommend, rather than otherwise.

Despite the growing importance of the income generated for the Royal from the increasing number of works subscriptions, the hospital still relied on numerous individual contributions and legacies to continue its operation. In 1848 James Cooke of the Royal Circus, Glasgow, staged a benefit show for the funds of the infirmary, which raised £32 14s 6d. At the other end of the scale, on her death in 1843 Miss Lucy Campbell of Gowan Bank, Campbeltown, left a sum of £1,000 to the Royal, given in exchange for the right of the Campbeltown Kirk Session to recommend 40 patients per year to the infirmary. In May 1843 the Royal's managers approved the terms of Lucy Campbell's settlement arranged by her trustees to allow the Kirk Session to recommend patients according to the terms of the bequest. In 1852 (possibly as a consequence of the Disruption in the Church of Scotland) the settlement was altered to secure the right of admission to the infirmary for those hailing from Campbeltown who had moved to Glasgow in search of employment.

> Occasionally paupers from this parish fall ill in Glasgow and there is no chance of getting an admission order from this Parish in time to be of service to them. It is proposed that if any such ill paupers apply to parishes in Glasgow or neighbourhood for admission, [this] should be granted them on

account of their membership of this Parish.

The overall financial position of the Royal changed considerably in the course of the period under review. In 1827 the infirmary had an income of £7,843. This was made up of £2,807 in annual subscriptions, £1,715 in legacies and donations, £311 in annual contributions, £550 from students' fees and diplomas; £400 in income from bonds, £78 in rents and £832 in sundries. In addition there was a bank balance of £1,131 and a cash balance of £15.

The infirmary's expenditure for the same year consisted of £2,994 on provisions, soap, candles etc.; £1,035 on medical provisions, including salaries, medicines, and wines and spirits; £688 for furniture and repairs; £178 for printing and stationery, £25 in legatees' annuities; and £307 towards the cost of building the Blind Asylum. The infirmary's bank balance was £2,612, and £2 remained in cash. The general state of funds seemed healthy, with over £17,000 invested in bonds and property, and including the infirmary's bank balance. By 1841 however the permanent funds of the infirmary had been eroded to less than £14,800, due to a working deficit for the year of £2,429. The volatile financial position of the infirmary in this period reflected the sudden drain on its resources which could result from outbreaks of epidemic fever. A major task of the Royal's managers was therefore to ensure that the institution had sufficient reserves to cope with the financial demands of the severest epidemic outbreaks and the sudden surge in unsubsidised admissions they occasioned.

The sums spent on medicines in the Royal serve as an indication of the limited level of curative treatment at this time. In 1841 an expenditure of £340 on drugs was exceeded by the £377 spent on liquors used for medicinal purposes. The position had not greatly altered by 1858, when £328 was spent on drugs and lint, while £332 was expended on port wine, whisky and beer. It is possible that some of this substantial amount of alcohol was for private consumption by the Board of Managers and the medical staff. The fact that a further £38 was spent on lemonade and soda water reinforces this suggestion. An indication of the changing face of medicine in the mid nineteenth century can be inferred by the £19 expended by the infirmary in this year on chloroform for anaesthetic purposes. Yet evidence of the application of this development in surgical practice is counterbalanced by reference to the purchase of 1,250 leeches at a cost of £11.

In 1860 the financial difficulties which had dogged the infirmary throughout the period remained. Although the managers ruled out a further approach to the Glasgow parochial boards for a church collection it was decided to make a concerted effort to target the small shopkeepers and traders in the city, in order to get 'that class' to contribute more funds than hitherto to the infirmary. Two additional collectors were employed as an experiment by the infirmary, to visit the small shopkeepers and traders personally, in order to increase the number of subscriptions from this group.

THE APPOINTMENT OF A MEDICAL SUPERINTENDENT

The increasing size of the infirmary, and the constant demands placed on hospital accommodation in this period of epidemics and increasing accident admissions, led to the introduction of the office of resident Medical Superintendent to oversee the administration of the institution. The creation of the post was first mooted in November 1830 by a meeting of the managers. The matter was remitted to a sub-committee, who approved the creation of the new post and drew up a series of regulations for the post-holder. The Superintendent was to be an unmarried man aged between 35 and 45, of active business habits, and a good accountant. His duties were to include the inspection of the wards for cleanliness twice daily, and to ensure the good behaviour of the patients. He was to pay all the domestic servants, and to supervise all the male servants of the institution. In addition he was to keep charge of all clerks' ward books, and to keep account of medical student fees paid, and of all medical materials supplied to the infirmary. He was to control access to the infirmary's 'dead room' (morgue), and to prevent any unauthorised dissection taking place. In return for these duties the Superintendent was to board at the infirmary, and to receive a salary of £100.

It was not until 1832 that the post was eventually advertised in the press. Even after re-advertisement, however, it was decided not to appoint anyone to the position, in view of the poor quality of the candidates interviewed, and the great responsibility of the post. It was not until 1838 that a suitable candidate, Robert Martin, 'a man of active business habits' was appointed by a decision of a large majority of the selection committee. He served until 1843, when he was suspended for an unauthorised absence from the infirmary, and tendered his resignation one week later. After this, the post of Superintendent was filled on a temporary basis by the infirmary Chaplain, Mr Blair. The demanding nature of the post as hospital accountant, administrator and personnel manager, and the level of remuneration which was therefore required, were such that the managers decided not to reappoint a Superintendent, but to adopt the less expensive alternative of distributing his duties among other existing members of staff at the infirmary, for example, that of personnel devolving upon the Matron. Most of the administrative duties fell on the infirmary's Apothecary, who after 1843 was given the title Superintendent-Apothecary.

NURSING AND OTHER STAFF

An indication of the pressures on the staff caused by the number of fever patients admitted in this period can be taken from the decision by the managers in October 1828 to increase the wage rates of nurses in the fever wards from seventeen shillings a month for day nurses to £1 per month. Night nurses received an increase from fifteen to seventeen shillings. There was no major review of the duties of the nursing staff until 1837, when it was recommended that a female medical Superintendent be appointed to oversee the work of the nurses employed by the infirmary. It was further recommended that the female superintendent take charge of the wines and spirits prescribed for patients, to ensure that there was no misuse of them by the nursing staff. No female superintendent was in fact appointed, and it was decided that the physician's clerks be put in charge of the administration of wines and spirits to patients. These comments suggest that the nursing staff were suspected of abusing the alcohol provided for medicinal purposes. In contrast, there were occasions when individual nurses were rewarded for their good service:

> On the motion of Dr. Perry [Physician]… it was unanimously resolved that Nelly —, the Nurse, receive a retiring allowance of £1 per month till further orders. To be laid out in such a way as the House Committee may from time to time [consider] as most eligible. This allowance being granted solely in consideration of her having served the House faithfully

for a continuous period of above 35 years—being the only instance of such lengthened service:—and not to be considered as a precedent.

In 1851, in what seems to have been an attempt to encourage similar long-term service, nurses' salaries were increased by an unspecified sum 'proportionate to length of service'. Other staff too received gifts for long service in the infirmary. In 1847 Miss Brodie, who had worked for many years as Matron, retired, and was awarded £100 in recognition of her sterling performance in this office. However, even towards the end of this period there was still little evidence to suggest that nurses were coming to be recognised as a distinct category of medical attendant. In the full accounts for the year 1858, while separate entries appear listing the salaries of the chaplain (£100), the matron (£60), and the janitor (£50), the wages of all 'Male servants, Female, Half-yearly servants, Nurses and other domestics' are quoted together in a lump sum of £1,095.

STAFF BACKGROUND

From the infirmary's inception, medical staff were invariably local residents. As the nineteenth century wore on however, there is evidence of medical appointments to the infirmary becoming less parochial. It is also the case that staff members often left to work elsewhere. In 1853 Dr Steele, the superintendent-apothecary, resigned his post in order to take up a similar position at Guy's Hospital in London. Candidates for the post as his replacement hailed from Dundee, Perth, Cumnock and Holytown, and two from Glasgow. Dr James McGhie of the Royal Lunatic Asylum at Gartnavel in Glasgow was appointed to the post. In 1856 candidates for the post of matron came from Edinburgh, Darlington, Glasgow and Limerick. Mrs Elizabeth Struthers from Edinburgh was appointed. The exception to this new trend was in the appointment of physicians and surgeons to the infirmary. As far as these positions were concerned, the hospital remained, with few exceptions, a closed shop of Glasgow-based medical practitioners. This was, no doubt, in part due to the fact that the Faculty of Physicians and Surgeons of Glasgow continued to limit appointments to these posts to Faculty members.[15] In 1859 two posts, one of physician, and one of surgeon, fell vacant for election. Of the twelve candidates listed as applying for these two positions, all, according to their

Medical Directory entries for that year, were experienced men, currently in medical practice in Glasgow.[16] Among the candidates for the surgeon's post was James Morton, a St Andrews medical graduate who practised in West Regent Street, and who lectured on Materia Medica at Anderson's College. Another candidate, George H.B. MacLeod of 10 Woodside Crescent, was a Glasgow graduate, who was surgeon at the Western Dispensary and the Lock Hospital, and Professor of Surgery at Anderson's College. He had formerly served as Senior Surgeon at the Civilian Hospital at Smyrna (now Izmir) and in the British army's General Camp Hospital before the battle of Sebastopol, during the Crimean War. Morton secured election for the post on this occasion, although MacLeod later served as surgeon, 1869 to 1874.

DISPENSARY PROVISION

A new service introduced in these years was the replacement of the former out-patients' service of the infirmary by a dispensary, and the appointment of physicians and surgeons to attend to this area of the infirmary's health care. In 1835 the decision was taken to add a dispensary to the Royal. Previously, out-patients were diagnosed and given a prescription to be made up at an apothecary's shop. There was no continuity of medical service for out-patients, who would most likely be seen by a different medical attendant on each visit to the out-patients room. A free dispensary service was introduced on a limited scale for a trial period of one year at the end of 1835. The scheme was not simply promoted by humanitarian ideals, it was clearly hoped the provision of a fuller out-patient service would lessen the pressure for admission to the infirmary as an in-patient.

> The Managers have to submit to the General Court [of contributors], for their sanction, a plan by which this part of our economy may be much improved, and rendered more satisfactory to the public. It is proposed that one of the Surgeons... shall take charge of the Waiting Room... giving advice to Medical and Surgical patients indiscriminately... That the prescriptions, after being put on record, be made up by a Dispensary Pupil, and the medicines so prepared be dispensed gratuitously to the Patient, or his friends, out of the stock of drugs kept at the Infirmary laboratory.

In 1837, 3,379 patients were attended to in the dispensary, with medicines amounting to a cost of £35 prescribed free to many. In 1840 the managers decided to end the provision of free medicines at the dispensary, due perhaps to the rising costs of this service which attracted increasing numbers of out-patients. This did not diminish the popularity of the new service however, and in 1852, 6,763 patients were treated at the dispensary.

> ...the benefits accruing from the department of Dispensary aid, as well as the popularity attending its operation among the industrious poor, are evinced by the large and increasing numbers who annually flock to the Hospital for advice from all parts of the west of Scotland.

In 1855 the dispensary provision was enlarged with the employment of one physician and one surgeon from the infirmary's staff to attend daily, except Sunday. The physician and surgeon served in the dispensary for one year, at a salary of £30 per annum. The doubling of medical staff led to an immediate increase in the number of patients treated from 7,380 in 1855, to 10,193 in 1856.

A PROFESSIONAL DISPUTE

It is no surprise that periodic professional confrontations and personality clashes came to the fore in the Royal as in any large institution. One of the earliest of these was a professional dispute between two members of the medical staff. Although settled in the end by committee investigation, the dispute threatened to lead to violence in the form of a duel between the two warring colleagues. One of the men involved, Granville Sharp Pattison, was remarkable for the figure he cut in early nineteenth-century Glasgow medicine. Despite his involvement in resurrectionist activities Pattison was appointed as a junior surgeon at the Royal in 1815 and on two occasions in late 1816 acted against the expressed wishes of Hugh Millar, senior surgeon and a manager of the infirmary. In two cases, those of John Young and Jean Goudie, Pattison carried out amputations and the outcome was fatal. Allegations of professional misconduct on the part of Pattison were made by Millar and an investigation by a committee of inquiry was undertaken. It was during their depositions before the committee that Pattison challenged Millar to a duel to settle what he viewed

as an attack upon his honour. The charges were that Pattison had not followed the recognised consultation procedures and disregarded the advice
of his fellow surgeons, acting on his own judgement in both amputations
(leg in the case of Young and arm in that of Goudie). After investigation,
in the case of Young, Pattison was found to have failed to comply with
the directions of the consultation by amputating further up the leg than
had been agreed. In the case of Jean Goudie, who was viewed by Millar
as a hopeless case who ought to have been left to die in peace and not
operated upon, no blame was attached, but Pattison ought to have
informed the two senior surgeons in view of the seriousness of the operation. Pattison was not removed from office, but was urged in future '…to
attend implicitly to the regulations of the House regarding consultations
and operations'. The managers' displeasure was further illustrated by the
absence of Pattison's name from the traditional vote of thanks to the medical members of staff in the Annual Report for 1816. Millar's triumph was
short-lived. Having been present as a manager at the meetings which
effectively censured Pattison in January 1817, he had to accept a resolution at the annual meeting a few days later that no person could be a
director and a medical attendant of the Royal at the same time. Millar
resigned as Director in October 1817.[17]

THE FACULTY OF PHYSICIANS AND SURGEONS OF GLASGOW VERSUS THE MEDICAL SCHOOL

The main area where the University of Glasgow medical school came
into confrontation with the Faculty of Physicians and Surgeons of
Glasgow in the Royal was over the provision of clinical teaching at the
hospital. A side issue was the method of selection of medical staff to the
infirmary, appointments which remained, with few exceptions, under the
control of Faculty. In this period, despite the acrimonious nature of the
struggle for influence over infirmary medical appointments and teaching,
the main focus of the rivalry was over the right to examine and award
degrees in surgery. This major dispute was played out in the courts,
including a resort to the House of Lords, but often the friction created by
the litigation was all too clearly in evidence in infirmary affairs.

In 1823 the medical committee of the Board of Managers met to discuss the possibility of opening the post of physician at the Royal to all
those medically qualified and of sufficient experience to be considered

eligible for the position. There was no mention of membership of the Faculty of Physicians and Surgeons of Glasgow as a requisite for selection. This proposal was not put into operation, but pressure for change in staffing and teaching methods at the infirmary was maintained. In 1824 the managers were presented with a report from the Principal of the University of Glasgow on the position of clinical lectures in surgery at the infirmary. The Principal's report concluded that clinical surgical instruction at the infirmary should be more closely integrated with surgical teaching at the University.

It was proposed that the Professor of Surgery, John Burns, be appointed an ex-officio lecturer in clinical surgery to the infirmary, with a remit to select those surgical cases which he deemed most appropriate for clinical instruction purposes. To encourage student attendance at the clinical lectures the University report suggested that they be made part of the requirement for a degree in surgery at the University, as was the case with the diploma at the Royal College of Surgeons in Edinburgh. This radical plan, which was influenced by the recent introduction of the new degrees of Master and Bachelor of Surgery by the University in 1817, was bitterly opposed by the Faculty of Physicians and Surgeons of Glasgow. Although the motives of the University Senate in setting up these new degree courses are not disclosed in their minutes, the imminence of the lawsuit regarding the rights of Doctors of Medicine to practise surgery within the territory of the Faculty was clearly an influential factor in the decision.[18]

The Faculty's response was to send a memorial to the Royal expressing their opposition to the University's proposal, and to the recent introduction of surgical degrees.

> The Managers will understand what is meant when they learn, that the University has lately assumed a power, which no other similar body in the United Kingdom has done—induced no doubt by some motive or title tho' unknown to the public—It is well known that the Faculty are the only accredited licensing body for Surgery in this western district of the Kingdom - the University, like every other, granting medical degrees alone. Within these few years however, they have begun to issue certificates which the students present as regular surgical licences. Whether the College hold these bona fide as diplomas, the Faculty cannot tell. It is certain however, that the University have encroached on rights, which the Faculty

alone have for two hundred years exercised by Royal Charter and Parliamentary authority. Should the Managers therefore, accede to the proposal now before them they will be giving an undue preference to a body, whose services in their Hospital have not been more valuable than those of the Faculty.

Under such pressures from both sides to change the methods of clinical instruction, the managers took time to reach their decision, and after appointing a fresh medical committee to discuss the question, it was decided in November 1827 to drop the issue for the meantime. Due perhaps to the pressure for change in clinical instruction, there were regular classes in medicine and surgery delivered at the Royal that year. The 1827 annual report noted that clinical medicine classes were taken by Doctors Brown and Balmanno, attended by 32 students, while clinical surgery lectures were delivered by Doctors Anderson and Couper, attended by 62 students. However, since clinical courses were not an integral part of the duties of those appointed to the medical staff, selected as they were from the ranks of the Faculty of Physicians and Surgeons of Glasgow, rather than from the staff of the University's medical school, the problem of the lack of regular and systematic instruction continued. In 1829, in recognition of the continued difficulties in implementing a unified course of lectures, the infirmary managers set up a plan to ensure that clinical teaching was provided on a more regular basis.

> The primary object of our Institution is to cure the diseased poor; but it serves also another public purpose, it forms a school for medical experience... To ensure the full benefit of Hospital attendance, Clinical Lectures have been found necessary, and on various occasions it has been attempted to put this branch of instruction on a permanent footing, and to render the Infirmary as useful to our Medical School, as similar Institutions are in other parts of the United Kingdom. These attempts, for different reasons, have always failed; the Managers, therefore, have lately adopted a regulation, by which it becomes imperative on the Medical attendants to give Clinical Lectures in both departments of practice; while, at the time the pupils are obliged to pay a fee for this instruction at the time they purchase a ticket for liberty to attend the house. Thus the Lecturers are ensured of hearers, and of some encouragement for their services.

The success of this proposal seemed assured in the short term. In 1831 the managers reported that the scheme of scheduled clinical instruction had generated an income of almost £900 from student fees, £300 of which was paid to the lecturers and £600 to the infirmary's funds.

The managers' pleasure at the implementation of the new scheme of instruction was not echoed by student appreciation. In 1833 a letter was received from students attending the infirmary complaining of the inadequacy of the clinical instruction provided at the hospital. In response to student pressure the medical committee of the Board of Managers decided that from the beginning of the winter session, the physicians and surgeons were to deliver two classes per week in each subject to the students. Later that year the provision of clinical instruction was placed on a more solid financial foundation. Student fees were raised to seven guineas (£7.35), three guineas of which (£3.15) was shared equally among the medical staff involved in clinical teaching (this was later changed to half of the student fees of five guineas per year). This arrangement ensured that there was an audience for clinical classes, and that only those medical staff willing to teach students in the Royal received this additional source of income.

The largely complacent attitude towards clinical teaching at the infirmary, based as it apparently was on numbers enrolled, not the standard of clinical instruction provided, was shaken in 1834 with a visit by a House of Commons' Committee on Medical Education to the infirmary. It was feared that the Committee would propose that medical education be centralised in the London medical teaching hospitals, to the detriment of the Scottish medical schools. Although this did not happen, the fears of the infirmary's managers were real. 'In opposition to such a change, the Corporation of the Royal infirmary have a right and interest to interfere, our Pupils' fees contribute to our Funds at an average nearly £600 annually.'

The dispute between the Faculty and the medical school did not disappear after 1833, indeed it was not resolved until 1840, when a final appeal by the University regarding the prosecution of its surgical graduates for unlicensed medical practice in Glasgow was dismissed by the House of Lords, with costs of over £1,600 awarded against the University.[19] The row over clinical teaching allowed other medical schools to benefit. Anderson's College Medical School, which had grown steadily since its limited entry into medical instruction at the end of the eighteenth century, and had appointed eight additional medical lecturers between 1819 and 1840, attracted more students than the University in the years between 1840 and 1860.[20]

'RELIGIOUS' DISCORD

Another area of controversy had implications for the position of religious toleration in the city of Glasgow. Unlike those of the Church of Scotland, and dissenting churches, there was no specific mention of collections being taken up at Roman Catholic churches in the minutes or annual reports of the infirmary, despite the high numbers of Irish patients (some of whom were presumably Roman Catholic) treated at the hospital. It is not clear whether this was because no collections were taken up at Catholic churches, or due to prejudice against the Roman Catholic Church among some sections of the community, which could account for the omission of references to the contributions received from the Catholic population of Glasgow in the official records of the infirmary. Certainly, there was a degree of sustained tension in the relationship between the Management of the Royal and various Catholic chaplains who visited patients in the hospital in the period.

The 1830s and 40s were a time of rapid increase in the number of Irish immigrants arriving in Scotland and in the west in particular. Driven from their homeland by the bleak economic prospects of a country backward in industrial development and slow to introduce new agricultural methods, there were 125,000 Irish-born people listed as living in Scotland in the census of 1841. By the time of the Irish famine in 1848, caused by the blight on potatoes, the staple Irish diet, there were up to 1,000 new arrivals a week from Ireland into Glasgow. The weight of numbers of immigrants was enough to attract unfavourable reaction from the local community. Alienated in terms of ethnic and linguistic barriers, the new arrivals (many of them unused to industrial employment) found that the unskilled work which was open to them created barriers between them and skilled artisan lowlanders. This was heightened by the fact that many of the new arrivals were from Ulster, and already inured to sectarianism. Ulster Protestant immigrants fed off and reinforced the anti-Catholic prejudices of the local populace. The Catholic Irish immigrants were thereby pushed into a ghetto mentality, closing ranks behind the protective arms of the Roman Catholic Church.[21]

Against this background, between 1836 and 1848, a series of allegations of misconduct were made against several Roman Catholic priests acting as chaplains to Catholic patients in the infirmary. The matter was first raised in October 1836:

> The Weekly Committee having brought before the Court of Directors for consideration of certain improper interferences said to have taken place on the part of a Roman Catholic clergyman... It was unanimously resolved:- That the patients in the Infirmary announce to the House Medical Clerk to what religious denomination they belong or from what Minister they wish religious visitation; and that the Ministers of the various denominations who visit the House be instructed that it is now resolved unanimously by the Directors that they shall confine their intercourse exclusively to those who belong to their respective denominations.

The occasion for this directive was a number of incidents involving Father Peter Forbes, who was alleged to have 'improperly interfered' with Protestant patients by approaching them to offer ministration, and on one occasion to have administered the rite of extreme unction to a Protestant patient, a woman named Taylor who was delirious with fever. A letter to the infirmary's managers from Bishop John Murdoch, the head of Glasgow's Roman Catholics, explained that the patient in question was mistakenly entered on Father Forbes' list of Catholic patients at the hospital. However, since this was not the first incident of this type, Father Forbes was barred from the infirmary, and despite a letter of apology for the actions which had so displeased the managers, his ban was not lifted.

In 1841, three years after Father Forbes' ban, another Roman Catholic priest, Father Long, was prohibited from attending patients in the Royal for a similar incident at the fever house. Father Long was interdicted from entering the infirmary in consequence of 'improper conduct' in the fever hospital, and a letter confirming this decision, to take immediate effect, was sent to Bishop Murdoch. Bishop Murdoch and Father Long then sought a meeting with the managers to put their case, but after further investigation the suspension on Father Long remained. A further consequence of the incident was the introduction of new regulations for all clergy visiting patients in the Royal, with the exception of the hospital chaplain. All visits were to be confined to two hours in the day under the supervision of medical staff, and Catholic clergy were to be strictly controlled in their activities in the fever house, requiring a letter of consent from the Medical Superintendent, before individual patients could be seen.

In 1848 Father William Lillis was banned from the infirmary due to another incident of undue 'interference' with Protestant patients. As in earlier incidents, the minute books do not record the details of the case, only commenting that Father Lillis' conduct towards a patient, William Shields, and his wife, was 'unwarranted and improper and contrary to the rules of this House... and [they] ... prohibit the porter from attending Mr Lillis into the Hospital on any pretence...' The frequency of these occurrences suggests that there was a distinct lack of understanding between the managers of the infirmary and the Catholic clergy who visited patients there. That no compromise was reached further suggests that there was an undercurrent of mistrust of the Catholic priests visiting the infirmary, and that their activities were closely monitored for fear of what were regarded as improper approaches to the Protestant patients in the hospital.

1816-60: CONSOLIDATION AND FRESH CHALLENGES

The years between 1816 and 1860 were a time of rapid change in the history of the Royal. In common with the early years in the infirmary's history there were the perennial concerns regarding the funding of the institution and the increasing pressure on beds due to the expanding population of Glasgow and its suburbs. However, the later period also witnessed dramatic changes in the type and background of patient admissions to the infirmary. The problem of ever-increasing fever admissions and the strain this placed on the Royal's accommodation was the dominating feature of the period, but there was also a substantial increase in accident cases treated by the hospital staff. Both of these factors owed much to the emergence of Glasgow as one of Britain's leading industrial and population centres. The increase in patients sent to the infirmary on the basis of workers' subscription to factories and public works in the city was another area where the rapid expansion of Glasgow changed the face of hospital admissions.

Often the hospital was forced to turn away fever patients for lack of beds to accommodate them. Yet throughout these years, the Royal's

This old drawing shows the ruins of the Archbishop's Castle, prior to their demolition in 1792, to make way for the Infirmary. The west towers of the Cathedral of St Mungo were demolished in 1846-48.

The Royal from Rottenrow, c.1800. The cathedral, and R J Adam's Barony Church, are on the right.

John Burns (1774-1850),
one of the Royal's first surgeons.

A Lister ward, c.1864

Joseph Lister (1827-1912), who developed the antiseptic system of preventing wound infection

*Glasgow Royal Infirmary Surgical
Block in 1861. The building on
the right is the Fever Block.*

*William Macewen, fifth from the left,
preparing to operate, c.1892. The matron,
Rebecca Strong, is second from the right,
and Macewen's protégé, S Hogarth Pringle,
is the third doctor on the right.*

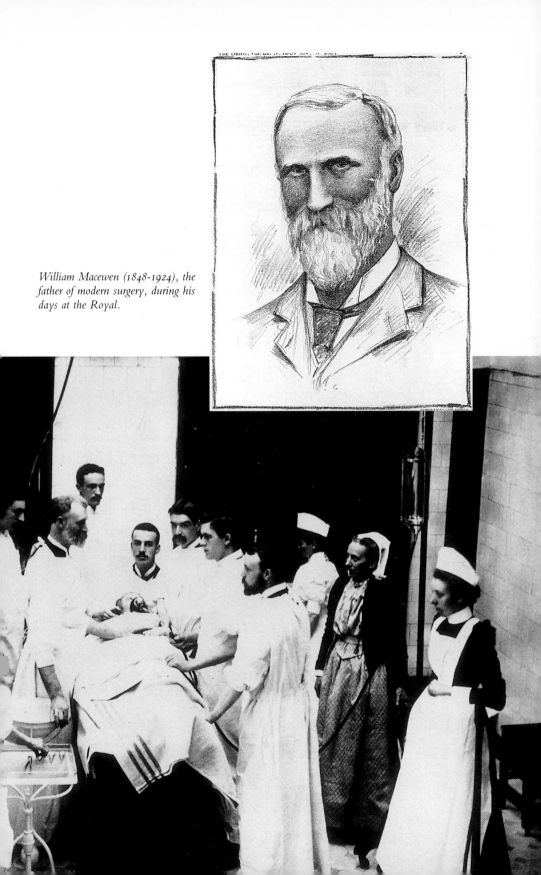

William Macewen (1848-1924), the father of modern surgery, during his days at the Royal.

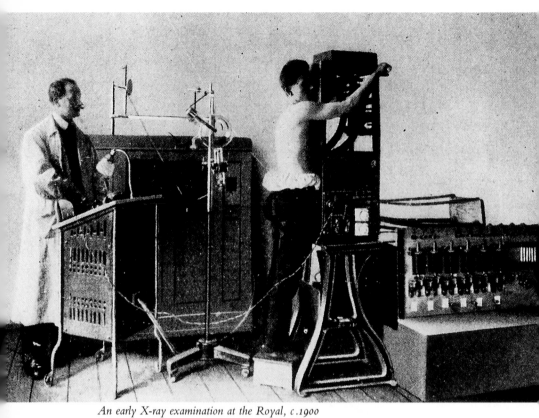

An early X-ray examination at the Royal, c.1900

Exterior of the X-ray department, c.1896

John Macintyre (1857-1928), set up the world's first hospital X-ray department

Miss Beatrice Clugston
(photographed about 1863), who formed the Dorcas Society
in the Royal to provide warm clothing for those in need

The Schaw Home, which opened in 1895

Programme for the Centenary ball, held in Glasgow City Chambers in 1894

Mabel Mackinlay, of the Dorcas Society, initiated the hospital's voluntary tearoom service for outpatients

The imposing new medical block, completed shortly before the First World War

The Dispensary outpatients waiting room, c.1914

Miss Jane Melrose and staff in the conservatory, c.1915

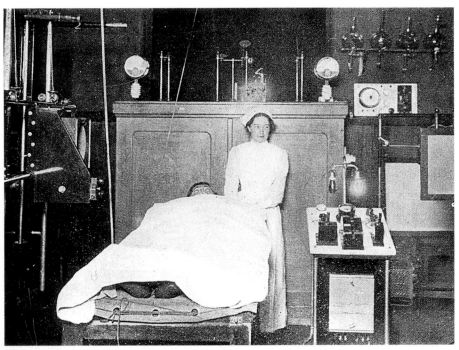

The X-Ray Photographic Room, c.1916

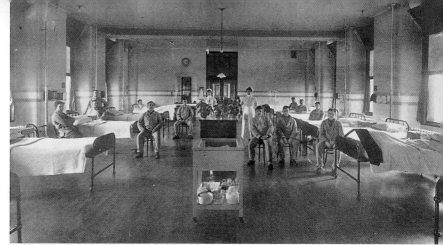

Ward B, for the treatment of wounded servicemen, 1915

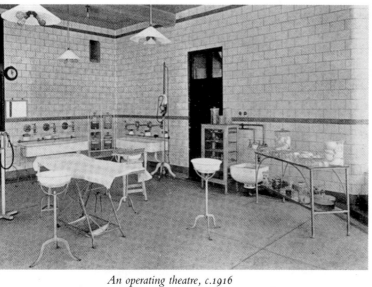

An operating theatre, c.1916

Below: *Nurses in the conservatory which connected the infirmary to the Nurses' Home, c.1916*

A nurse's bedroom, 1924

A classroom in the Teaching Department for Nurses, opened in 1927

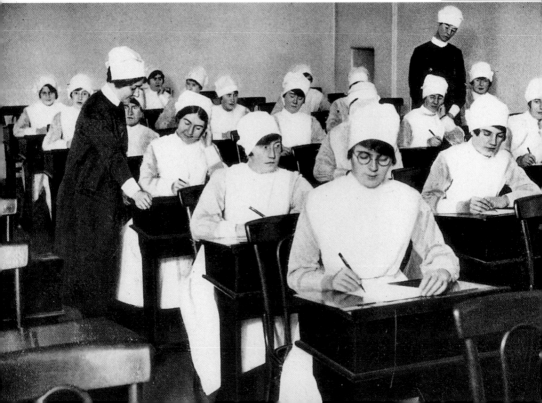

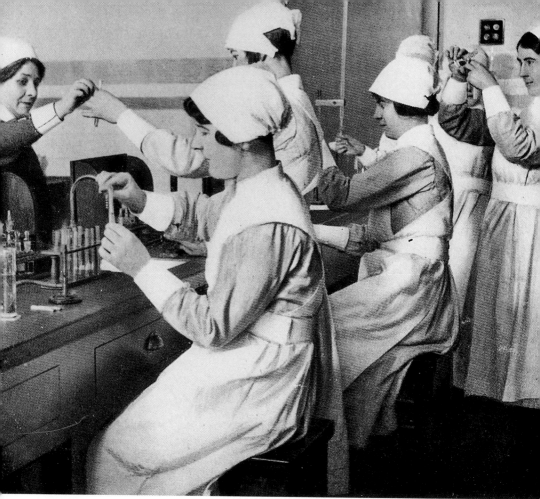

The laboratory in the Teaching Department for Nurses, 1927

The remains of the old Surgical Block, c.1925, awaiting demolition

David Cuthbertson (1900-83) at work in his laboratory, c.1930

Canniesburn Auxiliary Hospital from the air, c.1938

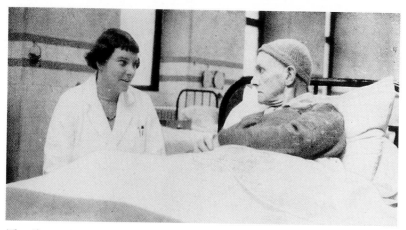

The Almoner interviews a patient, c.1950

The fourth-floor theatre in the surgical block, 1957

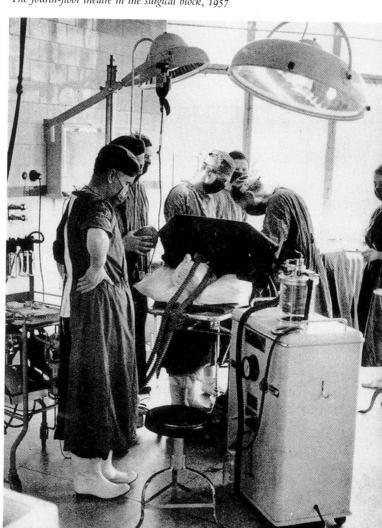

Aerial view, c.1950, when high density population surrounded the Royal. The canal has now been filled in to make way for the M8 motorway.

Medical laboratory, c.1950

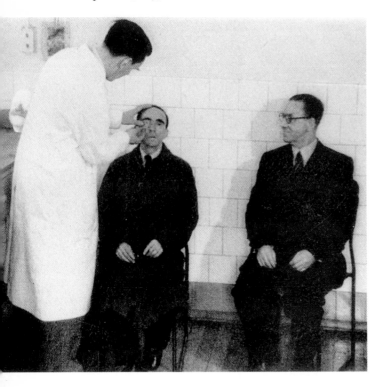

Technician fitting an artificial eye in the Plastic Surgery Department, c.1950

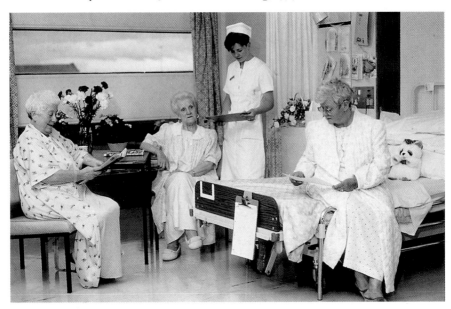

Modern day ward in the Queen Elizabeth Building, 1994

View of the Royal and Queen Elizabeth Building over the M8 motorway, 1994

Proposed design for the new maternity hospital, to replace Rottenrow

PERSPECTIVE

Common Services Agency, Building Division.
Architects

The recently developed Cathedral Square precinct, including the statue of David Livingstone, 1994

The hospital chapel, which provides a quiet retreat for all

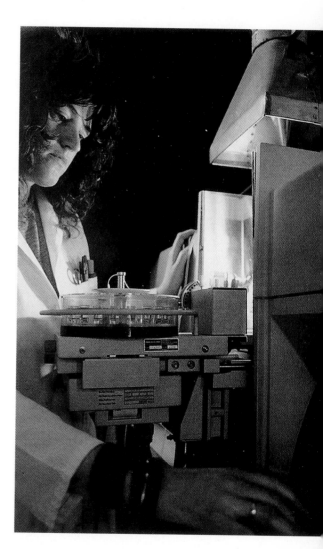

A Medical Laboratory Scientific Officer
tests a plasma sample for selenium using
an atomic absorption spectrometer

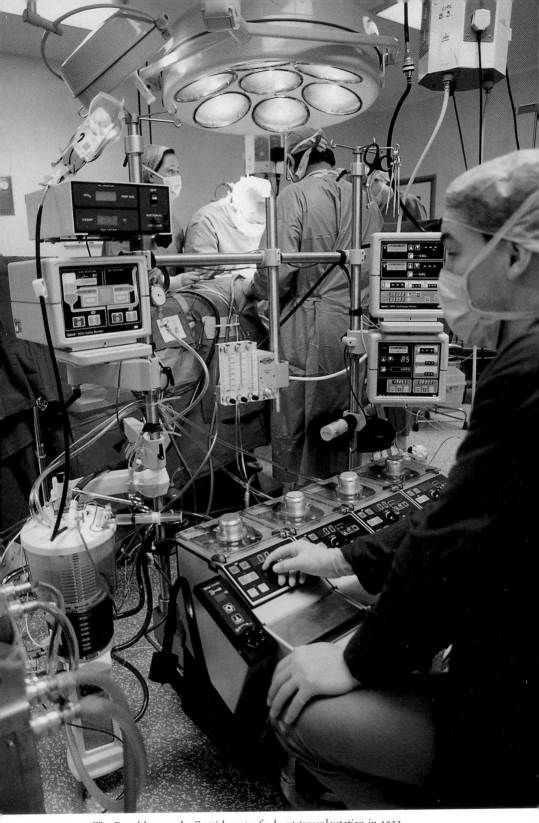

The Royal became the Scottish centre for heart transplantation in 1992

managers continually sought to meet the needs of the diseased poor by a programme of building expansion, both permanent and temporary, to house the growing numbers of those requiring treatment. In undertaking such a task, often in co-operation with local government agencies, the Royal remained the most important centre for public health provision in the city of Glasgow in the mid-nineteenth century.

3 | THE BIRTHPLACE OF ANTISEPTIC SURGERY, 1861–92

It may seem a strange principle to enunciate as a first requirement in a hospital that it should do the sick no harm.

Florence Nightingale, Notes on Hospitals, 1863[1]

In the history of the Glasgow Royal Infirmary 1861 was an auspicious year. With the opening of the Surgical Block, the managers confirmed their commitment to expanding the infirmary's role in the care and treatment of the 'sick or injured working classes'.[2] It was appropriate that the opening of the new block should be followed by the appointment of Joseph Lister as a surgeon. His work there, in the field of antiseptic surgery, firmly established the Royal's international reputation for excellence and innovation in surgical practice.

THE SURGICAL BLOCK

The Surgical Block, which was built for the considerable sum of £12,206 and opened on 21 May, provided staff and patients with the most modern facilities. The eight wards, each one 60 feet long and 28 feet wide, and containing sixteen beds, were more spacious, better lit and better ventilated than those in the Adam building and Fever Block. There was also a nurse's room off each ward and a resident's room on each floor; twelve rooms for private patients; and a basement flat containing twenty double rooms for those nurses who did not sleep next to the wards. Day rooms were provided on each flat of the north wing, and furnished with tables, books and newspapers, for the benefit of convalescent patients. The operating theatre, like its predecessor (which was converted to serve as a chapel), could accommodate over 200 students. The extra accommodation provided in the new building allowed the managers to reduce overcrowding in the old: two beds were removed from each of the small wards in the Adam building, and four from the large.[3]

106

While the surgeons were delighted with the facilities in the surgical block, they soon discovered that the wards provided no haven from the scourge of nineteenth–century city hospitals, the so-called 'hospital diseases'. Pyaemia, erysipelas, hospital gangrene and other suppurative and putrefactive conditions were endemic. Sir Hector Clare Cameron, who became a visiting surgeon at the Royal and Emeritus Professor of Clinical Surgery in the University of Glasgow, served as a surgeon's resident assistant at the infirmary in 1867. In the course of just one week, he saw five patients die from pyaemia in his ward.[4] The pioneering brain surgeon Sir William Macewen, who visited the surgical wards as a student during the 1860s, remembered that:

> suppuration in wounds was the rule, and very profuse it generally was. Dressing of the wounds had to be done daily, and sometimes several times a day. The handling of inflamed wounds was a source of pain, and the dressing was anticipated by the patients with an apprehesion akin to terror, especially since the exhausting process, with its accompanying high fever, reduced the resisting powers of the individual to a low ebb. The suppurative process invaded the deeper tissues, affecting the blood vessels, and produced septic thrombosis from which septic emboli were carried to distant parts. The dissemination of septic material was shown in the high temperature, the violent rigors, the profuse sweating, the sweetish, sickening odour from the breath, the yellow cachexia, emaciation, and final delirium which all too frequently ended in death. Sometimes every patient in a ward who had a serious operation performed upon him would be swept away...

Macewen added that, working in such distressing conditions, student dressers often had to leave the building, in order to gulp down fresh air and compose themselves. Many found it difficult to continue their training in the midst of such appalling human misery.[5]

Surgeons did not possess the scientific knowledge required to prevent the surgical wounds of patients from becoming septic. Although medical opinion generally recognised that hospital diseases were more prevalent in dirty and overcrowded wards, and it was commonly believed that exposure to 'bad air' was in some way responsible for infection, the existence of micro-organisms and the way in which they could invade a wound, and cause the decomposition of the tissue within, was not known. The importance of cleanliness in the operating theatres and wards had become evident to some practitioners, but the work of pioneers in the field of infection prevention, such as Alexander Gordon, Oliver Wendell Holmes and Ignaz Semmelweiss, was incomplete and not widely publicised.[6] Most surgeons continued to perform operations in old soiled coats, and were not always concerned to ensure that hands, operating instruments and dressings were thoroughly cleaned before being brought into contact with a wound. Dressers and nurses attending to suppurating wounds often passed directly from one patient to another, spreading infection through the overcrowded wards. Unaware of the cause of infection, many surgeons considered suppuration as a normal part of the healing process, and despaired of finding a means of preventing outbreaks of hospital diseases.[7] It was an Englishman, Joseph Lister, who dispelled the notion that nothing could be done.

Joseph Lister

Joseph Lister (1827–1912) studied medicine at University College, London, where he graduated MB in 1852. After a spell in private practice and as an assistant surgeon at the Edinburgh Royal Infirmary, where he worked closely with (and married the daughter of) the Professor of Clinical Surgery, James Syme, he was appointed Professor of Surgery at the University of Glasgow in January 1860.[8] Lister first applied for the position of surgeon at the Royal in August 1860. Despite the support of the Lord Provost, who nominated Lister, the managers voted instead to appoint the other candidate, Dr George Buchanan. Although he must have felt snubbed, Lister applied again the following year, and was supported by an address presented by his 161 medical students. He was nominated by the Lord Provost once more, and was elected on 5 August by fifteen votes to seven, in preference to Dr Ebenezer Watson. Lister worked as a surgeon at the Royal for eight momentous years.

Like the other three surgeons at the Royal, Lister had a male ward and a female ward in the Surgical Block, and a chronic condition ward for male patients in the Adam building, now generally known as the Medical Block. The conditions he met in the surgical wards upset him greatly, as his patients suffered the agonies of inflamed, suppurating and putrefying wounds. Many years later he wrote of 'the faint sickly smell commonly perceptible in surgical wards', and of 'the stench which prevails at the time of daily dressing' on account of the 'emanations from sores'.[9] A shy and reserved man, Lister rarely showed his feelings to staff and students. His correspondence, however, reveals that the suffering he saw in the wards moved him deeply, and strengthened his resolve to find a means of preventing the dreadful consequences of infection.

Before 1865 many surgeons used a variety of agents, such as chlorinated lime, alcohol and turpentine, in the treatment of inflamed or suppurating wounds. However, they did so unsystematically, without a true understanding of the nature of infection, and generally applied them in an attempt to arrest, rather than to prevent, the process of blood and tissue decomposition.[10] Lister favoured the application of wet or dry dressings to surgical wounds, applying poultices or sulphite of potash when signs of inflammation and suppuration appeared. When putrefaction began to spread, he applied pungent, fuming nitric acid as a last resort, in a desperate attempt to arrest its progress.[11] His search for a more effective means of arresting the process of decomposition led him to experiment with other agents.

Phenol is the active ingredient of carbolic acid, a coal tar derivative which was first advocated as a surgical disinfectant by the Frenchman Jules Lemaire during the 1850s. In 1864 Lister learned that carbolic acid had been used with success in treating sewage in Carlisle, to eliminate both foul odour and parasites before it was utilised as field manure. The surgeon obtained a quantity of the acid from Thomas Anderson, Professor of Chemistry at the University, for trials 'as a disinfectant' for wounds.[12] On 8 December 1864 he began to use carbolic acid in a number of different solutions with water, in the dressings of four post-surgery cases in both his male and female wards. The first experiments met with mixed success. In the cases of Mary Ann Lavander and nine-year-old Andrew Connel, the first patients described in the surviving records as having carbolic acid dressings applied to their wounds, the acid arrested the progress of suppuration after wrist excisions had been performed, but it also hindered the formation of healthy scar tissue on the wound. However, Lister's resident assistant noted that in an ankle amputation case, in which suppuration had taken hold, 'the powerful antiseptic properties of the carbolic acid were of such conspicuous advantage that it has been continued'.[13] Lister persevered with the use of carbolic acid as an alternative to sulphite of potash and nitric acid in the treatment of inflamed or suppurating wounds.

During these first experiments Lister was apparently unaware of the work of Louis Pasteur, the French chemist who demonstrated the role of micro-organisms in fermentation and the putrefaction of organic matter.[14] By the spring of 1865, however, it is clear that he had applied Pasteur's findings to his own research on wound infection and inflammation, and come to the conclusion that the decomposition of blood and tissue was caused by the invasion of the wound by micro-organisms, or 'germs'. He set about developing the means not only of counteracting infection, but of preventing the wound from becoming infected in the first place. He chose carbolic acid as the most suitable antiseptic agent, because it appeared to be a 'material capable of destroying these septic germs...yet not too potent as a caustic', and because 'it exercises a local sedative influence upon the sensory nerves'.[15]

Lister developed his antiseptic system of preventing wound infection by concentrating on one class of cases. In compound fractures of the limbs, the broken bone protrudes through the skin. Often in such cases, dirt gets into the wound, resulting in infection and, in the 1860s, compound fracture cases had a far higher mortality rate than simple fractures.[16] Lister set to work in March 1865. Charles Cobb, admitted with a compound leg fracture, had his wound dressed with cotton wool soaked in the acid. Although the limb was subsequently reset - after uniting 'by a false joint' - Cobb was discharged well on 17 June.[17] Neil Kelly, another compound fracture case admitted on 21 March, had a less happy experience. Lint soaked in carbolic acid was applied to the leg wound, but suppuration took hold, and Kelly remained in the ward for nearly twelve months before being discharged well. Lister stated later that the failure in this case was due to 'improper management'.[18] He resolved to continue his experimental treatment, but had to wait for five months, until a suitable compound fracture case was admitted to his care in the wards.

The first patient to be treated under Lister's improved 'carbolic acid plan' was an eleven-year-old potter, James Greenlees, who entered the infirmary on 12 August with a compound fracture of the tibia and fibula.[19] The wound was covered in lint soaked in carbolic acid, the leg was set and splints applied. After four days the boy complained of discomfort caused by the caustic effect of the acid, and so Lister applied a dressing with a weaker solution of carbolic, and when the wound remained free from pus, this was replaced by a third dressing, of lint soaked in a solution of carbolic acid and olive oil. The wound healed, and Greenlees was discharged from the infirmary on 2 October, fifty-one days after admission.[20]

Invigorated and encouraged by his success, Lister developed improved antiseptic ligatures, and a variety of carbolic acid cloth, plaster and putty dressings. Wounds were attended to under an 'antiseptic curtain' of cloth soaked in carbolic acid, and he experimented with materials such as thin sheet lead and block tin as coverings to prevent the dressings from drying out. The experiments were extended to all surgical cases, with such success that he could soon claim with confidence that '...hospital gangrene, like pyaemia and erysipelas, may be said to have been banished by the antiseptic system'.[21] In March 1867 he announced the success of 'the antiseptic system of treatment in surgery' in the columns of the *Lancet*, creating a sensation in the medical world.

GRAVE DIFFICULTIES

The unacceptable level of pyaemia, erysipelas and hospital gangrene which existed in the Surgical Block was most evident in the ground floor wards. The ward next to Lister's was closed, and investigations began in an effort to determine the cause of the dreadful death toll. A committee, appointed in 1867 'to enquire into the sanitary condition of the wards' ordered the construction of a deep drain from Castle Street to Vicars Alley, 30 feet to the north of the infirmary. During the excavation work it was discovered that victims of the cholera epidemic of 1849 had been interred in a mass grave near the old temporary fever hospital. The flimsy coffins were piled on top of each other, the uppermost lying only a few inches beneath the surface, just four feet away from the two ground-floor surgical wards. The burial pit was so large, and the bodies in such a state of decomposition, that the committee felt unable to order the clearing of the site. Instead, the pit was liberally soaked in carbolic acid and treated with quicklime, and a thick layer of soil up to five feet in depth was laid over it. Having thus reduced the risks, as they perceived them, of airborne infection, the managers also ordered the removal of a wall at the end of the Surgical Block, which was believed to prevent the free circulation of air outside the wards. A railing was erected in its place.

The fever grave was not the only one to cause concern. The Surgical Block lay next to the cathedral's old churchyard, and burial pits for paupers were filled only a few yards from the windows of the surgical wards. Lister visited the pits, which contained up to 5,000 bodies, on the request of one of the Royal's managers, and was appalled by what he found there.

> The pit, which was standing open for the reception of the next corpse, emitted a horrid stench on the removal of some loose boards from its mouth. Its walls were formed, on three sides, of coffins piled one upon another in four tiers, with the lateral interstices between them filled with human bones, the coffins reaching up to within a few inches of the ground. This was in a place immediately adjoining the patients' airing ground, and a few yards only from the windows of the surgical wards.[22]

In 1869 the interment of the Royal's 'unclaimed dead' in the grounds was discontinued, and the infirmary's funeral expenses consequently doubled, as corpses were taken instead to Sighthill Cemetery, about a mile to the north. In addition, Glasgow's magistrates were asked to discontinue pauper burials in the cathedral grounds, and burials in the old graveyard were finally discontinued in 1877.

LISTER'S LEGACY

In Lister's description of the pauper graveyard, his frustration at the conditions under which he worked in Glasgow was apparent. He was a dedicated surgeon, single-minded in his pursuit of the scientific knowledge he believed, correctly, would revolutionise the practice of surgery. By nature he was not a diplomat, and he was impatient of anything he believed would hamper his work. He may also have felt a victim of the ill-feeling which still existed between sections of Glasgow's medical establishment and the University which he represented as a professor. Inevitably, then, there was friction between Lister on the one hand, and some of the managers and staff of the Royal on the other. His comments in an article published in the *Lancet* on 1 January 1870, referring to the wards in the Surgical Block as 'some of the most unhealthy in the kingdom', and to the 'perpetual contests' he had to enter into with the authorities in order to prevent the overcrowding of his wards, alienated some members of the Board. They pointed out that they had gone to great lengths to improve the standard of nursing, the patients' diet, and the conditions of hygiene in the infirmary, and with justification they claimed some credit for the decline in mortality there. They asserted that they had been exceptionally lenient in their dealings with the surgeon, whose patients remained in the wards for much longer than those of his colleagues: indeed, as many as one third of Lister's patients remained in the Royal for longer than the recommended maximum of 60 days (and most of these long-stay patients stayed for more than 150 days), reducing the capacity of the infirmary to receive new cases.[23] Some of Glasgow's leading medical men, led by James Morton (a surgeon at the Royal 1859–67 and 1870–84, and Professor of Materia Medica at Anderson's University, 1855–88) and believing that Lister sought to denigrate their own competencies as surgeons, joined in the attacks on his published work on antiseptic surgery.[24] Significantly, however, his methods and their results impressed his students and fellow surgeons at the Royal in the late 1860s, when the evidence of his success was plain to see in the wards. Lister himself wrote in February 1870 that his complaints of conditions at the Royal referred to the early 1860s, and that 'I was fortunate to have excellent nurses from the commencement of my connexion with the infirmary...' and that he had 'sincere respect' for the managers, who had always shown him 'consideration and kindness'.[25]

Lister attempted unsuccessfully to leave Glasgow on two occasions; in 1864, when he applied for the post of Professor of Systematic Surgery at the University of Edinburgh, and in 1867, when he applied for the chair at University College London. In 1869, however, he was appointed Professor of Clinical Surgery at Edinburgh, after the resignation of his father-in-law James Syme, and he went on to improve and extend his revolutionary surgical methods in the wards of the Edinburgh Royal Infirmary, and later at King's College Hospital in London.[26] Contrary to popular belief, he did not begin to use the famous carbolic acid spray, to disinfect the area surrounding the operating table, until 1870 or 1871 – more than a year after his departure from the Royal.

Despite his clashes with the Board, Lister later remembered his time in Glasgow with affection. The managers appreciated his momentous achievements and the fame he brought by his association with the infirmary, 'the birthplace of antiseptic surgery'.[27] They were proud of the fact that the Royal allowed him the freedom, which might not have been permitted in another voluntary hospital, to introduce his radical innovations. Of even greater importance to the prestige of the infirmary was the fact that Lister's students, and most of the up-and-coming Glasgow surgeons, were deeply impressed by his success. Many of the residents, including Hector Clare Cameron, had actively participated in his work, and their contributions were generously acknowledged in the historic papers he published in the *Lancet* and the *British Medical Journal*, 1867–70. They were fired with the enthusiasm of men who had participated in a scientific revolution, and surgeons at the Royal were subsequently at the forefront of the movement to adopt and improve upon his surgical techniques. After Lister, the new breed of Glasgow surgeon saw himself as more than just a practitioner, but as a scientist who sought to apply the results of his own and of others' clinical research to the practice of surgery. With cleaner wards, better nursing and new surgical procedures, post-operative mortality at the Royal fell significantly, despite the increasing willingness of surgeons to perform more complicated operations. In 1861, thirty-nine of 212 patients (18.3 per cent) died after surgical operations, including twenty-nine of eighty-three amputation cases (nearly 35 per cent). Ten years later, the post-operative death rate had fallen to 10.7 per cent (forty-six of 429 cases), and the death-rate for amputees to 10.6 per cent (nineteen of 179 cases). In 1881 there were only forty-two deaths from 953 surgical operations (4.4 per cent), and nineteen deaths following 205 amputations (9.2 per cent).

Nursing

While Lister was developing his system of antiseptic surgery in Glasgow, there were further innovations in patient care in the wards of the Royal. Most important of all were the first steps to improve the training of nurses and the calibre of women entrusted with nursing duties.

The importance of obtaining the services of educated and committed hospital nursing staff had been reinforced by events in the Crimean War, 1854–6, when the shameful neglect of sick and wounded British soldiers was reported by newspaper correspondents, and became the matter of national scandal. Florence Nightingale (1820–1910) was hailed as a heroine for her work, with thirty female volunteers, in caring for those troops fortunate enough to be transferred to the barracks hospital at Scutari in Turkey. After her return to England she became a tireless propagandist for the better education of nurses.[28]

When the Surgical Block was opened in 1861 there were only forty-four nurses, most of them quite elderly, working in the Royal's thirty-one wards. Dressed in wide hoop-crinolines, they took copious amounts of snuff, a habit shared by many others who worked in the infirmary, to neutralise the fetid odours in the wards.[29] The nurses earned between fifteen shillings and seventeen shillings and sixpence per month, which was less than a female domestic servant might earn, and no more than one quarter of the wages paid to many workmen and artisans. Each nurse was attached to a single ward, and was on duty for eleven hours or even longer, sometimes being woken during the night to attend to a patient in distress. The nurses' duties included scrubbing the unvarnished wooden floors of the wards, washing clothes, fetching meals and changing beds. Patient care did not often extend much beyond feeding and washing the faces of the very sick. Most of the nurses were accommodated in makeshift bedrooms, 'in nooks and corners off the wards'[30] although some slept in the basement of the Surgical Block after it opened in 1861. The Constitution and Rules and Regulations of the infirmary, printed in 1864, stipulated that nurses should receive one and a quarter pounds of bread and half a pint of milk each day, as well as half a pound of beef four times a week, and a weekly ration of four pounds of potatoes, some herrings, eggs and cheese, and half a pound of salt butter.[31] But William McEwen, a prosperous drysalter and philanthropist who was twice elected the Dean of Guild and who became a manager in 1862, remembered later that the nurses did not receive regular meals, but 'got a herring one day, a bit of cheese another, an egg upon the third, and picked up on other days anything that was to be had or left over of the provision for the patients'. They had to supplement this meagre fare with their own food which they cooked for themselves in the wards.[32] It was said that, as their wages were small and they often went hungry, nurses were sometimes tempted to steal food intended for the patients.

Nurses shared an unfortunate reputation. James B. Russell, the medical superintendent of the Parliamentary Road Fever Hospital 1865–72, set forth the prevailing view in 1866 when he wrote that '...at present nursing is the last resource of female adversity. Slatternly widows, runaway wives, servants out of place, women bankrupt of fame or fortune from whatever cause, fall back on hospital nursing'.[33] Even so late as 1875, a special committee of managers at the Royal felt it necessary to recommend that 'the nurses throughout the house be warned that under no circumstances will slapping, whipping or threatening language towards patients be tolerated...' The harsh general criticism of nurses was not always deserved, and women such as Mrs Martin, the septuagenarian nurse in Lister's Ward 24, were kindly and efficient in performing their limited chores.[34] Nevertheless, the nature of the job, with its unpleasant duties, poor wages and unfortunate image, made it difficult to attract reliable and diligent women to serve in the wards.[35] By the 1860s there was a growing public awareness of the benefits of providing good nursing care for the sick, and a voluntary institution such as the Royal, which relied on public subscriptions and donations for its continued survival, could not afford to be seen to lag behind improvements elsewhere.

In January 1865 Mrs Struthers was 'removed' from office, after a dispute over her demand for a higher salary went to litigation. Miss Tait was appointed to replace her as Matron. The following year a grading system was introduced at the Royal, in an attempt to provide what might today be called an elementary career structure. Probationer nurses, who had served less than one year in the infirmary, were henceforth paid twenty shillings a month, and those who had completed their probationary period received twenty-five shillings. First-class nurses - those who had served for more than two years - earned thirty shillings. Promotion through the ranks from probationer was not dependent on length of service alone, but also on 'good conduct and thorough competency'. The following year further incentives were held out, in the form of annual prizes worth a total of £9, awarded to one day and one night nurse in each department 'for good conduct, kindness to patients, and cleanliness in their wards'. The prizes were discontinued in 1869, owing to difficulties experienced in discriminating between worthy candidates, and in their place the managers awarded their experienced nurses a pay rise: two shillings and sixpence a month for those employed in the infirmary for more than three years, and five shillings for those with more than five years service, the pay rises being dependent upon the recommendations of the matron and medical superintendent. In 1874 the Board accepted that a lady superintendent of day nurses should be appointed, and that the nursing staff should be increased, to provide a day nurse and a night nurse for each ward, with up to thirty-three assistant nurses to help them with their duties. Nurses did not have a uniform, but, for the first time, each was to be supplied by the infirmary with a cap.

Fever

The report of the increase in the wages of long-serving nurses was accompanied by that of an increase for those working in the fever wards. Staff at the Royal did not escape unscathed from the fever epidemics of the 1860s. There are no figures for staff mortality during the early years of the decade, although 'many of the officers and servants of the house were attacked' in 1864, during the typhus epidemic of 1864–5, and two physicians, five physicians' assistants and twelve nurses and servants took fever during 1865, when one of the physicians and four of the nurses died. The incidences of typhus, smallpox and scarlet fever at the Royal remained high in subsequent years, and as the admission of fever cases posed such a serious danger to the health of patients and staff, the managers explored ways of reducing the risks of infection.

Typhus was ever-present in Glasgow during the 1860s, causing nearly 7,000 deaths in the city during the decade.[36] Smallpox, too, remained a serious threat to public health, despite the Royal's enterprising free vaccination programme begun in 1857, and the introduction, by the terms of the Vaccination (Scotland) Act of 1864, of compulsory vaccination for infants. In 1864, at the height of the typhus epidemic, 2,847 of 7,104 in-patients (40.5 per cent) in the Royal were suffering from fever. The admission of large numbers of fever patients put enormous pressure on the Royal's financial as well as staff resources, and the Glasgow Police Act of 1862, which greatly increased the powers of the Glasgow Police Board in the field of public health, was warmly welcomed by the managers. In 1865 the Police Board opened a fever hospital in Parliamentary Road, providing 136 beds (later increased to 200). This permitted the managers to reduce the number of fever beds in the infirmary to 175. A second new municipal fever hospital, the Belvidere in the city's east end, opened in 1870. In May 1871 the Royal closed its wards to smallpox cases, after patients and nurses were infected during the latest epidemic to hit the city, and in 1876 it was decided that all fever cases from the city, other than typhoid, should be referred to the local authority hospitals. In 1884, in the face of heated opposition from the Chairman, William McEwen, and other 'lay' managers, the Board voted to exclude typhoid cases from the infirmary.

The closure of the wards to fever cases did a great deal to safeguard the health and peace of mind of both staff and patients, although the Royal continued to admit patients suffering from other contagious diseases, such as erisypelas and venereal disease. However, the exclusion of patients suffering from fever had wider implications, not least because it was a tacit admission that the Royal was not able to fulfil entirely its original purpose, to care for all the sick and injured poor sent to its doors. In encouraging the Police Board to open fever hospitals, the Royal demonstrated its willingness to see the local authority take responsibility for the care of a large class of patients who would previously have turned to the infirmary for medical assistance.

THE DORCAS SOCIETY

Although the Board made constant appeals to subscribers not to send chronic or incurable cases to the infirmary, nor to send those who were eligible for treatment at the parish poorhouse,[37] the wards and dispensary continued to admit large numbers of sick and injured from the very poorest classes. The condition of the sick poor during the early 1860s deeply moved a benefactor of the infirmary, Miss Beatrice Clugston, a devout Christian from a wealthy Glasgow family.

Miss Clugston was concerned that the professional staff at the Royal had neither the time nor the inclination to serve more than the immediate medical needs of the patients. For example, many people came to the infirmary clad in rags. On admission the patient was bathed and issued with infirmary clothing: his or her own clothes were taken away to be washed or fumigated. Sometimes the clothes fell apart during cleaning, and on other occasions they were considered to pose such a danger to health that they were burned. When the patient's clothing was returned on dismissal from the wards, it was often 'so scanty as to cause great danger of relapse, especially in winter weather'.

Inspired by the biblical story of Tabitha, or Dorcas, who 'was full of good works and almsdeeds' and made coats and garments for the widows of Joppa (Acts 9.36-43), Miss Clugston formed in 1863 the Dorcas Society of Glasgow Royal Infirmary, enlisting the support of doctors' wives and other ladies of comfortable means. The prime aim of the society was to provide clothing, particularly warm underclothing, for those in need. The Dorcas Society invited charitable donations of clothing from Glasgow's middle classes, and it persuaded the Board to make available a room at the infirmary, in which underclothes, dressing gowns and other items were made up for poor patients.

The Dorcas Society did not confine its activities to the clothing of the poor. In 1866 Miss Clugston launched a scheme to provide an invalid chair for every ward, and persuaded many of Glasgow's leading citizens, and a pair of infirmary physicians, to contribute. Lady volunteers visited the wards to lead prayers and bible readings, and offer spiritual comfort to the elderly and lonely. Later the society undertook the responsibility of supplying surgical appliances, such as artificial limbs, to those discharged patients who required them; visited convalescing patients in their homes; and raised money to pay the travelling expenses of those who had to make return visits to the infirmary.[38]

The Dorcas Society provided the infirmary with a rudimentary social work service, which did much to make life more comfortable for patients in the wards and which, by catering to the physical needs of discharged patients, ensured that many who might otherwise have relapsed, and sought readmittance to the wards, were able to recuperate at home. It remained the sole provider of social care and charitable assistance to patients until the creation, in the 1930s, of the Almoner's Department.

THE WESTERN INFIRMARY

During the 1870s the financial well-being of the Royal was threatened by two events beyond the control of the Board. One was a severe economic recession in the latter half of the decade; the other was the opening in 1874 of the Western Infirmary.

Lister left Glasgow shortly before the University made its long-awaited move from the city centre. For decades the proximity of slums, brothels and drinking dens in and around High Street had embarrassed the University authorities, who were also concerned that their site was hemmed in by tenement houses and industrial buildings. It was considered essential that young students should be educated in more salubrious surroundings, as far away as possible from corrupting influences. The Old College was finally sold to the North British Railway Company in 1864 (College Station was built on the site), and work began to erect new buildings on Gilmorehill, in a comparatively rural setting looking down on the city's fashionable west end. The University opened there in 1870.

The west of Glasgow and the neighbouring Burgh of Partick were growing at a rapid pace in the 1860s, as new shipyards were built along the north bank of the Clyde and industrialists sought greenfield sites for new engineering works. The University authorities were keen to have a teaching hospital near Gilmorehill, and were able to point to the growing population of the west end and the neighbouring industrial areas to justify the erection of a new infirmary there. A committee of Glasgow citizens set about the task of raising funds; building work began in 1871, and the Western Infirmary opened in 1874.[39] The establishment of a second voluntary hospital in the city did much to ease the immediate demand for beds at the Royal, but it posed problems which were to exercise the Board of the older institution for many years.

The University Senate originally intended that the new infirmary should be managed as a branch of the Royal. However, the two sides were unable to reach agreement over the allocation of staff posts and clinical instruction there, and so in 1874 the Committee of the Western Infirmary drew up a constitution which provided for the election and appointment of members to a separate Board of Managers. While there was no vulgar attempt to enter into competition for the support of subscribers and benefactors, the Royal soon felt the financial effects of having a rival for the affections of Glasgow's public-spirited citizens.

FINANCES

As an institution managed by representatives of Glasgow's political and business elite, and dependent on its citizens for funds, the Royal's fortunes were closely linked with those of the city's trade and industry. During the 1860s and for most of the 1870s the annual subscriptions and the contributions from public works' employees, which together accounted for most of the infirmary's ordinary income, increased steadily. Between 1861 and 1874 annual subscriptions rose from £3,632 to £7,499, and employees' contributions from £2,295 in 1861 to £7,358 in 1873. During the same period the stock account, consisting of surplus funds from legacies and donations, which were invested to provide an annual income, increased from less than £30,000 to nearly £61,000. These twin peaks were achieved as the local economy boomed during the mid 1870s, but this income slipped after the opening of the Western and as a recession in trade and industry began to have its effect on the local economy. The recession was exacerbated by the failure of the City of Glasgow Bank in 1878.

The City of Glasgow Bank, founded in 1839, had flourished and established a network of 133 branches. Its shareholders and customers included many of Glasgow's most prosperous businessmen and industrialists. When it was forced to close its doors on 2 October it was discovered that the directors had criminally mismanaged the bank's affairs, and the liquidators made a call to the shareholders of £500 for every £100 of stock held, in order to meet its liabilities. Many Glaswegians were ruined, and the collapse in confidence which accompanied the failure of the city's best-known bank served to deepen the economic gloom hanging over the city.

The worsening recession left the managers in pessimistic mood. The Annual Report for 1878 noted 'the commercial depression and disaster which our community have [sic] been passing through has tended to reduce still further our annual receipts in subscriptions and church collections...' Ordinary expenditure had continued to outstrip ordinary income since 1874. By 1880 annual subscriptions had fallen to £6,801, and employees' contributions to £4,880. Fortunately, these losses were more than balanced by an increase in extraordinary income. The stock account contained over £105,000 in 1878. Although it was slightly diminished over the following five years, as the Board had to dip into it to meet deficits in the ordinary income account, and although the managers were forced to make a special appeal for funds in 1881, a financial crisis was avoided. The costs of maintaining the infirmary continued to rise —ordinary expenditure increased from £9,142 in 1861 to £24,959 in 1883—but prudent financial management and the generosity of the Royal's supporters ensured that the infirmary continued to provide, and improve upon, the standards of care expected of it.

THE 'RELIGION' CONTROVERSY

The managers feared that the infirmary might suffer further financial loss as a consequence of a distasteful sectarian controversy which erupted in 1877. The influx of predominantly Roman Catholic Irish immigrants to Glasgow during the nineteenth century created tensions, in a community which had hitherto been largely Protestant in its religious affiliations. Sectarian feelings ran deep in many areas of society, fuelled by events in Ireland, and they surfaced regularly in political debate, pulpit demagoguery, and the occasional street riot. A major public institution such as the Royal could not avoid becoming embroiled in sectarian controversy, as had happened in the 1830s and 1840s. The events of 1877 created far greater controversy.

On 13 September of that year a letter from 'A.T.' was published in the *North British Daily Mail*, with a cutting from the *Belfast News* of 25 August. The article in the Irish newspaper alleged that the majority of nurses at the Royal were Catholics; that they burned Protestant religious literature; actively attempted to convert patients to Catholicism; and favoured Catholics when choosing those to be sent to convalescent homes. A flood of letters followed, and Henry Stewart, Honorary Secretary of the West of Scotland Protestant Association (which had instigated the controversy, and which the managers believed had 'planted' the original item in the *Belfast News*) called for an inquiry. The Royal's secretary, the respected local businessman Henry Lamond, replied tersely to the original charges, insisting that they were entirely inaccurate, and asserting that 'since its foundation the Glasgow Royal Infirmary has been conducted on strictly non-sectarian principles and that neither in the case of nurses or patients has there ever been any preference shown or religious test applied'.[40] The WSPA was not impressed, and Stewart wrote to the *North British Daily Mail* to insist that three quarters of the nurses at the Royal, and many other employees besides, were Catholics.[41] The managers, shocked that their word was not accepted on the matter, immediately mounted an investigation. One hundred and thirty members of staff were interviewed, and virtually every charge levelled by the WSPA was answered and shown to be groundless. Only about one third of the nurses—twenty-four of seventy-four—were Catholics, almost identical to the proportion of patients of that faith. To contradict the accusation that Catholic nurses were given preferential treatment in the allocation of duties, it was pointed out that twenty-three of the thirty-one day nurses were Protestants. The matron (a 'decidedly evangelical' Episcopalian) and the three nursing superintendents were Protestants, as were ten of the thirteen scrubbers, three of the four kitchen staff, two of the three housemaids, one of the two laboratory workers and one of the two serving maids, as well as the dining hall attendant. Nine of the twelve laundry women and the single bedwoman were indeed Catholics, although their preponderant presence in these 'dirty and sickening' jobs was entirely unconvincing as evidence of favouritism.[42]

The Board exhibited great dignity in refuting the charges of the WSPA and re-emphasising the non-sectarian character of the Royal. In the light of its measured response, the 'scandal' was revealed to be the product of wild and vindictive rumour-mongering. Sadly, however, the incident was damaging. A flood of letters supporting the WSPA's position appeared in the local press, containing emotionally charged statements such as that of 'J.R.M.', who wrote: 'To think that Protestant inmates [sic] are to be insulted, and Protestant money go to fatten these emissaries of the Pope, is surely more than can be tolerated for one hour. Let contributors withdraw their contributions until this blot is wiped out.'[43] At the annual meeting of the General Court of Contributors in January 1878, A.B. McGrigor observed sadly that 'throw plenty of mud and some of it will be sure to stick'. John Burns, the shipping magnate and a great-nephew of his namesake, one of the Royal's first surgeons, was one distinguished businessman whose patronage was lost: he revealed that owing to his strong feelings on the issue he would contribute to the funds of another institution in future. In the highly charged political climate of the time the Royal may have lost the subscriptions and legacies of others with strong sectarian prejudices, who were needlessly alarmed by tall tales of militant Popery in the wards.[44]

GROWTH AND DEVELOPMENT

The political squabbles and financial wrangles of the 1870s did not hold back improvements at the Royal. In 1861, 4,441 patients were treated in the wards of the infirmary, and 10,273 in the dispensary. The numbers increased to 6,104 and 13,630 respectively in 1871 (the year when the wards were closed to smallpox cases), and amounted to 5,130 and 20,629 in 1881, six years after the opening of the Western and five after the wards were closed to fever patients.

The increase in the number of patients admitted to the Royal necessitated the appointment of additional staff. In 1864, at the height of the typhus epidemic, the dispensary physician, Dr James Steven, was appointed fever physician. In November, he was appointed the fifth visiting physician; subsequently, the staff of visiting surgeons was also increased to five, and an apothecary was appointed in 1867, to relieve the superintendent of his responsibilities in the preparation of drugs. In 1868 the staff at the dispensary was further augmented by the appointment of two extra dispensary physicians and two extra dispensary surgeons, and the infirmary appointed a vaccinator to vaccinate staff and patients, to instruct students in vaccination, and distribute lymph to local practitioners. A dental and an aural surgeon were appointed in 1877, when Dr Ebenezer Watson opened a throat disease clinic. The following year, Dr James Stirton was placed in charge of a ward for 'diseases of women'. The dispensary staff provided their services for only a nominal fee of £30 per annum, but the visiting staff were more handsomely rewarded for their services: in 1875, in order to compensate for a drastic reduction in their earnings from student fees after the opening of the Western Infirmary, their annual salary was increased to £100.

GLASGOW ROYAL INFIRMARY SCHOOL OF MEDICINE

After the decision taken by the Board in July 1874, that the amalgamation of the Royal and Western infirmaries 'is not expedient or for the interest of either institution', and in anticipation of the departure of University students to seek clinical instruction in the wards of the new infirmary, steps were taken to set up a medical school at the Royal. A supplementary charter was obtained in August 1875, conferring powers 'to afford facilities and accommodation to individual teachers for instructing students in medicine, surgery, and the collateral sciences', and the Glasgow Royal Infirmary School of Medicine was instituted the following year. William McEwen, the Convener (or Chairman) of the House Committee 1866–85, launched a vigorous campaign to raise over £6,000 to provide separate accommodation for the school, and the building was opened in Castle Street, next to the infirmary, in November 1882. Initially the school proved popular with many medical students, as its fees were considerably lower than those of the University of Glasgow. However, the students could study only for the licence to practise medicine and surgery, awarded jointly by the Faculty of Physicians and Surgeons of Glasgow and the Royal College of Physicians of Edinburgh (from 1884, the licence was known as the 'Triple Qualification', after the Royal College of Surgeons of Edinburgh became the third licensing body), or for some Irish and English qualifications, as the school was not affiliated to a university. The absence of formal ties with a university ultimately hampered the development of the medical school. It was generally

124

held that a university degree carried greater status than a mere diploma. The University of Glasgow recognised only four of the departments of systematic study at the school, and University students preferred to receive clinical instruction from their professors (who were also University degree examiners) at the Western, rather than in the Royal.

In 1881 the trustees of Anderson's College, which had its own medical school and sent many students to the Royal for clinical instruction, negotiated with the Board with a view to merging the two schools. The negotiations were broken off in 1882, the managers believing that the other school had little to offer their own. Anderson's College of Medicine was subsequently detached from its parent (which became the core of the new Glasgow and West of Scotland Technical College) and in 1888 moved to a new building near the Western Infirmary. The relocation of Anderson's Medical College resulted in the exodus of many more students from the wards of the Royal to those of the Western, and therefore in the loss of even more income from student fees. It also provoked fears of an impending crisis in the provision of dressers to assist the surgeons in the wards, as this duty was traditionally performed, free of charge to the infirmary, by as many as forty promising students. Alarmed, the Board petitioned the Secretary for Scotland and the Lord Advocate in 1887, in an attempt to have a proposed Scottish Universities Bill amended to permit the erection of their medical school as a college of the University. They were fiercely opposed by the University Senate, and so in 1888 the managers promoted a Bill of their own for the establishment of a new independent college, St Mungo's, to take the place of the medical school. The ground and buildings of the medical school were subsequently made over to the college, and the Royal's direct responsibility for its affairs ended. The Board of Governors of St Mungo's hoped that it would subsequently be accepted as an extra-mural college of the University. The managers of the Royal hoped that the college would become more attractive to students than its predecessor, sending more young men to the wards to receive clinical instruction and bolstering the infirmary's failing reputation as a great teaching hospital.[45]

WILLIAM MACEWEN

After the departure of Lister the prestige of the Royal was further enhanced by one of the great surgeon's former students, William

Macewen (1848–1924). Macewen was born on the Isle of Bute, the youngest of twelve children. He studied at the University of Glasgow from 1865 until 1869, and became a house surgeon to Lister's successor, Sir George MacLeod. He was briefly the medical superintendent at Belvidere Fever Hospital, before resigning to concentrate on building his private practice. In 1871 he became a District Medical Officer, and a casualty surgeon to the Central Police Division, and in 1873 a dispensary surgeon at the Western Infirmary. Macewen returned to the Royal in 1875 as a dispensary surgeon, and the following year became one of the five visiting surgeons, and a lecturer in pathology at the infirmary's School of Medicine, at just twenty-eight years of age. During the seventeen years he spent at the Royal, the precocious young man became one of the world's most famous surgeons, and brought about a second revolution in surgical procedures.[46]

Macewen learned from Lister the importance of 'observation, investigation, experimentation and deduction' in surgery.[47] Convinced by the 'antiseptic theory' during his student days, he had participated as a resident in McLeod's experiments with antiseptic surgery, but must also have been impressed by his chief's view that 'disinfectants and antiseptics are unquestionably great aids in preventing purulent infection, but it is to the strenuous support of the strength by food and stimulants, by the ample supply of fresh air, by sustaining the courage, and enforcing cleanliness, that our attention should be chiefly directed'.[48] Macewen was one of several surgeons who sought to take Lister's work further, by striving to achieve 'aseptic' conditions—a germ-free environment—in the operating theatre. In an age when surgeons were not always scrupulous about hygiene in the theatre, Macewen insisted that his assistants and staff scrubbed up thoroughly before surgery, and wore sterilisable white coats during the operations. His aseptic procedures involved paying scrupulous attention to the sterilisation of surgical instruments, dressings, and of everything else in the room which might be a source of infection. In 1890 he persuaded the Board to purchase a steam dressing sterilizer and an instrument sterilizer.[49]

Macewen became famous for much more than his 'aseptic ritual'. He was a pioneer of brain surgery, removing a brain tumour in 1879, and of surgery on the spine. In 1888 he won international acclaim for his address to the British Medical Association in Glasgow, on 'The Surgery of the

Brain and Spinal Cord', and five years later he published the classic text-book, *On Pyogenic Diseases of the Brain and Spinal Cord*. Distressed by the high incidence of rickets in Glasgow, he designed his own instruments and developed a technique, known as 'Macewen's Osteotomy', for straightening deformed bones and enabling bow-legged and knock-kneed victims to walk upright. Macewen has been described as 'the acme of the scientific surgeon',[50] who refused to accept received wisdom if it flew in the face of his own research and the meticulous observation of clinical symptoms. He was knighted in 1902, and received honours from medical societies and academies throughout Europe and North America.

With an international reputation as the leading authority of his day on brain, spine and bone surgery, Macewen travelled the world to attend and speak at medical conferences. Although he was enormously respected his brusque manner did not, however, inspire affection among colleagues, and his single-mindedness and dedication to independent research encouraged his critics to complain that he failed to found a 'school' of collaborators. In fact, Macewen's influence on surgical theory and practice at the Royal was enormous, and many of his former students, such as James Hogarth Pringle (a surgeon at the infirmary, 1896–1923) adopted both his systematic approach to his work, and occasionally his maverick attitude to irksome infirmary rules and procedures.

REBECCA STRONG

Macewen's methods required the assistance of a committed nursing staff, well trained in the latest (usually his own) methods of pre-and post-operative patient care, especially for brain surgery cases which required close observation over prolonged periods to ensure accurate diagnoses. His opinions on the need to provide an advanced and systematic course of instruction for nurses were shared by the new matron, Rebecca Strong, who replaced Miss Tait after the latter retired in 1879. Rebecca Strong (1843–1944) was an Englishwoman, who trained at the Nightingale School of Nursing at St Thomas's Hospital in London in 1867, and was the matron at Dundee Royal Infirmary, 1873–9. William McEwen, the Chairman of the House Committee, and a leading advocate of nursing reform at the Royal, heard of her achievements in improving nursing standards and conditions at Dundee, and he visited her to persuade her to move to Glasgow. She made an immediate impact on nursing there.[51]

Despite the vast improvements made during the fifteen years before her appointment, the standards of nursing at the Royal fell short of Rebecca Strong's expectations. The superintendent, Moses Thomas, wrote in 1877 that 'in too many instances the applicant is one of a class who ... are not very elevated, either intellectually, morally or socially', and he admitted that, when there were no applicants to fill a vacancy, 'an intelligent scrubber' was sometimes promoted to serve as a night nurse. Thomas suggested that some systematic training should be offered at the Royal, and in 1878 a course of lectures on medical and surgical nursing was inaugurated, which was 'also open to ladies' on payment of a fee. A nurse was not permitted to take charge of a ward until she had passed an examination.[52] These reforms did not go far enough to satisfy the new matron.

Mrs Strong realised that her first task was to improve working conditions, in order to attract a better class of women. In August 1879 she persuaded the Board to provide suitable nurses' uniforms, and to purchase new ward furniture. In June 1882 she asked the managers to abandon a scheme to charge women sent to Glasgow from institutions in Edinburgh and London, and by Mrs Higginbotham's pioneering Glasgow Sick Poor and Private Nursing Association, for the privilege of training at the Royal. She pointed out that these trainees came to the infirmary precisely because they could obtain ward experience and instruction free of charge. They provided the Royal with intelligent probationer nurses who did not receive the £12 salary paid to the other pupils, and who came to work without pay at the Royal despite the fact that its reputation for training women was by no means firmly established, and there were not yet adequate sleeping quarters nor even a sitting room for the nurses. She argued that to introduce a charge for training would simply result in the trainees transferring to other hospitals with better facilities and recognised schools of nursing. Although the idea of imposing fees was dropped, Mrs Strong was to fight long and hard to win further victories for the nursing staff. Her first battle was with the residents and the superintendent.

THE RESIDENTS

Until 1862 the junior medical staff, or residents, at the Royal were referred to as clerks. This was a source of great dissatisfaction—in other hospitals, the title denoted someone of much lesser responsibilities than at the Royal—and in 1862 it was agreed that they should be known in future as physicians' and surgeons' assistants. It was also decided that the qualifications required for the post of resident assistant should be raised, with applicants required to have completed their four year course of study and have obtained the relevant medical degree or diploma before entering the Royal. The period of tenure of the residency remained just twelve months.

Young, newly qualified doctors were not always respectful of rules and authority, and over the years there were several who succeeded in incurring the wrath of the managers. The assistant to the physician, Dr Matthew Charteris, was dismissed in 1880, after an incident involving a probationer nurse outside the infirmary. The following year, Dr Hector Clare Cameron's assistant surgeon was suspended for refusing to apologise to the superintendent of nurses 'for interfering with her in the discharge of her duties and speaking to her in unbecoming terms'. He subsequently apologised 'for his conduct and language'. Two residents were dismissed in 1886 because they accompanied two nurses to the theatre, knowing full well that 'all outside engagements between the Assistants and the Nurses and female domestics [are] contrary to the rules of the house'. The nurses were reprimanded and their promotion suspended for one year.

The residents chafed under the regime of Mrs Strong. She believed that they were too young and inexperienced to have sole authority in the wards. They insisted they had the authority to deal with situations arising there, in the absence of their chiefs, and they resented the matron questioning their demands for the transfer of nurses when they, the residents, deemed assistance necessary. The medical superintendent, Dr Moses Thomas, was jealous of his rights as the executive officer of the infirmary to countermand the matron's decisions, and she became convinced that he would always take the residents' side in any dispute which arose. Matters came to a head at Christmas 1881, apparently after the matron issued an instruction that the residents' dining room should close at an early hour in the evening, and the residents became openly rude and discourteous to her.

In August 1882 Mrs Strong tendered her resignation, principally 'from a sense of personal discomfort arising from the conduct of the Residents in the hospital towards her personally...which they have exhibited rather as residents in the household than as professional men acting in the wards', and from the weakening of her authority as it was known that she and the superintendent did not agree on matters relating to the running of the hospital. Living up to her reputation for using threats of resignation as a means of negotiation, however, she delayed actually leaving the infirmary, and seems to have agreed to stay on after a report to the House Committee largely supported her position.[53] The superintendent, who complained she had 'a want of urbanity and a want of patience about her, and that she is impulsive and hasty' was criticised for his failure to defend the authority of the matron. Clearly, the responsibilities of the superintendent as the 'master of the house', and the matron as the 'mistress', required clarification. Mrs Strong was told by the managers that in future the responsibility for the allocation of nurses would be placed solely in her control, subject to the power of revision by the superintendent as chief executive of the infirmary. The matron had won a significant victory, establishing her authority over the junior doctors in nursing matters in the wards, and her right to communicate directly with the superintendent and visiting staff on matters relating to the nursing staff.

The matron's position at the Royal was made more difficult by the demands of William Macewen. The surgeon insisted that he could only proceed with his innovative surgery with the services of probationer nurses, to assist with observation work. Mrs Strong, in acceding to his requests, was left in the invidious position of appearing to favour him in the allocation of nurses, thereby incurring the wrath of other surgeons and their residents. Discipline also suffered.

'Macewen's' nurses became fiercely loyal to the surgeon. Macewen recalled many years after leaving the infirmary that, when he first joined the visiting staff, he failed to persuade the superintendent to supply him with a vessel in which he could sterilise his surgical instruments. To his surprise, some of the nurses clubbed together to buy him a fish kettle, ideal for the purpose.[54] Such loyalty was sometimes won at the matron's expense. She complained to Macewen in April 1882 that a relief nurse told her that 'she took her orders from Dr Potts [Macewen's resident], not Mrs Strong', and that this had happened before. She was distressed to discover, in August, that David Potts had announced his engagement to one of the nurses in his ward – for a matron who found that 'to govern ninety women under the most favourable circumstances is not an easy task', the prospect of her nurses forming emotional attachments with the residents was not one to relish.[55] Yet Macewen, often so fierce in pressing for the staff and facilities he felt essential for his work, was quick to acknowledge her contribution to his success, and in August 1884 he wrote to her from a conference in Norway, assuring her that 'you are so mixed up with everything I do in the surgery way. I look on you and the nurses as part of myself, and any honour which might be conferred on me as something which should be shared in Glasgow.'[56]

Rebecca Strong resigned again in January 1883, after the pressure of her work and a disagreement with Macewen brought her close to a nervous breakdown.[57] In July, after ninety-two of the nurses signed a petition asking the managers to refuse to accept her resignation, and Dr Charteris reported that 'she seems to have recovered from her mental depression and is anxious to continue her congenial work at the Infirmary', the matron returned to work. By then, however, the managers were embroiled in another and altogether more public controversy.

THE CHLOROFORM CONTROVERSY

On 6 March 1883 the *Glasgow Herald* published an editorial which must have worried the Royal's subscribers.

> It should no longer be an open secret that for some time past affairs have not been going well at the Royal Infirmary. Officials have not been drawing together, and resignations, only to be recalled again, have been frequent. The residents have been insubordinate and troublesome to govern; and their superiors, the 'staff', have been aggressive. The management itself has been ranged into two camps, each pursuing a different policy - one aiming to a stricter discipline and better internal government, even at the sacrifice of professional feelings; the other professing the same object, but tenacious of professional privileges and independence, and conservative of status and dignity.

The simmering feud between the visiting staff and management had come to the boil in late 1882. The Chairman, William McEwen, became concerned about the administration of anaesthetic in the infirmary, after three patients died under chloroform administered by residents unsupervised by experienced members of the staff. The inexperience or incompetence of many junior doctors entrusted with administering chloroform in British hospitals had attracted outraged comment in the columns of national newspapers. McEwen, ever sensitive to the Royal's reputation, took typically forthright action to ensure that safeguards were introduced to protect patients undergoing surgery in the infirmary. He succeeded in passing new rules to ensure that the residents were in future to be permitted to administer chloroform only in the presence of a visiting physician or surgeon, the superintendent or a member of the dispensary staff. He proposed that all residents, dressers and students should be given instruction in the administration of chloroform. In addition, he demanded that surgeons pay a second visit to the wards, in the afternoons of their receiving days, and that measures were taken to ensure the visiting staff attended the wards on a Sunday, as they were required to do by the Rules of the infirmary, as he felt residents were sometimes left to deal with situations which were beyond their abilities.

McEwen's new rules were opposed by the visiting physicians and surgeons. They complained that decisions regarding the medical policy of the infirmary should be taken by the medical staff, and not by 'lay' managers. Nothing daunted, McEwen then suggested that, as the percentage of surgical cases entering the infirmary amounted to 60 per cent of the total, and there were twenty surgical wards and only twelve medical wards, a sixth surgeon should be appointed, and the number of physicians should be reduced to four. Some medical men on the Board, led by the President of the Faculty of Physicians and Surgeons of Glasgow, Dr Robert Scott Orr, and the University's appointee Professor William Leishman, a former physician at the Royal, protested that the matter of the administration of anaesthetics was 'a purely professional one', and they were horrified at the attempt to alter the balance of the visiting staff. McEwen held firm, making it clear that 'the whole true explanation of this hubbub is a revived attempt on the part of the medical directors and the staff to get the whole control and management of the hospital'. The subscribers and contributors, ever suspicious of the motives of the medical establishment, and convinced that the infirmary's main responsibility was to the patient, and not to the training or professional advancement of the medical staff, seem to have supported him. Their feelings were summed up in an editorial in the *Glasgow Herald*, on 7 April 1883:

> It is proverbial that doctors differ, and, unfortunately, their differences are not confined to their prescriptions or the merits of the antiseptic system. They embrace a universal range.

Their inherent professional conservatism, their want of acquaintance with affairs, their deficient business qualities, all point to medical men being as a class peculiarly unfitted to form sound conclusions in matters of administration, especially when their own interests intervene...

The medical establishment fought back. Robert Grieve, one of the Faculty's appointees on the Board who supported McEwen's proposals, was told that he must stand down, and another Faculty appointee and McEwen supporter, William Eadie, was put under intense pressure to resign from the Board. When McEwen had to visit London on business in March 1883 his request for the postponement of the monthly meeting of the managers was ignored, and Scott Orr, Leishman and their allies succeeded in overturning the earlier resolutions, appointing instead a committee of medical men to investigate the chloroform question. McEwen resigned in disgust the following day.

The dispute became increasingly bitter after 19 March, with the publication in two newspapers of a letter from James Morton, the cantankerous surgeon who had been so vociferous in his condemnation of Lister's antiseptic system during the 1860s and 1870s. Morton accused McEwen of a variety of abuses of his power in the infirmary, using the most vituperative language. McEwen was furious, and in denying Morton's charges, launched a blistering attack on Morton's motives and accusing him of being an incompetent surgeon. Most of the managers deplored Morton's behaviour, and the Board issued a statement condemning the 'untrue' and 'offensive' statements he made. The episode was finally resolved in May. McEwen withdrew his resignation, returning to the Board in time to witness the adoption of new house rules on the administration of chloroform. In March 1884, in the face of continued opposition from the University's Professor of Medicine, William Tennant Gairdner, and other medical appointees on the Board, the number of physicians was reduced to four, and an additional surgeon was appointed to take charge of the lock (that is, venereal disease) and erysipelas wards, and the new burn ward. James Morton resigned at the end of his term as a surgeon, in 1884, and became President of the Faculty of Physicians and Surgeons of Glasgow, 1886–9. William McEwen, having firmly established the authority of the Board over the medical staff in matters of management policy, retired as Chairman and manager in January 1885.[58]

THE DEPARTURE OF REBECCA STRONG

Rebecca Strong, who had threatened to resign on a number of occasions during her six years at the Royal, finally left the infirmary in October 1885. One of the lady superindendents of nurses, Miss Wood, was promoted to take her place. Ostensibly, Mrs Strong departed to open a private nursing establishment in Glasgow, explaining that she was 'sorry my strength will not permit of my continuing so arduous and responsible a work for a longer time'. She wrote later that her decision was prompted by the Board's refusal to sanction work on the building of a new nurses' home, which the matron had insisted since her arrival in Glasgow was essential for the welfare of the nursing staff and the prospects for success of a school of nursing.[59] In fact the managers had gone some way to meet her demands. In 1882 a sitting room for off-duty nurses was built above the erysipelas wards, and the old dispensary was converted to provide nineteen bedrooms for nurses. Plans were also made for a new nurses' home, which would accommodate the thirty day nurses, twelve night nurses and ten probationers who remained in the bedrooms attached to wards, rather than 'collected together under proper supervision and other conditions more healthy than at present'. However, the managers were loath to fund the new home from existing funds, and were unable to raise additional revenue to meet the estimated cost of £5,000. They were distressed to lose Mrs Strong, but they did finally authorise the building of the new home in the summer of 1886. It was opened on 31 August 1888, providing eighty-eight bedrooms. A glazed covered way (variously known over the years as 'the conservatory', 'the greenhouse corridor', and 'the hen run') was built to connect the home with the main buildings, offering shelter to nurses going to and from the wards, and exposing their visitors to the scrutiny of the matron from her flat.

NURSES' DISCONTENT

After the departure of Mrs Strong, and despite the opening of the new nurses' home, the morale of the Royal's nurses plummeted. In some ways, the infirmary was the victim of its own success. The policy of improving working conditions and attracting younger women to work in the wards had paid dividends, and the nursing staff was better educated and provided with better training than ever before. However, the new generation of nurses had greater expectations of a life in nursing, and were less willing to tolerate the privations and arduous working conditions which older women had come to accept. On 2 September 1891 the *North British Daily Mail* published a letter from 'A Probationer' (later identified as Katherine Hunter), who wrote scathingly of the conditions she had to endure at the Royal. Her letter was followed by a flood of complaints and caustic comment from fellow nurses and former patients and residents. Certainly, the nurses had much to complain about.

A probationer began work at 6 o'clock in the morning, and finished at 8.30 p.m., with only half-hour breaks for breakfast and lunch and, sometimes, a one-and-a-half-hour break for rest and exercise. Often, owing to shortages of staff, she had to work on without a break until 10 p.m., and was then woken at dawn for 'special duty' to sit with a patient or assist in the ward until breakfast. A sixteen–hour day was not unusual, and yet she had to find time to attend lectures and study for her exam.

A night nurse was called at 8.45 p.m., and after supper at 9.15 p.m. she worked in the ward with nothing more than a cup of tea to sustain her. At 5 o'clock in the morning she was expected to make the beds, and after this to take patients' temperatures, wash their faces and sweep the floors. After breakfast at 7.30 she waited on the visiting surgeon or physician, who might remain in the wards until 2 o'clock in the afternoon.

There were no maids or cleaners in the wards after 10 a.m. on Sundays, and so the nurse on duty had to fetch meals, wash dishes and clean in addition to her normal chores. Patients who died in the wards in the evening were left in their beds overnight, unless a convalescing patient could be found to help the gateman remove the corpse and relieve the distress of both patients and nurse. The nurses had no separate toilet facilities, and so they had to use the patients' toilets when on duty, even in male wards and in wards reserved for infectious cases. The nurses felt unable to complain—the superintendent, Dr Thomas, was considered fierce and rude, and one former nurse complained that 'the matron's cold reserve positively frightened me, and every time I heard her voice in the ward I lay trembling until she was gone'.[60] They often fell ill under the strain of their duties—'underfeeding and overwork' were blamed for a daily sicklist which rarely contained less than twenty names—but received little sympathy from the authorities: it was alleged that sick nurses were routinely dismissed with the comment 'I'm afraid you are not strong enough for a nurse…'

The greatest criticism of all was levelled at the provision of meals. It was generally agreed that the food served to the nurses was quite adequate when Mrs Strong was matron, but deteriorated after her departure. Katherine Hunter described the meals as 'miserably cooked and poorly served'. Other former nurses recounted tales of beef, served to the nurses for three consecutive days, which had previously been used to make beef tea; of bad eggs and eggless puddings being served up; and of mustard mixed in a spittoon. Many former probationers complained that their entire salary was used to supplement their meagre diet. Former patients remembered that they suffered too: one wrote of 'tea and coffee like dirty water, without sugar, nauseating instead of nourishing to an invalid'. The *North British Daily Mail* was unequivocal in its support of the nurses. A thundering editorial on 3 September asserted that 'it is surely not necessary to kill the nurses in order to cure the patients'. It demanded an inquiry into charges that the penny-pinching attitude of the Board had left the nurses 'underfed and overworked'.

The nurses' cause was championed by the residents, who wrote letters to the press, sent memorials to the Board and started up a petition, all calling for better conditions for nurses. The skilfully orchestrated campaign forced the managers to take action. The cleaning and nursing staffs were increased by nine and eight women respectively. An inquiry into the nurses' grievances reported in October 1891. It was subsequently agreed to reschedule the 4 p.m. classes, which night nurses could only attend by disturbing their much-needed sleep; to provide the nurses with a monthly holiday from the wards; and to ensure that there was a greater variety and attention to quality of food available in the dining room. All nurses were to be permitted to take tea and bread and butter while on duty in the wards. Night nurses were reminded that the house rules required that they leave the wards at 10 a.m., and that they should break with the practice of lingering longer to wait upon the visiting physician or surgeon. Continuous night service was abolished, and day and night duties were rotated every three months.

Miss Wood resigned as matron 'due to continued indisposition' in July 1891. The job was advertised and, probably through the influence of William Macewen, Rebecca Strong made a late application and was reappointed in October. The return of Rebecca Strong was of vital importance to the Royal. Only she had the status to reassure women intending to enter the nursing school, and their parents, that the nurses' living and working conditions would be improved. Macewen was also reunited with the woman with whom he had collaborated on earlier innovations in nurses' education, and with whom he could work on the latest proposal—'an establishment for a systematic course of training for nurses to be followed by examinations', which he first suggested to the managers in April 1892, and which he presented in draft in October, only a few days before he resigned to become Regius Professor of Surgery at the University of Glasgow and a visiting surgeon at the Western. The new system was introduced in 1893, and it was to put the Royal at the forefront of the movement in the United Kingdom to provide preliminary training schools for nurses.

WOMEN STUDENTS

Improvements in training for nurses at the Royal coincided with a debate over the provision of facilities for clinical instruction at the infirmary for female medical students. Since the 1840s there had been many attempts by women to gain entry to British medical schools. The efforts of campaigners such as Sophia Jex Blake in Scotland met with limited success in the face of determined opposition from the medical establishment, but in 1886 the examination for the triple qualification was opened to women, and the Edinburgh School of Medicine for Women was established to offer systematic classes for women seeking a career in medicine.[61] Shortly afterwards the Royal's medical school became the first in Glasgow to permit women to matriculate for a complete course of medical study. The first woman to matriculate, in 1888, was a Canadian student whose name is not recorded. St Mungo's College continued the policy of its predecessor, and forty-three women attended classes there between 1890 and 1892, receiving clinical instruction alongside the male students in the Royal. Some women, particularly those from the Missionary Nurses' Training Home in Dennistoun, desired only to attend clinics at the dispensary, to provide them with a basic education in the properties of drugs and the treatment of injuries, to carry with them to missions overseas. The others, however, sought a complete medical education, to enable them to sit the examination for the triple qualification and to enter the medical profession. Alice Umpherston was one of the most successful of the women students, winning the class prize in Medical Pathology in the winter of 1891–2 and in the following summer session. Her classmates includes 'rebels' from the Edinburgh School of Medicine for Women, such as Elsie Inglis and the Cadell sisters, Ina and Grace.[62] The *Glasgow Medical Journal*, reporting on the general meeting of the Governors, staff and students at the close of the college's winter session, 1891–2, commented that 'from the hearty and kindly way in which the names of those ladies who gained prizes or certificates was received, it seemed pretty conclusive that no great difficulties have been met with in the conducting of mixed classes'.[63] Such an optimistic view did not take account of rising tensions at the College, precipitated by the arrival of the Queen Margaret girls.

The Queen Margaret College (QMC) was founded in Glasgow in 1883 to provide higher education for women, and introduced a medical curriculum in 1890. In August, the QMC asked for and was granted facilities at the Royal for the clinical and pathological instruction of its students, separately from the men. Like most Scottish hospitals the Western refused to allow women students to receive clinical instruction in the wards, and the QMC students were allowed only limited facilities at the Maternity Hospital; so the Board's decision was a major victory for those who sought to gain equal opportunities for women to study medicine in Glasgow. Clinical classes for the QMC students began in November 1890. There was a hostile reaction to this success from many of the male students at St Mungo's College.

In March 1891 a majority of the male members of the St Mungo's College Medical Society voted to send a memorial to the College governors and the infirmary's managers, listing the disadvantages they suffered from attending mixed classes at the College and in the Royal. They complained that the women were given preferential treatment in the examination of patients; that the men were often too embarrassed to ask pertinent questions regarding the patient's condition when the case involved 'certain organs'; and that because the classes in the gynaecological clinic were segregated, the smaller number of women students (there were fifteen in all, four of them from the QMC) received a higher standard of instruction than did the men in their large class. The memorial also complained that a large number of the women were not 'bona fide medical students'—a reference to the trainee missionaries. For these reasons, the memorial called on the Board to discontinue mixed classes at the Royal. The managers were persuaded by a memorial from the women students of St Mungo's to decline the society's request, and permit them to continue 'if so inclined' to attend mixed classes during the 1891–2 session.

In August 1892 a memorial from fifty-one of the male students threatened to leave St Mungo's if mixed classes were continued there. The College governors, without the resources to pay for separate systematic instruction for women and fearful of losing almost 50 per cent of their students if mixed classes continued, decided to exclude women from the medical courses. At a special meeting the managers of the Royal responded with a resolution, carried by five votes to two, to exclude all women from classes at the infirmary. The decision, taken only a few days before the British Medical Association voted to admit women to its membership, provoked a public outcry. Strongly worded complaints were received from former women students, the QMC (which became The Women's Department of the University of Glasgow in 1893), the Faculty of Physicians and Surgeons of Glasgow, and the Missionary Nurses' Training Home. In the face of such widespread opposition, the managers agreed unanimously in September to continue to permit women students to receive clinical instruction at the Royal, but only in separate classes. Although the College governors complained in 1893 that too many beds were set aside for the clinical instruction of women, to the exclusion of the College students, and suggested the women should be sent instead to the wards of the Victoria Infirmary, the managers refused to restrict the facilities made available to the students from the QMC. The first women to graduate in medicine from a Scottish university, Marion Gilchrist and Alice Louisa Cumming in 1894, received their clinical instruction at the Royal, as did most of those to follow in their footsteps at the University of Glasgow.[64]

The end of an era

Between 1861 and 1892 the standards of comfort and care offered to patients at the Royal improved almost beyond recognition. In 1861 the sick and injured were sometimes more at risk in the wards, from fever and infection, than they were in their own homes. The decision to exclude fever cases, and the advances in antiseptic and aseptic procedures made by Lister and Macewen, made the infirmary an altogether safer place. Patients were better cared for in 1892: the nurses were better trained, the standards of cleanliness were higher, and more attention was paid to providing the patient with a healthy diet and pleasant surroundings. The situation was far from perfect—the deterioration of the fabric of the buildings was becoming a particular source of concern to the managers—but it was certainly true that by 1892 patients could be effectively treated for more illnesses and injuries, and stood better chances of recovering their health, than ever before in the history of the Glasgow Royal Infirmary.

4 'THE COSTLY PILE
AT CASTLE STREET', 1892–1918

Oh, the Auld Hoose, the Auld Hoose,
That noo they're pu'in' doon,
Mair than a hunner years its been
The glory o' the toon...

The New Hoose, the New Hoose,
It's big and braw and high;
But, oh, it's chiefest glory is
That it's the G.R.I.

Extract from a poem by Dr John Fergus, on the reconstruction
of the Royal.

By 1892 Glasgow was firmly established as 'the commercial and manu-facturing capital of Scotland, and in point of wealth, population and importance, the second city of the British islands'.[1] Since 1861, and after a series of boundary extensions, its population had increased by over 66 per cent, to 658,073 people,[2] and independent suburban burghs such as Partick and Govan were growing at a similarly rapid pace. Industry and trade were booming, creating vast fortunes for businessmen, industrialists and entrepreneurs, and relatively secure employment for tens of thou-sands of office workers and skilled tradesmen. The economic prosperity of Glasgow was given a physical expression in the new city centre, in the streets laid out in a classical grid pattern around George Square, which were adorned with fine public and commercial buildings. The great International Exhibition of 1888 confirmed its claim to be one of the world's great cities – hundreds of thousands of people flocked to Kelvingrove Park that summer, to visit the spectacular buildings which served as showcases for Glasgow's art, commerce and industry.

The area around the Royal's Townhead site was transformed after Lister's departure from the infirmary. In 1866 the City Improvement Trust was created to demolish many of the old city-centre slum areas, and promote the erection of new homes. Despite a delay resulting from a long recession in the building industry during the late 1870s and 1880s, much of High Street was cleared (a process in which the railway companies joined, acquiring land for new city-centre lines and stations) and new, less densely crowded tenement buildings were being erected in 1892. The steep slope of the Bell o' the Brae, that part of High Street leading up from George Street to the infirmary, was reduced from a gradient of 1 in 14 to a more gentle 1 in 29, and the square in front of the medical block was enlarged. The Trust also addressed the nuisance posed to health by the Molendinar Burn, which had become little more than an open sewer. The stretch of the burn behind the infirmary was culverted over in 1878, and Wishart Street was laid out along its course, to connect the newly-built John Knox Street with Alexandra Parade.[3]

Vicar's Alley, the lane which passed along the western side of the infirmary and had become 'a resort for bad characters', was shut off to the public in 1880. Another public nuisance was dealt with ten years later. Since Lister's day, the volume of traffic clattering along Castle Street had increased substantially, disturbing the rest of patients in the wards. In an attempt to provide the in-patients with some respite, the city's Police Board agreed in 1890 to pave the roadway with wood, from Mason Street to a point 30 feet north of the Surgical Block.

Glasgow's public transport improved beyond all recognition between 1861 and 1892. A passenger railway network was largely completed by the 1890s, with College Station (now High Street Station), which opened on the old University site in 1871 and was rebuilt on the City of Glasgow Union line in 1886, the most conveniently situated for the Royal. A horse-drawn tram system, inaugurated in 1872 and comprising 60 miles of tramway by 1892, offered fast and cheap services to all parts of the city. It was taken over by Glasgow Corporation in 1894, and was subsequently electrified and extended to serve most of the suburbs.[4]

The development of an extensive and inexpensive public transport network had important consequences for the Royal. The inhabitants of distant areas of the city or the suburbs had in the past been deterred from going to Townhead in search of medical assistance by the difficulties involved in travelling while ill or enfeebled. With better public transport, more felt able to leave their sickbeds and seek medicine and advice as out-patients at the infirmary. In 1861 there were 10,273 attendances at the dispensary. Thirty-one years later the figure had risen to nearly 38,000.

Glasgow's economic progress was achieved at the expense of considerable human misery. The population included large numbers of poorly paid unskilled workers with little job security, and unemployment was often high. Despite the activities of the Improvement Trust in the city centre, slums such as those in Cowcaddens and around Glasgow Cross remained among the most overcrowded in the country, and the levels of social degradation to be found there shocked even the most hardened social commentators. Alcoholism, crime and the illnesses and diseases associated with overcrowding and undernourishment were rife in slum areas. With thousands of coal-burning industries, a fog of atmospheric pollution hung over the city, and this, too, took its toll on the health of the citizens. Dr John Barlow, an assistant surgeon in the dispensary, noted in 1892 that 'the majority of patients who came for advice [to the dispensary] were not living in healthy homes. They were poor, and badly nourished, and, in most cases, very dirty.'[5] The infirmary's annual report of that year reveals that pulmonary tuberculosis and bronchitis together accounted for 20 per cent of the 2,052 cases treated in the medical wards, even though the Royal would not admit chronic cases.

During the second half of the nineteenth century tubercular joints and bone disease, and abscess, tumour and ulcer cases, remained common in the surgical wards. Advances in surgical technique pioneered by Lister, Macewen and others also permitted a much greater range of operations, such as brain, thoracic and abdominal surgery (the latter including appendectomies, first performed at the infirmary in 1891), to be carried out with comparative safety. However, to many benefactors and subscribers, the Royal's most important work was in the treatment of industrial injuries. Accident prevention and the safety of employees was seldom high on the list of Victorian industrial management priorities. Consequently, the expansion of Glasgow's heavy industries was accompanied by a steady increase in death and serious injury. Almost every day, local newspapers carried reports of male and female workers who suffered dislocations, burns, fractures and other horrific injuries at their workplaces. Hundreds of these cases were taken to the Royal each year, by cab, commercial vehicles or, after 1882, in the horse-drawn vehicles of the St Andrew's Ambulance Society.

By 1892 the Royal had been relieved of many of the responsibilities it had accepted in 1794. After the passing of the Poor Law Amendment Act in 1845, Glasgow's parochial boards (which became parish councils in 1894) took an increasingly active role in providing hospital care for sick and infirm paupers. Ward accommodation at the old Town's Hospital and in the Barony Poorhouse in Barnhill (which opened in 1853) was extended. Although the standard of care they provided fell far short of those in the voluntary infirmaries, there was a commitment to providing an improved standard of hospital care, which resulted in the erection of a new general hospital of 1,700 beds at Stobhill, and smaller district hospitals at Duke Street and Oakbank, in the first years of the twentieth century. The Govan Parish Poorhouse, with a small hospital which was later to become the Southern General Hospital, opened at Merryflats in 1872 and provided similar accommodation for the chronic sick and infirm poor of the area.

In addition to the growth of Poor Law hospitals, and of municipal fever hospitals after 1865, there had been a dramatic increase in voluntary institutions during the last quarter of the nineteenth century. Many were specialist hospitals, such as the Hospital for Sick Children, the Glasgow Ear Hospital and the Samaritan Hospital for Women. The city's third voluntary general hospital, the Victoria Infirmary, opened in Langside on the south side of the river in 1890.[6] But these additions to Glasgow's hospital accommodation and medical facilities were scarcely sufficient to meet the needs of a rapidly increasing population, and in 1892, despite the opening of new institutions in other areas of the city, and the expanding role of the city and the parochial boards in meeting the need for hospital provision for infectious disease, chronic and ordinary pauper cases, there was a waiting list of up to 150 for admission to the wards of the Royal.

The departure of William Macewen in 1892 marked the end of an era at the Royal, but the managers were fully aware of the dangers of allowing the infirmary to rest on its laurels. The need to maintain, extend and to improve upon the services which the Royal had traditionally offered, and the pressure to offer new specialist treatments, provided them with their agenda for the approach of the twentieth century.

NURSING

William Macewen's final achievement at the Royal was to gain acceptance for the course of systematic training for nurses which he had devised in association with Rebecca Strong. The scheme was introduced in January 1893. Prospective students had to satisfy the matron that they possessed a knowledge of grammar, spelling, composition, dictation and the 'three r's', before they were accepted to a preliminary course of instruction. The first part of the three-month course comprised lectures in elementary anatomy, physiology and hygiene, laying great stress on what Rebecca Strong called 'observation and correct reporting'.[7] If she passed the exam on these subjects, the student embarked on a second, more advanced series of lectures and demonstrations on clinical and surgery cases, ward work and cookery, and sat a further examination. The fee for the first course was two guineas (£2.10) and for the second, three guineas (£3.15). Only after attending the courses and passing exams in the relevant subjects was the student accepted to work as a probationer in the wards, working for a salary of £12 during the first year, and £20 in the second. At the end of the second year, if the probationer could pass a final examination, she was presented with her certificate as a trained nurse. The course was made still more attractive in 1894, when E Nilsson, a graduate of the Royal Central Institute of Stockholm, was appointed teacher of massage treatment, so important in physiotherapy.

The new scheme was very successful, both in improving the standard of nursing at the Royal and in encouraging intelligent young women to train there. This success in itself posed a problem for the matron. In September 1896 she asked the House Committee to consider the establishment of a nurses' registry office in the infirmary. Her reason was that the Royal was now attracting 'a more enterprising set of nurses', who were less likely than their predecessors to remain for long in the wards after completing their training, but eager to move on to further their careers in other hospitals or in private or district nursing. The matron believed that the establishment of the registry would enable them to maintain some contact with the infirmary after moving on, foster a greater esprit de corps among current and former members of staff, and bolster the growing reputation of the training school. The proposal was not accepted, but it was typical of the matron's ambition to improve the attractions and status of nursing at the Royal.

THE OPHTHALMIC INSTITUTION

Shortly before Macewen's departure the Royal acquired a new department. Many patients suffering from eye diseases or injuries, the latter often the result of accidents at engineering workshops, sought medical attention at the Royal. However, it had neither the specialist staff, nor instruments and equipment, to provide treatment for serious cases. As the Royal relied heavily on industrialists and their employees for funds, and they expected the infirmary to provide a complete range of medical care for sick and injured workers, the managers were eager to provide the necessary facilities. There were two eye hospitals in Glasgow, the Ophthalmic Institution and the Glasgow Eye Hospital, and the Board decided to seek amalgamation with the smaller of them, and thus avoid the expense of setting up and equipping a department from scratch. The Ophthalmic Institution was founded in 1868 by Dr John R. Wolfe. In 1890 a provisional agreement was reached whereby the Royal would acquire the assets and the responsibilities of managing and maintaining the Institution, and would erect a new building at the infirmary to provide the same number of beds—thirty—as were provided in the existing West Regent Street premises in the city centre. The amalgamation was completed in March 1891 when the Institution became the infirmary's ophthalmic department, although it continued to be funded by means of separate voluntary subscriptions. The ophthalmic surgeon attended the out-patient department at the Royal on two days each week, and clinical instruction was made available to students in West Regent Street. The undertaking to build additional premises for the department at Townhead was not honoured until the 1960s.[8]

JOHN MACINTYRE

The most dramatic medical breakthrough to be made at the Royal in the late Victorian era was achieved in the unlikely surroundings of the Electrical Department. The department was still in its infancy—it was established in 1887—but it was here, in March 1896, that what is believed to be the world's first hospital X-ray, or radiology, unit was established. The man responsible for opening the unit was John Macintyre (1857–1928).

Macintyre was born near the Royal, the son of a Highland tailor. It is

146

said that he became an apprentice electrician after leaving school, but subsequently decided to study medicine. After graduating MB, CM from Glasgow University in 1882 he spent three months at sea as a ship's surgeon, and then pursued postgraduate studies in London, Vienna and Paris. He returned to Glasgow in 1884 to take up the post of Surgeon for Diseases of the Throat at the Anderson's College Dispensary, and two years later became an assistant surgeon and the Demonstrator of Anatomy at the Royal's School of Medicine.[9] Fascinated by the potential uses of electricity in medicine, particularly in his area of special interest, laryngology, Macintyre published a paper in the *Glasgow Medical Journal* of January 1885 on the subject of the illumination of the cavities of the body by electric light. Later that year he was appointed to the new post of electrician at the Royal, and began to collect the equipment required for electro-therapeutics and diagnosis.[10] In 1887 the 'department for the application of medical electricity' opened. It was enlarged in 1894, and a gas engine, dynamo and other equipment installed.

In 1895 Wilhelm Röntgen of Würzburg discovered short-wave electro-magnetic radiation, which could pass through opaque material, such as skin and tissue, and could thus be used to obtain photographic impressions of the bones and some of the vital organs of the body. The discovery of what Röntgen called 'X-rays' created excitement throughout the scientific world, and scientists rushed to assemble the electrical equipment required to duplicate and develop his research. Shortly after the publication of Röntgen's discovery Macintyre and a friend, Dr Archibald Fauld, working in Macintyre's own laboratory, succeeded in photographing the bones of Macintyre's hand by means of X-ray apparatus. Macintyre explained and demonstrated the potential uses of X-rays in medicine at a meeting of the Glasgow University Medico-Chirurgical Society in March 1896. He also worked on a paper with Lord Kelvin's nephew, the electrical engineer James T. Bottomley, and Lord Blythswood, who had his own well-equipped electrical laboratory, and they presented their paper 'On Roentgen X-rays, or the new photography', to the Philosophical Society of Glasgow in 1896.[11]

By March 1896 Macintyre was at work setting up a laboratory in the electrical department, for 'the new process of surgical photography', and in April secured the appointment of Faulds and Dr George McIntyre as his unpaid assistants. The laboratory was fitted with the latest equipment, and important breakthroughs made there included, in 1896, the first X-ray cinematograph – in the first instance, 40 feet of film of the moving legs of a frog. However, the laboratory was not devoted entirely to scientific experiment, and by 1901 over 1,400 X-ray photographs of patients were taken each year.[12] In 1902, in recognition of its success in the diagnosis and treatment of a variety of injuries and illnesses, a modernised X-ray department was installed in the new Electrical Pavilion. The cost was borne by a number of wealthy benefactors.

THE SCHAW CONVALESCENT HOME

The establishment of the X-ray laboratory was accompanied by an improvement in the facilities available for convalescent patient care. The staff had long been under pressure to discharge convalescing patients before they were fully fit to leave, owing to the long waiting list for admission to the infirmary. In November 1891 Miss Marjorie Shanks Schaw met the managers to discuss her proposal to provide a convalescent home for patients from the Royal, where they might spend a week or two recovering their strength before going home. Miss Schaw offered to put £40,000 towards the project, to purchase a site in Bearsden, build the home, and provide an endowment to help meet the running costs. The institution was to be known as the Schaw Convalescent Home, in memory of her brother Archibald.

Schaw Home was set in 12 acres of land on the outskirts of Bearsden, a small village near Glasgow. The Gothic building, three storeys high, was built on a hilltop with stunning views from its impressive square tower. Day and recreation rooms were on the ground floor, with male and female dormitories offering accommodation for fifty patients on the upper floor. The home opened to patients in August 1895. Reporting the official opening ceremony in March of the following year, the *North British Daily Mail's* correspondent wrote, without a trace of irony, that 'the basement contains a smoking room for the men and a large work room for the women'.[13]

The managers were happy to have such a magnificent addition to the buildings in their care. Sadly, it did not immediately find favour with its neighbours. Bearsden was one of Glasgow's most exclusive suburbs, and the residents of the fine villas in the vicinity of the home had moved there to distance themselves not only from the polluted atmosphere but also, no doubt, from the more 'uncouth' elements of the city's population. The influx of convalescing 'sick poor' patients, who came mostly from the industrial districts of Glasgow, created tensions in the community.

In April 1896 the Board received complaints from a number of Bearsden residents that patients from Schaw Home were loitering at the gates of their houses. Two years later, in August 1898, another complaint was received, of 'patients from the Convalescent Home blocking the footpath of the railway bridge, expectorating all over the place, and frequently making rude comments on passers-by...' Finally, as complaints continued to come before them, the Board decided in June 1899 to confine the patients to the grounds of the home. It would appear that the two communities were able to co-exist relatively amicably after this, and Schaw Home became one of Bearsden's best-known landmarks. After her death Miss Schaw's trustees allocated a further £40,000 to the Royal, to endow the three wards on 'the Schaw Floor' of the Surgical Block at Townhead.[14]

RECONSTRUCTION

The Schaw Floor was named in 1917, after the Royal had been entirely rebuilt. The replacement of the old infirmary buildings had become a matter of urgency in the 1890s, due to the inadequate operating facilities, the requirement for additional bed space, and to a general deterioration in the fabric of buildings which were no longer deemed suitable for the requirements of a modern hospital. Despite the irrefutable case presented by the Board in favour of reconstruction, however, their decision to rebuild the infirmary at Townhead generated a good deal of controversy.

In March 1897 the Board was informed that the Lord Provost, David Richmond, wished to commemorate the sixtieth year of the reign of Queen Victoria with a scheme to replace the historic Adams' Medical Block with a modern hospital building. In April 1897 the executive committee of leading Glasgow citizens which was formed to promote the scheme issued an appeal for donations to the Queen Victoria Diamond Jubilee Fund, to meet the cost of the reconstruction work. The managers agreed that the Medical Block had become obsolete, but considered that the other buildings were also in need of replacement. Accordingly, the Board proceeded to work on the preliminary details of a scheme to rebuild the entire infirmary.

The scheme met with difficulties from the beginning. Sketch plans of the interior arrangements of wards, theatres and departments were presented to the staff in January 1898, when they made their objections known and offered preferred alternatives. In April 1899 the criticisms were more strongly expressed, with ten members of the medical staff signing a memorandum to the effect that 'the plans do not...fulfil the requirements of a modern hospital...', and Rebecca Strong stating that 'the plans as amended are still defective...' In 1900 the Lord Provost's executive committee invited designs from architects for the new Medical, or 'Jubilee', Block, supplying amended sketch plans of the interiors to those who entered the architectural competition.

The assessor appointed by the executive committee to act as a technical adviser in the competition was Sir Robert Rowand Anderson, an architect famous in Glasgow for his Central Station Hotel and other public buildings. To Anderson's chagrin his choice of the winner of the competition was ignored by the executive committee, which chose instead to accept the proposals of a local architect, James Miller, whose previous work included railway buildings such as the ornate St Enoch's Station on the Glasgow Subway, and who had been commissioned to extend Anderson's Central Station Hotel. Miller's plans for the Jubilee Block caused an outcry. Anderson protested that the proposed six-storey block would dwarf and overwhelm the cathedral, and he chastised the committee for 'wasting money on the ghastly absurdity of a baronial infirmary'. The executive committee replied that the aesthetic merits of an architectural style were a matter of opinion, but they felt Miller's proposals best suited the infirmary's practical needs. A heated debate began in the press, as leading architects and cultural organisations bemoaned the detrimental effect that the Miller building would have on its historic surroundings.[15] In 1904 the Board commissioned the architect Sir Henry Burdett and Dr Donald Mackintosh, the medical superintendent of the Western Infirmary, to report on Miller's plans for the Jubilee Block and the other new infirmary buildings. They in turn presented a critical report in February 1905, and in July the Office of Works in London summoned the architect and James Hedderwick, the Chairman of the House Committee, to hear the reservations of the Commissioners of Works regarding the height of the proposed Jubilee Block.

The intervention of the Commissioners resulted in the removal of some of the more fussy architectural details from the exterior of the Jubilee Block, but the managers refused to contemplate a reduction in its height. Nor were they willing to consider the complaints of a large body of professional medical opinion, supported by many of the medical staff of the infirmary and most forcibly expressed by the University's Professor of Medicine, Sir William Tennant Gairdner. These protestors argued that all but the accident and emergency wards of the infirmary should be removed from the present cramped site, away from the noise, heavy traffic and atmospheric pollution of Townhead to a new, more spacious location in the suburbs. Like the arguments of the architectural critics, those of distinguished medical authorities in favour of relocation were dismissed by the Board. In November, while the debate on the architectural and practical merits of the scheme raged on, work finally began on the first phase of the project, the new Surgical Block.[16]

There is no doubt that the Royal was in desperate need of reconstruction by the early 1900s. In 1912 the Clerk of Works reported to the managers that the old Medical Block, then in the course of demolition, had been in an extremely dangerous condition.

> All the central portion, which has the appearance of heavy masonry, is really a skeleton, and has had to be shored up to prevent a mishap in removing. The pediment face which is nearly all cement is impossible to save, parts of it crumbling away in the men's hands. Bond timber, originally built in with iron and lead straps, was the only thing that held it up, and a sample of the timber, which is severely decayed, herewith will show the state the building was in. The only thing that kept this building up in my opinion was Faith, and it is a good thing it is now being demolished, as something serious would certainly have happened.

Clearly, the economies which Robert Adam had to introduce in the 1790s, at the insistence of the managers, had resulted in the construction of a building which, although pleasing to the eye, was far from suitable for continued use in the twentieth century.

St Mungo's College

While the debate over the architectural and locational merits of the new infirmary continued, another controversy arose at the infirmary. St

Mungo's College had, almost from its inception in 1889, struggled to attract sufficient numbers of students to meet the costs of running the school. During the early years of the twentieth century the situation deteriorated. Aspiring young doctors continued to prefer to study for a University of Glasgow degree, rather than the triple qualification. The expense of university fees had previously created a barrier to entry to courses there, but the introduction in 1901 of Carnegie Trust grants to meet class fees permitted many talented students of modest means to matriculate at Gilmorehill. The College had initially attracted many English, Irish and Welsh students, but the opening of new medical schools in Ireland and in English provincial cities at the end of the nineteenth century had resulted in a decline in the number of students coming to Glasgow from other parts of the United Kingdom in search of a medical education. With less than ninety students matriculating at the College each year, and its capital stock declining, the College was in the words of the Royal's Chairman, James Hedderwick, a 'sickly youth'.[17]

In 1905 the College governors renewed their efforts to secure affiliation with the University. Relations with the Royal deteriorated the following year, however, when the Board declined a request to give financial assistance to the hard-pressed College. They also refused to permit its professors of surgery, clinical surgery and clinical medicine to remain on the visiting staff, and therefore to retain clinical teaching facilities in the wards, as they had reached the official retirement age for visiting staff (set in 1898) of sixty. University professors did not retire until the age of seventy, and the governors believed that it would be impossible to obtain affiliation with the University if it was established that professors' clinical teaching facilities were to be at the mercy of the Board of the Royal. They hinted that the College might be forced to close. The infirmary's managers, however, refused to bend the rules, and they let it be known that they would be content to see the College offer only elements of the course of study for University of Glasgow students, rather than a complete course for students intending to sit the examination for the triple qualification or another licence to practise. A joint committee was set up to examine relations between the Royal and the College in February 1906, but the deadlock could not be broken.[18]

Fortunately for the Royal's future reputation as a teaching hospital the Muirhead Trust was persuaded to intervene. The trust was set up to build and partially endow a college for the medical education of women, according to the wishes of the late Dr Thomas Muirhead. During the early 1890s it proved impossible to reach agreement with the Victoria Infirmary, the favoured location for clinical teaching for the college students: the founding of a medical school at St Margaret's College, where students had the opportunity from 1894 to study for a University degree, and the introduction of Carnegie Trust grants for university students in 1901, rendered the scheme redundant. In 1906, however, the Muirhead Trustees agreed to consider applying the endowment to St Mungo's College, on condition that the name Muirhead was associated with the College; that there was a connection with the University of Glasgow; that the College could match the endowment of £40,000 from the trust; and that all the teaching facilities at the College were open to women on equal terms. The University, meanwhile, had become concerned about the large size of clinical classes at the Western, at a time when the current vogue in medical education was for small classes and individual ward instruction. The University Principal, Sir Donald MacAlister, who was also president of the General Medical Council, strongly supported the movement to re-establish close links between the University and the Royal; of particular attraction, of course, was the vast amount of 'clinical material' which would become available to students in the wards. There was some delay in completing arrangements, as the College governors sought to settle their dispute with the Board of the Royal, and the Muirhead Trustees resisted a challenge from the Victoria's governors to the legality of their offer to the Royal.

In 1910 the University received an Order permitting the alteration of the constitutions of the deeds of endowment of the chairs of Clinical Medicine and Clinical Surgery. The two chairs were transferred from the Western to the Royal and further endowed by the Trust and by the College, and two new chairs were created at the infirmary. In September 1911 Robert Kennedy was appointed to the St Mungo Chair of Surgery; Walter Hunter to the Muirhead Chair of Medicine; John Munro Kerr to the Muirhead Chair of Obstetrics and Gynaecology; and John Teacher to the St Mungo (Notman) Chair of Pathology. Subsequently arrangements were made with the University of Glasgow to have classes at the Royal on the subjects of venereal disease, diseases of the ear, diseases of the throat and nose, and skin diseases, and by 1930, five more clinical lectureships had been attached to the infirmary. The Royal became a centre for clinical and systematic instruction during the final two years of the University medical curriculum, and its future as a great teaching hospital was secured.[19]

NEW MANAGERS

In the autumn of 1898 the Glasgow and West of Scotland Association for the Return of Women to Local Boards informed the Board of the Western Infirmary of their intention to put forward two of the Association's members for election as managers. The nominations were greeted with some hostility, but the two candidates were elected the following year. The managers of the Royal were also initially hostile to the idea of women sitting with them on the Board, but legal advice was obtained to the effect that all 'contributors' were eligible for election. The Royal could not afford to alienate liberal middle class opinion by opposing the election of women. Nor could the managers ignore a growing tide of opinion in favour of granting representation to the employees of public works which contributed to the infirmary's funds, particularly after the Victoria Infirmary opened on the city's south side in 1890, with three 'Workmen's Governors' elected by men from local industries. In 1901 the managers obtained a supplementary charter enabling them to add four new members to the Board, two of whom were to be women, and two representatives of working-men contibutors. At an extraordinary meeting of subscribers in July, Mrs Mather, Mrs J W Napier, James Reilly of the National Labourers' Union and William Binnie of the Milton Ironworks were elected managers.[20]

The number of working-men representatives was subsequently doubled, in 1911, when the constitution of the Royal was altered once again to meet the requirements of the agreement with the University of Glasgow and the Muirhead Trust, and to improve efficiency in the management of the infirmary's affairs. The number of ex-officio managers was reduced from thirteen to four, with the withdrawal of the privilege enjoyed by the seven members of Parliament for the city, and the Professors of Medicine and of Anatomy at the University of Glasgow, to appointment without election to the Board. The number of nominated managers increased from eight to fifteen: the University Senate's representatives were increased to two; the University Court was also permitted to elect two, in place of the ex-officio posts which had been held by professors; Glasgow Corporation's nominations were increased to three; and the Muirhead Trustees were given the privilege of electing one manager, and the Faculty of Procurators the privilege of electing two. The privilege of the Church of Scotland in Glasgow to elect one of its ministers was withdrawn. The addition of two more representatives of working men raised the number of managers elected by the general court, comprising the contributors and subscribers, to sixteen.[21]

THE FINAL DEPARTURE OF REBECCA STRONG

On the advice of Rebecca Strong the official title of charge nurse was changed in April 1907 to that of 'sister'. This was her last recommendation as matron. In June, after returning from prolonged leave, she wrote to the Board to say that 'the work is too fatiguing. The three months leave of absence did much for me in building up my strength but I have not just fully regained my usual powers of resistance to either strain or climatic changes. I do not think I can stand another winter's work...' Her resignation was accepted with regret, and Miss Jane Melrose, the assistant matron, was invited to take the post in July.

Rebecca Strong was sixty-four years of age when she resigned in 1907, but the grand old lady of nursing continued to devote her life to promoting the improvement of nurses' education and welfare. In 1918, she helped found the Scottish Nurses' Club in Glasgow and in 1921 she was in the chair at the inaugural dinner for the Glasgow Royal Infirmary Nurses' League. She continued to attend international congresses and to give interviews on the subject of nursing until only a few years before her death in 1944, and in 1939 she was awarded the OBE.[22] In the latter years of her career at the Royal she became a figure of fun to the residents, who mocked her long-standing habit of offering her resignation (and almost immediately withdrawing it) over relatively minor disagreements with the infirmary authorities, and her over-zealous attempts to maintain strict Victorian standards of discipline and morality among her charges.[23] Few, however, would dispute her achievements at the Royal. She forged a prestigious role for the matron in an institution which had hitherto considered that position subordinate, in virtually all matters of any administrative importance, to the superintendent and the medical staff. The preliminary training school for nurses which she devised with

William Macewen was studied and imitated in hospitals around the world.

THE COST OF REBUILDING

In 1892 the Royal had reserves of £145,993 lodged in the stock account. Although ordinary expenditure continued to exceed ordinary income —the former rose from £32,247 in 1892 to £43,674 in 1909, and the latter from £20,852 to £30,033—the continuing flow of endowments and legacies into the extraordinary income account, greatly in excess of the demands for extraordinary expenditure and the deficits which had to be met in the ordinary income account, permitted the reserve capital to be increased from nearly £146,000 to over £298,000 (yielding an annual income of £30,308) during the same period. There was a slight fall in ordinary income after 1908, but the greatest blow to the infirmary's finances was self-inflicted, a consequence of the rising cost of the reconstruction scheme.

Rebuilding the infirmary was a massive task, but it was undertaken on the assumption that the costs would be met through the generosity of Glasgow citizens. It quickly became clear, however, that Glaswegians did not have bottomless pockets and the project was in danger of being halted for lack of funds. In 1904, in the midst of a period of severe recession in local industry, an appeal was opened by the Board to raise the money required to build the other infirmary buildings, supplementing the income raised by the Queen Victoria Diamond Jubilee Fund for the reconstruction of the Medical Block. When it became clear that costs were likely to exceed the income from both these funds, drastic measures were taken. In January 1909 the Board sought authority from the General Court of Contributors to transfer up to £150,000 from the stock account, to the supplementary reconstruction fund—a move which would halve the amount of invested capital, and therefore the income derived from it, and, as the *Glasgow Herald* pointed out, raised the legal question of whether capital from a fund created from endowments and bequests, and intended for the maintenance of the institution, could be allocated to meet construction costs.[24] Nevertheless, the Board received the necessary approval from the subscribers and contributors, and in consequence the annual reports on the stock account were thereafter presented to show both restricted funds—bequests and endowments on which only the interest was available—and unrestricted funds. Nearly £100,000 was transferred from the stock account to the supplementary reconstruction account in 1909–11, and the remaining sum had been transferred by the end of 1914, leaving just £78,666 of free capital. Even then, however, the final bill for the erection of 'the costly pile at Castle Street'[25] was not settled, and it was to remain a matter of deep concern to the Board until the late 1920s.

NATIONAL INSURANCE ACT, 1911

The Board's problems after 1909 were exacerbated by the Liberal Government's growing interest in the state of the nation's health services, which resulted in the National Insurance Act of 1911. The Government's concern for the health of the working classes was stimulated by the scandal of the poor health and physique of men who volunteered to fight in the Boer War, 1899–1902, and fears that the physical condition of the average British worker had become inferior to that of his fellows in countries such as Germany and the USA. Free school meals and a school medical service were introduced in 1906 and 1907 respectively, to help remedy the situation. In creating a state-supported national unemployment and health insurance scheme in 1911, the Chancellor of the Exchequer, David Lloyd George, announced that he intended to banish 'the four spectres [which] haunt the poor: old age, accident, sickness and unemployment', but he was also concerned to safeguard and improve the health of the working population. One of the features of the National Insurance Act of 1911 was the introduction of medical benefit to regularly employed persons over 16 years of age, and to all manual labourers, earning less than £160 per annum. Each member of the scheme was to receive 'ninepence for fourpence', paying fourpence (less than 2p) per week into an insurance fund, which received an additional threepence from his or her employer and twopence from the state. The insured employee was entitled to receive free medical treatment from a general practitioner, chosen from a panel of local doctors. While most working people seem to have welcomed the Act, and many employers could appreciate the potential benefits of establishing a national insurance scheme as a means of improving the health and social welfare of the nation's workforce, the voluntary hospitals found themselves in a difficult position.

The Royal was required under the Act to pay national insurance contributions for nurses and other employees, which resulted in a further increase in staff costs. A greater worry, however, was that many workers and their employers, who were now legally obliged to contribute to the National Insurance scheme, would be less inclined to contribute to the coffers of voluntary institutions such as the Royal. Yet the National Insurance Act did not include hospital care among the benefits available under the scheme, and non-contributors, including the insured worker's spouse and children, were not covered. It was essential for the Royal that it was made perfectly clear that the infirmary still provided a vital service for working people and their families, and was worthy of continued, generous subscriptions and charitable donations.[26]

The new legislation had profound consequences for the dispensary, where many of the out-patients were workers covered by the provisions of the Act, and therefore should properly have gone to their 'panel' doctor for treatment and advice. During 1912 the possibility of closing the dispensary to insured men and women was discussed by the Board, but not agreed—such an action would have had a serious effect on subscriptions from local industries. Instead, after the National Insurance scheme was implemented in January 1913, it was decided that an insured person would be granted a consultation only if he or she had a certificate or letter of introduction from a general practitioner; that the insured person would receive treatment only on the first attendance; that the general practitioner would be advised of any treatment recommended at the dispensary, which would not take responsibility for following up the case; but that treatment would be given as before to every accident case, and to acute medical and surgical cases. The effect of the new regulations was immediate: the number of first attendances at the dispensary fell from 28,157 in 1912 to 16,581 in 1913, and total attendances from 78,762 to 48,524. Attendances at the specialist clinics also fell, the exception being, unsurprisingly, the clinic for diseases of women, where the number of first attendances and of total attendances continued to rise.

THE RESIDENTS

In 1888 the residents' official title was changed once more: henceforth, they were officially referred to as house physician or house surgeon, to avoid confusion with the dispensary staff, whose titles had been changed to those of assistant physician and assistant surgeon in 1884. The residents served for one year, received free board and lodging, and usually assisted both a visiting physician and surgeon, each for a session of six months. The life of the resident was a hectic one, and is comically recorded by one of the infirmary's most famous 'old boys'.

Osborne Henry Mavor, later to achieve fame as a playwright under the pseudonym James Bridie, spent a term in the wards of the Royal as a student, and in 1913 he returned as house physician to Dr William Jack. In his autobiography, *One Way of Living*, he gives the following account of the working day of a resident before the Great War:

> He was awakened by a probationer banging at his door in an agitated soprano calling out that the chief had passed the front gate. He tore off his pyjamas, flung himself into the bath, half dried himself, pulled on a shirt, trousers and socks, put on his white jacket, brushed his hair and met his chief at the top of the stair with an alert and respectful smile. If it was the time when students were being taught, he made a show of listening to the first few bars of the lecture and then retired to the ward kitchen for a breakfast of scrambled eggs. He then picked up sufficient information about the patients from the sisters or the charge nurses, visited those who were more seriously ill and was primed for the ward visit. After the ward visit he took coffee with his chief and saw him off the premises. From half past twelve till half past two he examined patients, wrote reports, carried out treatment and had lunch. From three till six he slept or amused himself at a novelty called the cinema. If he dined in mess he was allowed one bottle of beer. There was a fine if he did not dine in mess. If there were sufficient numbers in mess, songs were sung or polo played. Polo was played in the pathology department. The residents sat in cane-bottomed chairs and propelled themselves along the slippery waxed floor with their feet... Round about midnight he attended to work that was in arrears and at about half past one paid his night visit.
>
> But the ward was usually quiet at the night visit, a long dim vista of white and scarlet lit only by the night nurse's red shaded reading lamp. The resident took his microscope into the ward and sat doing blood counts and talking to the nurse in whispers. Half an hour in the test room with chemicals followed, then the resident felt hungry. He strolled round the hospital with his master key till he found a ward kitchen that was making supper. There he had bacon and eggs and tea. At

intervals he had to bolt for the linen cupboard when the night sister came round unexpectedly. But there was a system of secret telegraphy in the hospital that followed that devoted woman on her rounds. Nothing could happen at the remotest spot in the hospital that was not immediately reported half a mile away. The resident poured his troubles into sympathetic ears and went to bed before the probationers came on duty at four o'clock in the morning, soothed and comforted, half cabbage, half king. On receiving nights he worked from midnight to midnight, and on symposium nights he rioted exclusively in male society.[27]

Mavor's hints that the overworked residents often 'let off steam' in raucous fashion, are confirmed in the pages of the Minute Books of the Residents, which survive for the years 1894 to 1914 and record the social events of each session. Symposium nights—boisterous affairs held in the dining hall or in a resident's room, at which there was usually much singing, drinking and dancing—were a much-loved feature of life in the infirmary. Along with billiards and tennis, the residents were known to stage wrestling and even boxing bouts, and to play football, in their dining hall. During the summer session of 1911 the residents organised cat hunts in the corridors and basements of the infirmary, and one dead kitten was found tucked up in the bed of an unsuspecting colleague. Occasionally the jollification went too far, provoking complaints from 'Mamma' (the residents' nickname for Rebecca Strong) about the noise. As one residents' tradition was to haul a piano on to the tennis court in the quadrangle, in the early hours of the morning, and serenade the elderly matron in her bedroom above, it is hardly surprising that she complained.

The behaviour of the residents was generally good, and minor breaches of infirmary rules were put down to youthful high spirits. When they overstepped the bounds of tolerable behaviour—for example, when the nursing superintendents were locked in their rooms in 1905—stern reprimands were dispensed by the superintendent, and on a few occasions a resident was asked to leave the infirmary. In 1898, however, things went rather too far. One resident became unpopular with his fellows because of his unwillingness to accept erysipelas cases into his chief's ward. At a mock trial conducted by the others he was sentenced to a cold bath, and was promptly stripped to his underclothing and thrown into a tub. The victim responded to the indignity by pressing charges against his tormentors. In September 1898 twelve residents appeared in the St Rollox Police Court charged with assault and, pleading guilty, they were fined a guinea each. The case attracted a a great deal of press comment, particularly as it re-opened the old debate about the supposed 'picking and choosing' of patients by residents, the latter intent on supplying their chiefs with 'good clinical material' for teaching purposes. The Board was quick to issue a statement that the resident on duty on his ward's receiving day had no power to turn away cases at the gate, but required the authorisation of an assistant physician or surgeon in the dispensary to do so.[28]

The first female resident at the Royal was Marion Ross, a graduate of the University of Glasgow, who acted as a locum in the summer of 1898, during the absence on holiday of a male resident.[29] Another Glasgow graduate, Anne Louise MacIlroy (who went on to serve with distinction in the First World War, became a leading obstetrician and gynaecologist, and was created a Dame of the British Empire in 1929), became a resident assistant to the specialist in diseases of women, James Kelly, in the summer session of the following year.[30] Subsequently, a woman resident was usually appointed to serve for six months as assistant to Kelly.

GANGLAND

Mavor's reminiscences confirm that, contrary to much popular belief, Glasgow's gang culture did not have its origins in the 1920s, but was thriving before the First World War. The staff at the Royal, in the heart of gangland, were only too aware of the problem.

> In the spring of 1914 I moved from the medical wards to a composite office called at the time Casualty House Surgeon. I was at the disposal of the Skin and Ear, Throat and Nose Departments, and was responsible for the organisation of the Gate. The Gate was the most romantic of the occupations. In a white pinafore and rubber gloves I strolled with lordly grace through an endless variety of scenes. I was the link between the hospital and the outside world, and a lively outer world it was.
>
> The neighbourhood of the Royal Infirmary was largely controlled by street gangs. Our protectors in my time were the

Chelsea Boys, and we could go in and out at any hour of the day or night under their watchful eye. The gangs of those days fought with cross-cut saw, broken bottle necks, cobblers' knives, knuckle dusters and iron shod boots. The day of the little gigolo with the leather shoes, flannel trousers and a couple of razors in his waistcoat pockets had not yet arrived. The common injuries were scalp wounds, abrasions about the ribs and often a curious little series of stabs in the shoulders and upper arms made by the cobblers' knives...

One day the Garngad boys, becoming critical of the treatment of one of their comrades in the hospital, invaded a ward, threw down the screens, pulled off the bed-covers and put the nurses in a state of terror. The whole affair took less than five minutes, and they escaped before the police came. That night they drifted one by one into the Gate, thoroughly stamped with the trade marks of the Chelsea Boys. We bore them no ill feeling and stitched them up tidily.[31]

PROGRESS WITH REBUILDING

Mavor's contacts with Glasgow's gangster underworld were made in the new Gatehouse or Admission Block, which opened in 1909. The reconstruction of the Royal was organised so that no department had to close, each new building being completed before an old one was demolished and work began on the next stage of the project. The six-storey Surgical Block opened on 23 June 1909, with male and female wards on each floor, six operating theatres and a total of 237 beds. It was named the Robert and James Dick Block, in recognition of the decision in 1909 of the trustees of the late James Dick, to allocate £80,000 to the fund for the infirmary's reconstruction and thus ease the financial crisis brought on by the escalating costs of reconstruction. The new laundry, power house, Gatehouse and an extension to the nurses' home to provide one hundred additional beds, were also completed that year. The cramped Pathology Department was replaced by a modern, spacious Pathological Institute, which was inaugurated on 4 October 1911. Sir William Osler, Regius Professor of Medicine at the University of Oxford, waxed eloquent in his speech at the opening, declaring that:

an institute was something more than a deadhouse, and very much more than an ordinary pathological laboratory - it was the cerebrum of the infirmary, the place where the thinking was done, where ideas were nurtured, and thoughts were materialised into researches upon the one great problem that confronted the profession in each generation, the nature of disease.[32]

The Third Ward Block of the surgical buildings was also completed that year. In June 1912 the Special Diseases and Administration Block opened, and was named the Templeton Block, in honour of the Bridgeton carpet manufacturers John and James Templeton (the former serving on the Board), who made generous donations to the supplementary reconstruction fund. In 1913 the southern section of the block was opened to

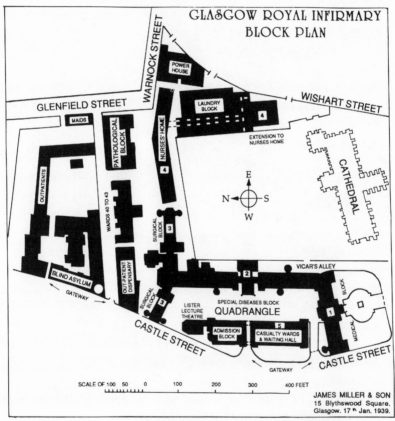

The new Royal, 1939

Map Reference: (1) The Queen Victoria Block
(2) The Templeton Block
(3) The Robert and James Dick Block
(4) Nurses Home
(5) John Ross of Lochbrae Block

medical cases. In December 1911 the last objections to the plans for the Jubilee Block were withdrawn, and the city's Dean of Guild Court gave permission for work to begin on the controversial building.[33] The reconstruction of the infirmary was largely completed in 1914, and the new buildings were formally opened on 7 July by the King, Queen and Princess Mary. The King consented to the naming of the new Electrical Department in the Jubilee Block as 'The King George V Electrical Institute', and the Queen to Ward 3 bearing the name 'The Queen Mary Ward'.

IN THE WARDS

The reconstruction of the Royal was achieved due to the determination and sense of purpose of the Board, which refused to be deflected from the scheme by the complaints of the critics, nor by the difficulties encountered in raising funds to pay for it. In the colourful words of James Hedderwick, the Chairman from 1901 to 1914, 'the board had marched together like a wall, and wheeled like a gate'.[34] The fact that the 'new' Royal was erected with very little disruption to the day-to-day work of the infirmary was due in no small measure to the powers of organisation of the matron, Miss Melrose, and to J. Maxton Thom, who replaced Moses Thomas as superintendent in 1902. It owed much, too, to the forbearance of the nursing and medical staff, who carried on in the midst of what was, at times during the nine years of reconstruction, one of the city's largest building sites. Even before it was completed the new infirmary was busier than ever. In 1913, 9,661 patients were admitted to the wards, compared to 5,270 in 1892, and the daily average number of in-patients rose from 560 to 656.8 during the same period.

The in-patient's life in the infirmary was more comfortable than it had been in the nineteenth century. The daily routine in the medical wards was described in 1916 by Dr Walter Hunter, the senior physician. Patients were woken at 4 a.m., and given a glass of warm milk. The wards were then swept and dusted, the beds made, and the patients washed. Breakfast was at 8 o'clock and the doctors' rounds began one hour later. After the visit of the doctor, convalescent patients were permitted to go to the day room, where they were served dinner at 1 p.m.; those who were confined to bed had their meals served in the wards. Visiting hours were from 3 to 4 o'clock, every second day, and tea was served at 5.15 p.m., followed by supper at 7. Lights out was at 8.30 p.m.

In 1931 G.H. Edington, who had been a house surgeon in the Royal in 1891, told the delegates of the employee contributors of the changes he saw in the Royal. In the old infirmary it was quite common for cuts and minor injuries to be attended to while the patient sat on a chair in the middle of the ward floor, in full view of the other patients. On receiving days the fearsome-looking surgical instruments were laid out on the ward table. Emergency admissions requiring the amputation of a limb or some other form of major surgery were wheeled past the beds, to one of the small operating theatres which had been set up, since Lister's day, in rooms and corridors off the wards. In the new infirmary those in need of attention for minor injuries were treated in rooms in the Gatehouse. A patient requiring indoor treatment was transported from the Gatehouse, by way of an underground passage, to one of the surgical wards. Each of the six floors in the Surgical Block constituted a hospital unit, under a single surgeon, with his own operating facilities. Operations and minor surgery were conducted, mercifully, out of the sight and hearing of the other patients.[35]

The first world war

The Royal Visit of 7 July 1914 took place in an atmosphere of rising public concern about the possibility of a great European war. On 28 June 1914 the assassination in Sarajevo of the Habsburg emperor's heir, Archduke Franz Ferdinand, provided the Austro-Hungarians with a pretext for crushing the upstart Balkan state, Serbia. Austria-Hungary declared war on Serbia on 28 July, and Germany declared war on Serbia's ally, Russia, on 1 August. The Germans declared war on France two days later, launching an offensive on their western neighbour through neutral Belgium. Britain, which had guaranteed Belgian neutrality, responded by declaring war on Germany. Soon, the war had spread around the globe, as far-flung imperial possessions and allies of the great European powers were involved in the conflict.

Shortly after war began the Board placed 120 beds in the Royal at the disposal of the military authorities, and began to draw up plans for temporary buildings, in which additional casualties could be treated. Forty beds were also reserved for convalescent servicemen at Schaw Home. In rather more mean-spirited mood, the managers decided in October to dismiss the gardener at Bearsden, Mr Lange, on the grounds that he was a German. It was subsequently pointed out that the unfortunate man was born in Schleswig-Holstein before it was ceded by Denmark to the German states, in 1864, and therefore he was a German citizen only by force of conquest. The managers relented and reinstated the gardener. This was a time of widespread public alarm about spies and saboteurs, however, and Lange was forbidden to enter or work on the building for the duration of the war.

During the early months of the war the number of Scottish volunteers for military service was much higher, as a proportion of the total male population, than those from any other part of the United Kingdom. The staff of the Royal were as keen to 'do their bit' as anyone else. Before the end of 1914 twenty-one members of the medical and surgical staff enlisted for military duties, and five with the Red Cross. The matron became Principal Matron of the 4th Scottish General Hospital at Stobhill, for which one of the Royal's nursing superintendents acted as matron. Five nurses left to serve in the Queen Alexandra's Naval Nursing Service Reserve, fifteen in the Queen Alexandra's Military Nursing Service, and seventeen in the Territorial Force Military Hospitals. The Royal received its first 327 military patients by the end of December.

It soon became clear that far from being 'over by Christmas', as optimists had predicted, the war in Europe was going to be a long and bloody affair. After the first Battle of the Marne in September 1914, when the advancing German army was checked by French and British forces, the two sides dug hundreds of miles of trenches and settled down to a long war of attrition on the Western Front. British troops also saw action in the Middle East, in the disastrous Gallipoli campaign in Turkey in 1915–16, and in Italy and the Balkans. The Royal Navy, after the Battle of Jutland in 1916, was active mainly in blockading Germany's ports. British casualty figures were horrific—nearly seven hundred and fifty thousand died and more than two million were wounded during the four years of war— and the infirmary's staff were increasingly involved in caring for sick and injured servicemen, both in the infirmary and in foreign lands.

Between August 1914 and the end of 1919, 2,345 servicemen were admitted to the Royal. The casualties often arrived at night, by hospital train, and were carried from the railway station to the infirmary in fleets of ambulances and other vehicles. The X-ray department was utilised to the full during the war, and each time a train-load of casualties arrived at the infirmary, up to eighty photographs were taken the following afternoon, to assist in the diagnosis of fracture, gunshot and shrapnel wounds. The men were accommodated in the main buildings and also in the old Surgical Block, which had been scheduled for demolition to make way for an extension to the Admission Block, but was retained to meet the demand for additional beds. The Scottish Command paid four shillings per day—the average daily cost of a bed at the Royal—for each serviceman admitted to the infirmary. The Ministry of Munitions paid the same amount for men and women engaged in the manufacture of explosives, who were admitted for the treatment of toxic jaundice, caused by TNT poisoning.

The volume of work resulting from an influx of servicemen placed a great strain upon the medical and nursing staff, whose numerical strength was sapped by the departure of many men and women to serve with the forces and independent medical services. Night operations increased dramatically in 1917, as many of the remaining surgeons were engaged during the day in the city's military hospitals. The volume of night-time operations took its toll on the health of the nurses, who were required to work through every sixth night, and until midnight on most other days. Partial relief was offered by allowing nurses who attended night operations to leave the wards at 2 p.m., and to stay away until the following morning. However, the departure of experienced nurses to take up posts in military and other war hospitals meant that those who remained worked far longer hours than would have been tolerable in peacetime.

In February 1917 an outbreak of diphtheria in the nurses' home forced the managers to ask the military authorities to remove wounded servicemen from the wards, and transfer them to other hospitals. In May, when many of the sick nurses had returned to work, it was still not possible to re-admit servicemen, owing to a shortage of surgeons. In October, however, the managers were persuaded to relent, after being informed by the Assistant Director of the Medical Service that military hospitals were full to overflowing.

THE ROLL OF HONOUR

The signing of an Armistice with Germany in November 1918 practically ended Britain's involvement in the First World War. In just over four years, the Royal lost many valued servants: the sacrifices of one extra dispensary physician, twelve resident assistants, one non-resident assistant, four nurses (two of whom died at Stobhill) and four employees are commemorated on the Roll of Honour in the Jubilee Block. Staff Nurse Agnes Climie is perhaps the most famous of those who died in the war. She worked with the 58th Scottish General Hospital in France, and was killed while on duty on 30 September 1917, during a German bombing raid.[36]

On a happier note, the services of the infirmary staff were recognised in the awards of a number of medals. Eight nurses (including the matron) received the Royal Red Cross; twenty-six were awarded the Associate of the Royal Red Cross and one the bar to the RRC; one received the Croix de Guerre; and one the Military Medal. Twenty-five staff were mentioned in dispatches.

WAR'S END

The end of the First World War brought to a close the most stressful period in the history of the Glasgow Royal Infirmary. Most of the reconstruction of the infirmary had been completed prior to 1914, and the staff and managers had coped admirably with the disruption caused by large scale demolition and building work. The future of St Mungo's College, which seemed bleak at the turn of the century, had been rescued by the agreement of 1911. Finally, the demands on its services, created by the greatest war in history, had stretched the human and material resources of the Royal to breaking point. That the Royal succeeded in meeting each of the challenges it faced was a tribute to the resourcefulness of the managers and the resilience and loyalty of the staff. These attributes were to be tested in different ways, but on many more occasions, in the post-war world.

5 PROGRESS AND CHANGE, 1918–47

The old boundaries that marked off the local authority from the voluntary spheres of work are fast disappearing.

Editorial, Glasgow Herald, 8 February 1926

Although the Allies signed an Armistice with Germany in November 1918, much of Europe remained wracked by war or was consumed by revolution. At the same time a deadly form of influenza swept the Continent, having reached Glasgow in the late spring. Many of the staff at the Royal fell ill, three nurses and the acting superintendent died, and the managers had to close the infirmary to visitors and new cases from the armed services. The epidemic was accompanied by outbreaks of other debilitating illnesses such as encephalitis lethargica, or 'sleepy sickness', and by an outbreak of diphtheria in the city.[1] During the following months a daily average of forty nurses were too ill to work. The influenza epidemic did not subside until the middle of 1919, only to be followed in 1920 by an outbreak of smallpox in the east end, which resulted once again in the closure of the wards to visitors.

The end of the war brought only a brief respite for the depleted staff. Overcrowding in the wards had reached its wartime peak in 1916, when there was a daily average of 767.7 patients in the wards. From 1918 the number of servicemen in-patients began to fall, and the last soldiers were discharged in January and the last sailors in April 1919. The departure of casualties from the armed forces was one reason for the slight fall in the number of in-patients, with a daily average of 696.4 in 1918 and 665 in 1919. Nevertheless, there was a continuous stream of cases seeking treatment and advice at the dispensary and clinics, where the number of first attendances rose from 38,813 in 1918 to 46,067 the following year.

The pressure on the Out-Patient Department was increased by the Board's agreement to play a key role in Glasgow Corporation's scheme to improve facilities for the early diagnosis and treatment of venereal disease.

There was a worrying increase in the incidence of venereal disease during the war, and the Scottish local authorities were charged by the Local Government Board with the responsibility of providing special treatment centres. Before the war the Royal had dealt only with acute VD cases, but in 1917 an Outdoor Treatment Centre was opened in the dispensary under the Venereal Diseases Scheme. The number of VD new cases seeking treatment at the clinic rose dramatically, reaching a peak in 1920 when there were 3,447 new cases (14.5 per cent of the total number of first attendances at the dispensary), and total attendances of 42,794 (over 41 per cent of all dispensary attendances). Although the infirmary received payment from the local authority for each attendance, to meet the cost of drugs and dressings, and also to meet the expenses of those admitted to the fifteen beds in the male venereal disease ward, the work placed a huge burden on staff resources. The Royal withdrew from the scheme in 1925, and the beds in the VD ward were allocated to other cases.[2]

THE POST-WAR WORLD

While the medical and nursing staffs struggled to cope with the demands placed upon them, the Board had to find the means to limit the damaging effects of rampant war-time inflation. Between July 1914 and July 1919 prices increased by approximately 250 per cent, and wages by about 215 per cent. Prices and wages went on to reach new peaks in 1920, before falling back with the onset of a severe economic recession and the introduction of deflationary measures by the Government.[3] The managers estimated in December 1919 that the demolition of the old Surgical Block and the erection of an Emergency Block at the gate would cost three times the price estimated in 1914. The Annual Report for 1919 noted that, although public works employees' contributions had almost doubled since 1915, to £16,549, and the total ordinary revenue amounted to £52,802, the ordinary expenditure had risen to an unprecedented £98,676, leaving a record deficit of £45,874. In commenting that 'the managers deplore the critical position of the funds', the report drew particular attention to the fact that ordinary and extraordinary income together fell short of the year's expenditure by nearly £23,000, and the unrestricted funds in the stock account had shrunk to a book value of only £35,862—less than half the balance in 1914. The outlook appeared bleak, and the report warned that 'if the loss on working is to continue for the next year at the same rate the whole available free capital will have been consumed and the closing of some wards will become inevitable'.

NURSING

Along with a deterioration in the value of financial reserves, there were other matters which it had not been possible to deal with during the war, but which the managers had to address with urgency after 1918. One of the most serious involved the working conditions and morale of the nursing staff. Most nurses worked a seven day, fifty-eight hour week which, the Board agreed, should be shortened in the interests of the nurses' health, and of the efficiency of the infirmary. However, the Royal could not afford the expense of employing and providing accommodation for more nurses, and so hours remained largely unchanged. In March 1920 the House Committee was informed that many nurses were leaving the infirmary (one hundred left in 1919 alone), and it was increasingly difficult to find suitable replacements for them, because nurses could earn higher salaries in other hospitals. Money was found for small pay rises, but the staffing problem eventually eased as a result of a nation-wide growth in unemployment and the fall in prices and wages after 1920: the reduction in the opportunities for women to obtain relatively well-paid jobs elsewhere made nursing a more attractive proposition for young women in search of work. In 1921 there were 270 on the nursing staff, with a waiting list of fifty women seeking entry.

The nursing profession received a boost in 1919 with the passing of the Nurses Registration (Scotland) Act, which created the General Nursing Council for Scotland and introduced a national system of examinations (the first nurses to sit the state examination at the Royal did so in 1924) and a national register of nurses.[4] The Act gave the profession a greater status, and it was passed at a time when Scottish women were becoming more self-confident in pursuing careers and asserting their rights to a more independent life-style. Nurses at the Royal were increasingly reluctant to accept the more irritating rules and regulations left over from the pre-war era, and this was exhibited in a number of ways. In 1924 it was reported that the matron, Miss Mary Donaldson (who replaced Jane Melrose on her retirement in 1921), was having 'a hard task' in maintaining discipline. Although the doors to the nurses' home were locked at 10.30 each evening the abuse of late passes by some nurses was a particular matter of concern to the matron. Miss Donaldson resigned after only three years, and Miss Margaret Williamson was appointed her successor.

A sense of fellowship between the resident physicians and surgeons and the nurses continued to grow after the war, and was reinforced by a remarkable show of solidarity on the part of the latter in 1921. Some residents took the New Year's Day festivities too far, breaking into the nurses' home and entering bedrooms in the early hours of the morning. Four residents and one non-resident assistant were dismissed for this serious breach of the infirmary's rules. The nurses petitioned the managers to show leniency, however, and those junior doctors who had not completed their terms were reinstated, with a severe warning as to their future conduct.

The lister ward

Another item of business left over from the pre-war years, and requiring the careful attention of the managers, involved the future of the Lister Ward in the old Surgical Block. There were many Glaswegians, supported by prominent medical men and educational institutions around the world, who believed that Ward 24, where Lister introduced his pioneering surgery methods, should be saved for posterity. The managers were not willing to preserve the ward, pointing out that the ground was required for additions to the infirmary and that provision for the treatment of the sick must be given priority over the commemoration of past glories. The demolition of the building was delayed by the war: it remained open for the reception of wounded servicemen, and the campaign to save the ward, as a museum or in some other form as a tribute to Lister's achievements, was revived during the 1920s. The managers had originally hoped that the University would re-erect it, stone by stone, at Gilmorehill, but that scheme fell through in 1921. In December 1923 they reaffirmed their decision of 1914 to demolish the building, and in January 1924 it was razed to the ground, leaving only the basement walls standing. Work began shortly afterwards on an extension to the Admission Block, with the erection of a lecture theatre on the site of the historic Ward 24. When it opened in 1927 the theatre was given Lister's name, and a plaque was placed on the wall facing Castle Street, and another on the wall facing the quadrangle, to identify the site and its historical significance. In 1926, some ward furniture from the old Surgical Block was sent to the Wellcome Historical Medical Museum in London, where it was put on display in an historical recreation of the 'Lister Ward'.[5]

RECOVERY

The infirmary was rescued from its desperate financial plight at the end of the war by the generous response of its supporters to appeals for greater financial assistance. In 1920 the Secretary and Cashier, R. Morrison Smith, introduced a scheme of voluntary assessment in public works. The employee was invited to contribute according to a graduated scale according to income, rising from a penny a week for those earning thirty shillings, to sixpence for those with a weekly wage of more than £7. To encourage working men and women to take a greater interest in the infirmary, and to demonstrate appreciation for their support, the Royal inaugurated annual meetings of the 'delegates of working-class contributors', where they were kept abreast of the latest developments in the infirmary and addressed by distinguished guest speakers. These efforts to woo working-class contributors were highly successful, and in 1920 contributions from this source nearly doubled, to £30,000. Renewed efforts to persuade more people to contribute to the infirmary's funds through subscriptions and donations also met with success. Despite recurring periods of economic depression in the west of Scotland, ordinary revenue held firm at between £81,000 and £90,000 during the decade. Annual deficits on the ordinary account of between £22,000 and £35,000 were met from increased extraordinary income, and the infirmary's unrestricted capital increased to £135,789 in 1924, before dropping back to £111,256 in 1926. The restricted capital funds also grew, from £161,871 in 1919 to £272,649 in 1926. They were boosted by the growing popularity of a scheme, inaugurated in 1891, which permitted a donor to endow a bed in the infirmary, and receive the privilege of recommending five patients for admission each year, for the sum of £1,250. The success of fund-raising efforts during the ealy 1920s enabled the Royal to make further strides in improving patient care facilities.

Insulin treatment for diabetics was introduced at the Royal, Victoria and Western infirmaries in February 1923. The services of skilled chemists were required to undertake research projects in relation to this treatment and others in the field of physiological chemistry, and so in July 1926 the University appointed a clinical biochemist and Lecturer in Pathological Biochemistry, Dr David Cuthbertson (1900–1989), to work at the Royal. His Biochemical Department, with a small laboratory in the Institute of Pathology, was established the following year. Cuthbertson was later permitted to establish a self-contained metabolism unit, with its own kitchen, and from 1930 he became involved in post-injury studies, on the metabolic consequences of fractures and injuries to the muscles. Cuthbertson demonstrated that a 'negative nitrogen balance' accompanies traumatic injury, and that the replacement of protein was vital in the treatment of serious injury. In 1934 he left the infirmary to become Grieve Lecturer in Physiological Chemistry at the University of Glasgow, but he maintained connections with the Royal throughout a distinguished career which culminated in his appointment as Director of the Rowett Research Institute in Aberdeen in 1945 and a knighthood in 1965.[6]

In recognition of the importance of special dieting in the treatment of many cases, a dietetic kitchen was set up in the main kitchen in 1926, under the supervision of a trained dietitian. That year the King George V Electrical Institute was doubled in size and re-equipped, after the number of patients attending the department had risen in two years from over 33,500 to more than 61,800. The new equipment included facilities to carry out deep therapy, for cancer and other cases. Also in 1926 the first wireless receivers were installed in the wards, and in the nurses' and maids' homes, and BBC radio programmes proved popular with staff and patients alike. In 1927 separate wards were provided for burns cases, establishing the first burns unit in the United Kingdom, and a resuscitation room for burns and scalds cases opened in 1929. In 1928 a urological clinic and a clinic for nervous diseases were established, thus expanding still further the Royal's facilities for providing specialist advice and treatment.

In meeting the costs of new facilities and departments, the Royal was in effect paying the price of keeping pace with advances in medical science. In 1939 the delegates of working-class contributors were told that 'no sooner was the infirmary equipped with every possible contrivance than some gentleman in a distant country invented some highly expensive appliance which the specialist concerned would certainly desire to have'. The latest radiological and electrical equipment, much of it imported, was particularly expensive to acquire and maintain, and the machinery often had a short working life. Nevertheless, the Royal's reputation as a centre of medical research and a leading teaching hospital required it should keep abreast of the latest developments in medical technology. The managers made frequent appeals to the munificence and the civic pride of its wealthy benefactors, to secure funds to establish prestigious new departments, or obtain expensive items of equipment.

The first important building project of the 1920s was the erection of another nurses' home, facing Wishart Street. The home provided an additional 100 bedrooms, a recreation room and guest room, and was opened on 1 January 1926. In October 1928 the Secretary of State for Scotland, Sir John Gilmour, opened the Lister Lecture Theatre and lecturers' rooms, and the long-awaited Casualty Block. The block contained two units of casualty wards, for sixteen male and sixteen female patients, and a large waiting hall to hold up to 500 visitors. It was dedicated to John Ross of Lochbrae, whose trustees made generous donations to the unrestricted funds during the 1920s to enable the construction work to proceed.

The modernisation of the infirmary and its services was achieved without any let-up in the more mundane, but equally important, everyday work of the wards and clinics. Life at the Gatehouse was the subject of a humorous poem written in 1930 by Miss Christian Fleming, a physician in the Out-patient Department.

> *A motley throng is passing thro',*
> *From gutter snipe to hooknosed pew,*
> *From a babe-in-arms with its musical strains*
> *To the grizzly dotard with varicose veins.*
>
> *They fill the benches in the hall:*
> *The rooms are full, not least of all*
> *Is that essence of bedlam called 'No 5',*
> *With wailing humanity, too alive.*
>
> *While room No 2 rather baffles description -*
> *A cut to be stitched, or a wheezy prescription,*
> *A bone in the throat, a scald or a burn*
> *Waiting each to be treated in turn.*

With fractured femur or finger in two
They come to ask us, what can we do? -
With aches and pains and appendicitus,
Sebacious cyst and dance of St Vitus.

An epithelioma of tongue,
A 'touch of phthisis' in one lung.
Pes equinus, a swallowed penny,
And inguinal hernias - far too many.

Or - 'please its Tam wi' his back in a rash',
An abscess, or a razor slash
From sternal notch to antitragus -
Or nothing at all but desire to plague us.

Policeman hovering notebook complete,
A drunkman dithering on the seat.
A lacerated wound that has gone septic,
Pains abdominal - purely peptic.

A.D.B.A., and theatre's on,
Not a room left, and the houseman's gone,
And Nurse is wondering what's to be done
When the ambulance comes with another one.

The X-ray plates are as black as night -
They've taken the left and I've stated the right;
The scissors are blunt and the knives won't cut -
We may say 'Damn!' or we may say 'Tut!'.

Still,
The nurses come and the nurses go,
Physicians look in - now'n again, ye know!
But patients be many or patients be spare,
The surgeons go on for ever, there.

FINANCES

Although the reputation of 'Red Clydeside' as a hotbed of revolution has often been exaggerated, there was a great deal of industrial unrest in Glasgow and the west of Scotland after the war. Inevitably during the 1920s the infirmary had difficulty raising funds from those areas affected by strikes and lockouts, and from those sections of the workforce suffering from high rates of unemployment. However, no industrial dispute had such a severe effect on its finances as the protracted and bitter miners' strike of 1926. Contributions from employees in the collieries, steelworks, railways and other industries in the west of Scotland fell; the costs of boiler fuel rose due to shortages; and the number of patients from industrial areas increased, as unemployed and striking workers and their families suffered 'lower vitality and illness brought on by deprivations during the strike'. Appeals launched to alleviate distress in the mining areas attracted huge public support, and large charitable donations which might otherwise have been sent to the infirmary.

The problems arising from the miners' strike preceded another raid on the capital reserves of the infirmary. In 1917 the general court had voted to transfer £26,000 to the Reconstruction Fund, and a further transfer of £30,000 had been approved in 1925. In February 1927 it was necessary to plunder the reserves once again, and £65,000 was subsequently credited to the Reconstruction Fund, as the total cost of building the new infirmary soared beyond the £500,000 mark. This final transfer brought the total amount removed from the unrestricted funds, to meet the shortfall on income raised by special appeals for the reconstruction scheme, to the huge sum of £271,000. The infirmary's liquid reserves were left depleted, to such an extent that the free funds sank to £14,176 in 1927, and the following year to just £4,071.

The second financial crisis within a decade persuaded many observers that the Royal, like many other voluntary hospitals, was not capable of putting its finances on a secure footing unless there was a fundamental reassessment of its place in the city's hospital system. To avoid recurring periods of crisis it was necessary to recognise changing economic circumstances, and introduce radical changes in the nature of the services it provided, and in the methods of funding them. The dilemma was brought into even sharper focus by other developments which appeared to challenge the whole ethos of the infirmary.

LOCAL AUTHORITY HOSPITALS

In the aftermath of the war the provision of health care in Scotland was the subject of radical reappraisal. There was a chronic shortage of hospital beds in Scotland, and the voluntary hospitals, with long waiting lists for admissions and with overcrowded out-patient clinics, had not the financial resources to meet the country's urgent requirements. The

Scottish Board of Health was created in 1919 to co-ordinate health services, and in 1924 the Hospital Services (Scotland) Committee, chaired by Lord Mackenzie, was appointed to investigate the situation and offer suggestions for improvement. In its report in 1926 the committee estimated that there was an urgent need for 3,600 additional general hospital beds in Scotland. It pointed to the need for the local authorities to be given a greater role in the provision of hospital accommodation, and for greater co-operation between the voluntary hospitals and local authorities to create a co-ordinated hospital service.[7] The report was influential in the framing of the Local Government (Scotland) Act of 1929, which became effective the following year.

The Act, among other things, transferred to county councils and the town councils of large burghs, the Poor Law hospitals and medical services which had previously been the responsibility of parish councils. Glasgow Corporation's Health Department was given charge of seventeen hospitals and asylums, the schools medical service and an outdoor medical service for the sick poor. Under the leadership of the Medical Officer of Health, Alexander MacGregor, the department set to work with great enthusiasm to develop a comprehensive municipal medical service. The Southern General, Stobhill and other former Poor Law hospitals were renovated, new services and facilities were introduced and by 1938, although the service fell short of the department's ambitious goals, 1,000 hospital beds had been added to those available in Glasgow ten years earlier.[8]

The 1929 Act permitted the local authority hospitals to provide treatment for all inhabitants, not only those applying for poor relief as paupers, and so to accept patients who might once have been able to obtain treatment only at a voluntary hospital. The Royal, like its sister institutions, was determined to retain its independent voluntary status, but had to face up to the fact that a large part of its traditional role in caring for the sick poor was being assumed by the Corporation. To circumvent calls for the amalgamation of local authority and voluntary hospitals, in the interests of rationalising services, it was clear that the voluntary hospitals must be able to point to areas of expertise which the local authorities did not or could not provide.

REDEFINING THE INFIRMARY'S ROLE

In 1932 Dr John Cowan, a consulting physician at the Royal, sum-
marised the view of many of the managers and medical staff, in a
memorandum calling for a major reappraisal of the aims and services of
the infirmary. The points he made provided an agenda for a wide-rang-
ing debate during the 1930s, and the formulation of new policies and
strategies to secure for the Royal a pre-eminent position in the city's
expanding hospital network.

Cowan began by asserting that 'the year 1930 marks the termination
of an era of the voluntary hospitals, for in it their primary function, the
care of the necessitous sick, passed to the municipal and county authorities'. He insisted, however, that the voluntary hospitals still had a vital role
to play, in the education of doctors and nurses, and as centres for research
into disease. To fulfil this role required a fundamental change in the ethos
of the voluntary hospital. 'At present, many patients who are not desirable are admitted to the wards; patients with incurable chronic diseases;
and those with trivial disorders who should be treated in their homes.
Others, a nuisance to their doctor, are sent to hospital to get them out of
the way.' He insisted that 'the policy of the open door must cease', as the
overcrowding of the wards and the overwhelming of the dispensary and
clinics with chronic and trivial cases (he made special reference to the
'absurd' numbers of cases of cuts and contusions and tonsillitis) was a
drain on human and financial resources; it distracted staff from the types
of work best suited to their specialist talents; and it prevented them from
making maximum use of the infirmary's advanced and expensive facilities.

Economic facts of life forced the managers to act upon Cowan's most
radical proposal, that the cherished principle of 'the open door' should be
abandoned. The infirmary's capacity was set at 664 beds during the 1920s,
but the daily occupancy rate seldom fell below 700. With the completion
of reconstruction in 1929, the official capacity was raised to 700 beds, but
by 1934 the average daily occupancy had risen to 830, with as many as
905 cases in the wards during the busiest days. There was a daily average
of over 1,000 (mostly non-urgent) cases seeking admission to the infirmary during the late 1920s.

The superintendent's report on the work of the infirmary during 1931 illustrates the extent to which the other departments of the Royal were in danger of being overwhelmed by the workload placed upon them. Approximately one in ten of Glasgow's population of 1.1 million—a total of 111,135 people—attended the dispensaries and other out-patient departments that year, each on an average of more than three occasions; 16,823 in-patients were treated, with an average of just over 800 in the wards each day. The infirmary suffered for its own success: every improvement in its services increased the attractions of hospital treatment, and the number of patients seeking assistance there. There were many who believed that one way in which to limit the overcrowding was to introduce more rigorous vetting of prospective patients.

Since the earliest days of the Royal there had been complaints from the managers and staff that there were many people who could afford to pay for private medical care, but took advantage instead of the open door policy at the Royal—as one critic complained in 1883, 'many invalids of comparatively good means who can afford to pay a doctor's bill are willing to assume their worn and discarded clothes, and mix with the needy throng in the infirmary, for the purpose of receiving gratuitous medical attention'.[9] The opportunity to be treated by some of the city's leading surgeons and physicians, the introduction of advanced and expensive treatments, and the vast improvements made in hygiene, diet and the quality of patient care encouraged people from those social classes who might in the past have preferred to receive treatment, and even some types of surgery, from private practitioners in the home, to seek attention in hospitals. While the rich and more prosperous middle classes could afford the expense of entering private nursing homes, an increasing number of men and women of more modest means sought entry to the voluntary hospitals. They were not always honest about their personal circumstances.

The Royal required that relatively well-to-do patients seeking entry to the infirmary should pay the standard subscription of one guinea, to assist with the cost of their treatment. Nevertheless it was widely believed that many who could afford to pay 'were selfish enough to use the services of the infirmary without offering anything towards their maintenance'.[10] One method by which these patients could be dissuaded from entering the Royal and obtaining, free of charge, services for which they were not eligible, was for the infirmary to establish its own nursing home.

PAYING PATIENTS

In 1925 John Glaister, the Professor of Forensic Medicine at the University of Glasgow, and a manager since 1901, summed up the philosophy of the traditionalists when he told a meeting of the delegates of the working-class contributors that 'whenever an institution began to receive paying patients it ceased to be a voluntary hospital'. However, since the 1840s the Royal had made provision for 'separate accommodation' for patients in single rooms off the wards, on payment of a fee, in the 1920s, of two guineas (£2.10) per week, and there were many at the Royal who agreed with the Scottish Board of Health (which became the Department of Health for Scotland in 1929) that the voluntary hospitals should take the responsibility for providing more pay-beds for patients of moderate means. Pay-beds were common in England, accounting for 5 per cent of the income of London's voluntary hospitals as early as 1890,[11] and in 1931 the Victoria Infirmary in Glasgow opened a wing for paying patients, extending it four years later.[12] The idea had much to commend it to the Scottish voluntary hospitals, providing a means by which more beds could be reserved for emergency and 'deserving' acute cases, while patients of moderate means would be able to take advantage of the expert care and facilities of an infirmary while contributing to its income. James Macfarlane, the bread and biscuit manufacturer who had been a manager on the Board of the Royal since 1899, and its Chairman since 1914, was particularly enthusiastic about the idea of providing beds for paying patients. In 1922 he told members of the staff that 'there is a... very large class in the social scale, just above those for whom our infirmaries are intended, who are quite unable to pay for private nursing homes as we know them. I have long felt that an hospital for paying patients, and devoted exclusively to the service of this class, is much needed...'[13] Macfarlane announced that he and some members of staff had already drawn up plans for such a hospital, and he had secured an option on a greenfield site for it at Canniesburn, Bearsden.

CANNIESBURN AUXILIARY HOSPITAL

In 1925 James Macfarlane and his brother George gifted land at Canniesburn to the the Royal. Subsequent gifts increased the site area to 44 acres by 1934. During the 1920s the Scottish Board of Health encour-

aged the voluntary hospitals to open satellite hospitals in rural surroundings, where convalescents could be sent to free more beds in the city
centre for casualties and emergency cases,[14] and Macfarlane's intention
was to build both an auxiliary hospital and nursing home there. In 1932
the managers obtained a supplementary charter which authorised them to
co-operate with the Corporation and other local authorities 'for the provision of accommodation, maintenance and treatment for sick persons...
on such terms and for such payment... as may be agreed upon...', and to
'afford accommodation to and to admit and maintain any person not nec-
essarily of the poorer classes requiring medical or surgical treatment... in
consideration of such charges for maintenance, accommodation and
treatment as may be arranged... and it shall be in the power of the managers... to erect, equip and maintain any building or buildings... or to set
apart any building or section of the buildings erected or to be erected and
occupied for the purposes of the said infirmary... for the purpose of
accommodating all or any such persons...', on condition that the
accounts of paying patients' accommodation and treatment were kept
separate from those of the infirmary proper.[15]

The perilous state of the infirmary's finances delayed the commencement of the project until 1935, five years after the opening of the Victoria
Infirmary's satellite Philipshill Auxiliary Hospital near East Kilbride.[16]
Lady Macfarlane (her husband had received a knighthood in 1932) cut
the first sod at Canniesburn on 5 April, and the foundation stone was laid
by the Duke and Duchess of Kent on 28 May, on the same day that they
opened the extension to the paying patients' wing at the Victoria.[17] The
buildings, designed by the architect James Miller, consisted of three
blocks, linked by a corridor: the central block contained the administrative departments, kitchens and other facilities; the east block, named the
Zachary Merton Home in recognition of a donation of £40,000 from
the Zachary Merton Trust towards the cost, contained eighty beds and
facilities for convalescents; and the west block was the nursing home,
with forty-six single rooms (for which the patient was charged five
guineas per week), two rooms containing two beds (four guineas), and
four rooms of four beds (three guineas), and its own theatre, X-ray
department and other facilities.

The convalescent and nursing homes were opened by Sir Iain
Colquhoun of Luss on 18 January 1938. Only forty beds were initially

made available to paying patients – the others were required for nurses' accommodation, until the Royal could raise funds to pay for the construction of a nurses' home.

ALMONERS

The provision of beds for paying patients was only one feature of the campaign to reassess the services which should be provided by the Royal, and to reduce overcrowding and costs. Another innovation was the inauguration of a hospital almoner service.

In 1935 it was reported that 31 per cent of in-patients at the Royal were receiving unemployment benefit or state allowance. Although the treatment of the sick and injured poor had been the mission of the infirmary since 1794, the social needs and conditions of patients were generally believed to be outwith its area of prime responsibility, and it was felt that they were properly the concern of charitable bodies such as the Dorcas Society. The work of the society had expanded greatly since 1864, to include the provision of surgical appliances such as artificial limbs, and helping meet the out-patients' rail and bus fares to and from the infirmary. After the First World War, however, there was a growing awareness in the medical profession that social circumstances were often fundamental to the nature of the patient's illness, and to the prospects of his or her full recovery after being discharged from the wards. It was recognised that amateur volunteers could not be expected to carry out the delicate task of investigating and identifying the personal circumstances and problems of patients, and for this reason, in 1932, the society engaged a qualified hospital almoner to work at the Royal.

The Royal Free Hospital in London appointed the country's first hospital almoner in 1895, and almoners were subsequently employed by hospitals throughout England.[18] Miss Esther Hamilton, who was appointed by the Dorcas Society in 1932 primarily to follow up radium therapy cases, was engaged by the Royal two years later, when the infirmary set up its own Almoner's Department 'as an aid to the medical and surgical staffs, [to undertake] social work for the patients in the wards and a follow-up service by which patients are helped and directed after leaving the infirmary'.

By making home visits and through correspondence, Miss Hamilton and her assistant helped ensure that discharged patients followed the treatment recommended to them on their discharge from the wards, thereby reducing the chances of relapse and readmission to the infirmary. But the managers expected the almoners to fill another important role. In the Almoner's Report for 1936, Miss Hamilton asserted that 'the only form of abuse of the services of the medical dispensary which is considerable, is carried out by patients who are in receipt of public assistance and thereby entitled to treatment afforded by doctors in the Public Assistance Department'. When the almoners began work in the Out-Patient Department in October 1935, therefore, they did so 'mainly with a view to curtailing the number of attendances'. The almoner was expected to interview the patient on arrival at the infirmary: although no one could be turned away before an examination was carried out by a member of the Gatehouse staff, those cases whom she discovered were receiving public assistance, and were not in urgent need of treatment, were sent to the Public Assistance Department, to be referred to the appropriate local authority service. Children too ill to wait for an appointment at the school clinic were also received, but the almoner made sure that they did not return to the infirmary as out-patients once the emergency had passed. The almoners did not only stand guard against the admission or return visits of the ineligible young and poor: patients they discovered to be of comfortable economic circumstances were gently encouraged to make a donation to the infirmary's funds.

The almoner service played a key role in the Royal's strategy of freeing beds and out-patient facilities for what were considered suitable cases for treatment at Townhead, and such was its success that the department employed six women by 1939.

THE MEDICAL STAFF

Cowan's memorandum called for one other break with tradition, the introduction of salaries for junior doctors. By 1931 the residents at the Royal Hospital for Sick Children and the Victoria and Western infirmaries received honoraria, and Cowan insisted that only by introducing some form of recompense at the Royal could the infirmary continue to attract the cream of the city's young graduates. The managers were concerned at the growing difficulty experienced in filling vacancies among junior staff, and they acted immediately. A scale of payments was introduced, with the residents, and non-residents working in the surgical and

ENT wards, receiving £25 for each term of six months. The decision to award honoraria marked a further break with the voluntary tradition, although the fact that members of the visiting and dispensary staff had since the early nineteenth century received payment for their services made the reluctance to pay even a token sum to junior doctors appear iniquitous.

The inter-war years also witnessed an advancement, if at a slow pace, in the status of women doctors at the Royal. The appointment of women to posts in the dispensary and special clinics was accelerated by the war, when there was a shortage of male staff. In 1928, however, the managers agreed with Professor John Glaister, the University Senate's appointee to the Board, that women should not be appointed to the senior posts of assistant physician or surgeon 'and ultimately have charge of wards', and Miss Ellen Orr's application for a post of assistant surgeon was turned down. This decision was rescinded in 1930, but it was not until October 1934 that Ellen Orr became the first woman to join the senior medical staff as an assistant surgeon. The first woman to be appointed to a chief's post was Dr Alison Hunter, who became Surgeon in Charge of the wards for the diseases of women in 1946.

New technology and services

The west of Scotland's industry and trade suffered severely in the great world-wide economic depression which followed the notorious Wall Street Crash of 1929. Although the managers anticipated a steep fall in income and so kept a careful eye on expenditure during the early 1930s there was only a slight fall in annual income before the first signs of economic recovery became evident in 1934. A relatively steady flow of funds permitted the managers not only to pay for additional staff and accommodation for the ever-growing number of patients seeking treatment at the infirmary, but to invest in new and improved equipment and facilities.

A School of Massage for men opened in 1931, offering instruction in massage, medical gymnastics, medical electricity and light therapy under the direction of the Medical Officer of the Orthopaedic Department. It was the only school of its kind for men in Scotland. In 1932 the Royal became a National Radium Centre, and a medical officer-in-charge of radium treatment, Daniel Lamont, was appointed. Radium, then in very short supply, is an important aid in the treatment of cancer, but it is also a dangerous radioactive element which requires careful handling. The radium delivered to the Royal was contained in hollow platinum needles, to ensure the rays could be accurately directed to the area under treatment, and a lead-lined safe weighing 2 tons was required to store the needles safely when they were not in use. In 1939 the Royal appointed a full-time radiologist and awarded McGhie Cancer Research Fund scholarships to two men engaged in the field.

The X-ray department continued to prove a valuable asset but also a heavy drain on the infirmary's funds. Over 26,000 X-ray examinations were carried out each year, consuming up to £5,000 per annum for film alone. The equipment was very expensive, due to high protective tariffs on foreign imports during the 1930s, and it was pointed out to the delegates of the working-class contributors in 1935 that, whereas John Macintyre was able to purchase an X-ray tube for thirty shillings during the 1890s, the price of modern tubes had risen to as much as £200 each.

In 1934 the Board announced the purchase of the Blind Asylum building adjoining the infirmary site on Castle Street, and a plan to convert it to accommodate the Out-Patient Department, Ophthalmic Institute and other departments. The following year the managers agreed to take over the work of the Glasgow Central Dispensary, which occupied the old Anderson's College Dispensary in Richmond Street. However, due to delays in beginning work at the Blind Asylum, the Central Dispensary remained open until 1940. The Opthalmic Institute's move was subsequently postponed indefinitely, when other departments were given priority for relocation.

During the 1930s the Royal admitted more than 3,000 fracture cases each year. However, it was acknowledged that patients often required a long period of recuperation after an accident, before they could return to work. The Board, heavily dependent on subscriptions and donations from industrial workers and their employers, was concerned to improve the recovery time of fracture cases. In 1935 the honorary consulting surgeon John Patrick brought to the attention of the managers the recommendations of a report by the British Medical Association, suggesting fracture cases should be segregated and treated separately from other cases, and that a specialist follow-up service should be created to ensure a more rapid recovery of the use of damaged limbs. In 1937 a sub-committee on the rehabilitation of fracture cases reported that there were forty fracture clinics in England, and one had recently been set up at Aberdeen Royal Infirmary, with impressive results. The managers were told that 'there was practically no orthopaedic apparatus' at the Royal, 'and no operations were performed in the Orthopaedic Department, which was in reality just a Massage Department'. The surgical staff, however, opposed the creation of a specialist unit as unnecessary, asserting that 'there were in effect six fracture clinics already', in their surgical wards. The hostility of the surgeons to specialisation in this area effectively blocked the creation of a specialist unit for several years. Instead, it was decided to take the less adventurous step of opening a rehabilitation centre, 'which would in effect be an up-to-date Orthopaedic Department' concerned only with the after-care of fracture cases, in the new Out-Patient Department in the Blind Asylum building.

IMPROVEMENTS IN STAFF CONDITIONS

In 1936 the matron, Miss Margaret Husband, who had succeeded Miss Williamson in 1932, submitted a report to the Board on a recurring problem, the recruitment and retention of the services of suitable probationer nurses and maids. The managers agreed to pay probationers a salary from the date of entry to the School of Nursing, rather than from the end of the three-month preliminary course. In answer to the complaints of night nurses, that they were required to work for nearly twelve hours, from 9 o'clock in the evening until 8.30 a.m. with only thirty minutes' break for supper, the night staff was increased by fourteen to allow longer breaks. A night operating staff consisting of a sister and three nurses was also appointed, to relieve the workload of the theatre staff. In 1938 another source of irritation to the nurses, the requirement that probationers purchase their uniforms from the infirmary for £6 13s, was removed. Subsequently the probationers and pupil nurses were supplied with uniforms free of charge.

The perennial problem of accommodating the Royal's growing army of nurses—nearly 450 strong by 1937—was addressed by commissioning the architect James Miller to draw up plans for a new nurses' home. The imposing building, to be erected on a site behind Provand's Lordship and facing Cathedral Square, was intended to accommodate 270 nurses, and The Lipton Trust offered to donate £100,000 to meet the expense.[19]

However, war broke out before work could begin on the new building, and the project was abandoned.

To retain the services of domestic staff, it proved necessary in 1938 to increase the salary for out-sleeping maids by £10, to £40 with meals, and with annual increments up to £52. In-sleeping maids beginning work at the infirmary did not receive an increase in their salary of £25, but annual increments were introduced, to a salary ceiling of £34. The matron was concerned about the working conditions as well as the pay of domestic staff, and she stressed that 'in her opinion the time for the hand polishing and washing of floors by ward maids was long past'. The managers resolved to purchase an electrical floor polisher to provide relief from this back-breaking work.

THE EVE OF WAR

The efforts made in the 1930s to redefine the role of the Royal, improve and focus services, and place the infirmary on a sound financial footing, were remarkably successful. The provision of expensive equipment and specialist facilities was made possible by the improved state of the infirmary's funds: by 1939, despite continuing high levels of expenditure, there was more than £110,000 in the unrestricted capital account, and over £440,000 in the restricted account. Annual subscriptions and other ordinary income had returned to pre-1930 levels, and legacies and other financial gifts continued to flood into the coffers. The completion of most of the building modernisation work, the introduction of increasingly effective measures to control costs, and the first confident steps to carve out a niche for the Royal in the new order of health service provision in the city, encouraged confidence in the Royal's future as a major teaching hospital, under voluntary management. The optimistic mood soon evaporated, however, with the outbreak of a second world war.

THE SECOND WORLD WAR

In 1938, as the threat grew of a war with Nazi Germany, the Government sought to ensure the nation's hospitals were prepared for the expected influx of wounded servicemen, and of heavy civilian casualties in the event of mass air strikes on British cities. In June 1938 the Secretary of State for Scotland assumed responsibility for the organisation of an

Emergency Medical Service to receive and treat casualties in the event of war, and the EMS was established in May 1939.[20] Under the EMS new hospitals were built across Scotland, and hutted annexes and temporary wards were also opened in existing hospitals. In August 1939 the Royal had control of 1,400 beds, including those at Schaw Home and Canniesburn. It was expected that the Germans would launch massive air attacks on British cities once war was declared, and 850 beds were reserved at Townhead to receive civilian casualties.

On 26 August 1939, with all diplomatic attempts to avoid a war in Europe exhausted, the Royal and Western evacuated all patients who were fit to return home. On 1 September the Germans invaded Poland, and Britain and France declared war on the aggressor two days later. Immediately after the declaration of war, the Royal was placed under the control of the Department of Health for Scotland, and all but 170 of the in-patients at Townhead were evacuated to Canniesburn, and to Schaw, East Park and Lenzie convalescent homes, to leave beds free for casualties. There were relatively few British casualties during the opening months of the war, however, and the hospitals were permitted to admit war workers, and later ordinary civilian cases, to reserved beds. By January 1940 the number of beds reserved at the Royal under the EMS scheme had been reduced to 300 of the total of about 1,050, and the number of civilian patients in the wards had risen to 700. The long waiting list for admission to the infirmary was actually reduced the following year, when EMS wards were opened to those awaiting treatment in voluntary hospitals.[21]

It was in January 1940, during what became known as the 'phoney war' period from September to April, that the manager John Stewart told the meeting of delegates of the working-class contributors about the unforeseen irritations of running the infirmary in a time of national emergency. He reported that 'the black-out has been as big a trouble as Hitler; whist drives and dances could not be held and collections had to be made during the hours of daylight. The money did not come in so easily but we had to deal with all the accidents caused by the blackout.' The dramatic increase in road traffic accidents was a particular cause of concern to the Government—20,000 were believed to have died on Britain's roads in the first two years of the war[22]—and thousands of the injured were treated at the Royal, which was often unable to recover the full cost of treatment from the insurance companies. Further expense was incurred in purchasing sandbags and blackout curtains, and in building air-raid shelters at the infirmary.

Extra nurses were taken on to work under the EMS scheme at Canniesburn and Schaw Home, and there were fears that the Royal might have to find considerable sums of money to build or rent accommodation for them. Fortunately, Sir Archibald Campbell came to the rescue by offering Garscube House near Dawsholm as a temporary nurses' home, which could accommodate up to seventy women. The Royal accepted his offer, and purchased a second-hand bus to take the nurses to and from Bearsden. The nurses were not entirely happy with conditions at Garscube House, and complained of cold bedrooms, dampness, a lack of hot water, poor lighting and insufficient bed linen and meals. Action was taken to improve their conditions.

The Royal and its satellites were able to offer vital services on the nights of the great air raids on Clydeside, on 13–14 and 14–15 March and 5–6 and 6–7 May 1941, when over 1,000 people died and over 4,000 were wounded. During the infamous 'Clydebank Blitz' in March, 122 casualties were received at Canniesburn, where medical and surgical teams from the Royal were assisted by porters, tradesmen and civilian volunteers. In all, however, only 237 civilian casualties were admitted to the wards at Townhead during the war; far fewer than had been predicted in 1939. The infirmary itself survived the war unscathed, although in 1941 firefighters were called upon to extinguish a blaze on the roof, after incendiary bombs fell nearby.

The war years witnessed the opening of important new facilities at the Royal. Work on the conversion of the Blind Asylum building, to hold the new Out-Patient Department, began before the outbreak of hostilities. It was opened in June 1940 by the Right Honourable John Colville MP of Colville's Ltd, the iron and steel manufacturers which had contributed to the cost. The new facilities were a distinct improvement on the cramped and scattered quarters which the departments occupied before the war. The surgical department was located on the ground floor, the medical and medico-electrical on the first, and the gynaecological on the second. The third floor, added to the building during the conversion, housed the X-ray department and the rehabilitation clinic.[23] The rehabilitation clinic (which became the orthopaedic department after the war) was seen as an essential part of the Government's 'drive for industrial efficiency', helping injured men get to work in vital war industries, and it received 7,000 new cases in 1942 alone. Under pressure from the Department of Health for Scotland, which sought further improvements in fracture treatment, the managers persuaded the surgical staff to withdraw their opposition to a specialisation in fracture treatment. In March 1943 the Secretary of State for Scotland, Tom Johnston, opened male and female rehabilitation wards, providing the Royal with a fracture unit at last.[24] In recognition of the fact that up to 24 per cent of the 5,000 fracture cases at the infirmary came from Lanarkshire, satellite fracture clinics were established in health centres at Motherwell and Coatbridge, and also at Kirkintilloch, so that recuperating patients were not forced to travel long distances to receive their treatment in Glasgow.

In 1941 the bacteriologist Dr Leonard Colebrook was sent to the Royal by the Medical Research Council, to investigate the treatment of burns and wound infection, under the Surgeon in Charge of the burns wards, Mr Alfred Clark. Clark was already collaborating with David Cuthbertson on research into traumatic shock and developing an improved dressing for burns, and Colebrook became involved in the latter project. One result was the production of MRC Cream No. 9, which became widely used in the treatment of burns. The unit was given an experimental supply of penicillin in 1942, two years before it became generally available for use in treatment in the wards. Members were also engaged in early research in plastic surgery, and Tom Gibson, who worked at the Burns Unit in 1942–4, went on to become one of the country's leading plastic surgeons.

In 1940 Dr Sloan Robertson was appointed to take charge of a neuro-surgical clinic in the Out-Patient Department. However, the Glasgow hospitals later agreed to pool their resources in this important field, and in April 1942 Sloan Robertson established a neuro-surgical unit containing forty beds at the EMS hospital in Killearn, under the supervision of Professor Charles Illingworth. Other wartime innovations included the creation of a blood bank, under the National Blood Transfusion Scheme. The project was organised by Dr Alice Marshall of the Pathology Department in September 1940, and involved the storage of ten bottles of blood and twenty of plasma at the Royal, and a commitment to supply up to fifty bottles of blood at eight hours' notice.

191

THE NATIONAL HEALTH SERVICE

The Royal had a proud war record. Despite severe shortages of staff and vital medical supplies and equipment, a range of excellent services was maintained, for civilians and servicemen alike. For all its achievements, however, the infirmary was no longer master of its own fate.

The managers' response to the Report of the Committee on the Scottish Health Services in 1936 had been broadly favourable. The committee's opinion that 'the peculiar function of voluntary organisation and voluntary effort [is] to anticipate, to experiment, to educate... [and] to cooperate and to supplement in various ways the work of the local authorities and state',[25] fitted well with the redefined, more specialist role which the infirmary had attempted to adopt since 1931, and a recommendation that the Treasury contribute substantial funds to meet capital costs was attractive for an institution seeking greater financial security. However, the future of Britain's health services was the subject of radical reappraisal during the war. The famous Beveridge Report of 1942, on Social Insurance and Allied Services, stated that a prerequisite of the plan to introduce a social security scheme was that 'medical treatment covering all requirements will be provided for all citizens by a national health service organised under the health department...'[26] The exact shape which this service should take became the matter of heated debate, but the success of the EMS, under the direction of the Department of Health for Scotland, convinced many that an element of state control was not only necessary but desirable. This view was shared by many idealistic young doctors, but certainly not by the managers of the Royal. Like those entrusted with the management of other voluntary hospitals, they feared that the loss of local, elected management control would prove disastrous. The Annual Report for 1944, referring to the proposals set down in the Government's White Paper on a proposed 'National Comprehensive Health Service', put their case succinctly:

> The voluntary hospitals have behind them a wealth of experience, buildings, equipment and staff, and it would be a catastrophe if this great system were to be superseded by a state or local authority service because such a service must necessarily be run on bureaucratic lines. The voluntary hospitals are the most democratically controlled institutions in this country.

THE POST-WAR WORLD

The White Paper on the creation of a National Health Service was pub-lished in February 1944, affirming the principle that medical treatment and advice should be made available free of charge at the point of use to those in need, and that the voluntary hospitals, supported by generous state grants, should retain their place in the nation's hospital service. The managers pointed out that if such a 'free' health service was introduced, then subscriptions and contributions would inevitably dry up, leaving the voluntary hospitals almost entirely reliant on the state for funding.

In the immediate aftermath of victory in Europe, while the final shape of the new National Health Service was being determined, the Royal faced serious difficulties in maintaining the range and quality of its ser-vices. As had happened in the First World War, there was very little expenditure on vital maintenance and building work between 1939 and 1945. Staff costs rose inexorably, as did the costs of new instruments, appliances and other essential equipment. Penicillin (which was intro-duced in the wards three days after D-Day, in June 1944) and other expensive sera, which were paid for by the Government during wartime, had now to be purchased from the Royal's own funds. The Government's EMS contributions, towards the cost of reserving beds and the treatment of service and civilian casualties, were discontinued.

In October 1945 the Finance Committee reported that the resources of the Royal were near exhaustion, and that it might be necessary to cut back on services unless the infirmary received a large contribution from the Government or some unexpected financial windfall. The House Committee, referring to the acute shortage of nursing staff, warned that ward closures might be necessary even if additional funds were raised. In November the managers were informed of a sit-down strike by in-sleep-ing maids at Canniesburn, and of the monotonous and unimaginative meals served up by the kitchen staff, struggling to produce nourishing meals from supplies available under food rationing regulations. In December the matron reported that 170 nurses were awaiting leave to go on long-overdue holidays, and that many would be unable to continue working if extra staff were not found, allowing them to take their holi-days.[27] At the same meeting the superintendent was told to make provision for the closure of six surgical wards, and to begin reducing admissions. The deficit on ordinary expenditure increased from nearly £47,000 in 1945 to £121,500 in 1946 and to £209,600 the following year. The situation was grave, and the Royal was only able to continue in 1947 courtesy of a maintenance grant of £74,659 from the Department of Health. Even with this additional income, the deficit for the year amounted to £58,569.

The inability of the Board to increase revenue during a period of rising costs was due in large measure to Government policy relating to its future within the National Health Service. Since the publication of the White Paper in 1944 there had been a belief that the state would contribute generously to the costs of running the voluntary hospitals, and this may have discouraged benefactors from making gifts and donations. In the General Election of July 1945 the Labour Party won a landslide victory, and still more radical proposals emerged. The new Government was committed to a programme of social reform and nationalisation, and the job of forging a new comprehensive health service was entrusted to one of the party's most idealistic and commanding figures, Minister of Health Aneurin Bevan. Bevan had no time for those who argued for the retention of the voluntary hospitals. He believed that 'a patchwork quilt of local paternalism is the enemy of intelligent planning. It is repugnant to a civilised community for hospitals to have to rely on private charity.' The National Health Service (Scotland) Bill, introduced in December 1946 (nine months after a sister Bill for England and Wales), proposed that all Scotland's hospitals be brought under the control of local boards of management, which were responsible to one of five Regional Boards, which were responsible in turn to the Secretary of State for Scotland. Once it became known that the hospital's upkeep would soon be the responsibility of the taxpayer, that endowments would be 'reallocated' once the infirmary came under state control, and that subscribers' lines would no longer be required to obtain treatment, it was inevitable that subscribers, contributors and benefactors would become reluctant to offer increased financial support. The last months of independence were miserable ones for all concerned at the infirmary, as the problems of running a hospital during the harsh winter of 1947–8 were compounded by a chronic shortage of funds. It was a sad end to more than 150 years of voluntary effort.

In the Annual Report for 1947 the managers set out the 'assets' which would be inherited by the NHS. The Royal had 862 beds. There were five general medical, six general surgical, two gynaecological, a skins, a urological, a plastic surgery and an orthopaedic unit. Radiological and radiotherapy departments, pathological, bacteriological and biochemical laboratories, and cardiology, endocrinology and neuro-surgery clinics offered other vital services. The infirmary also had a large Out-Patient Department, rebuilt in 1940, and flourishing schools of physiotherapy and nursing. Canniesburn, Schaw Home and the Ophthalmic Institute provided additional facilities for specialist care and convalescence. It was estimated that the buildings, equipment and other material assets of the Royal amounted to the vast sum of £6 million. The value of the skills and accumulated experience of the staff was beyond calculation.

The last monthly meeting of the managers was held on 2 July 1948, and the Royal and its auxiliary institutions were transferred to the Western Regional Hospital Board three days later.

6 UNFULFILLED
EXPECTATIONS, 1948–74

Whatever its faults, and there are many, the hospital service as I know it, is better staffed, better equipped, and with an equally good spirit as before 1948. In many respects the hospitals today are far in advance of the hospitals of yesterday. It would be extremely disappointing if this were not so.

A A MacIver, Secretary of the Board of Management for Glasgow Royal Infirmary and Associated Hospitals, 1974

THE BOARD OF MANAGEMENT

After all the arguments and disputes, the new National Health Service was launched early on the morning of Sunday 4 July 1948—the Appointed Day—with a broadcast to the nation by the Labour Prime Minister, Clement Attlee. Despite the slogan in the official advertising, 'This Day Makes History', Attlee and his supporters within the Government were determined to maintain a conciliatory tone to ensure that the NHS got off to a good start. Indeed, reassured by the Government's concessions, a good many doctors had been won over. Alexander K Bowman was appointed Senior Administrative Medical Officer for the Western Regional Hospital Board responsible for all hospital services in the West of Scotland. He was soon an enthusiastic advocate for the NHS:

> For the first time it was said, men felt secure so far as the medical care of their families is concerned, and women felt freedom in this regard in respect of their children which they had never before experienced. I was quite touched, and hoped inwardly that we should be able to see to it that everyone had in fact a fair deal.

Such emotional idealism was topical. In the west of Scotland the shipyards and engineering works were bustling with activity, making good the ravages of wartime, and heralding the prospect of full employment, on which depended the nation's ability to finance improvements in social welfare, education and living conditions. In the streets surrounding the Royal Infirmary there was a great deal to be done to fulfil the Labour Government's ambitious social agenda. Much of the housing was in appalling condition and in many places street violence was accepted as part of the pattern of life. Under the new structure of the Western Regional Hospital Board the Royal joined a group of hospitals, principally serving the socially deprived east end of the city. To the existing hospitals and institutions, managed by the Board of Management of the Royal (the infirmary itself, Canniesburn Auxiliary Hospital, the Glasgow Ophthalmic Institution, Schaw Convalescent Home) were added the Eastern District Hospital, the Belvidere Infectious Diseases Hospital, the Bridgeton Orthopaedic, Rheumatic and Foot Clinic, and the Glasgow and West of Scotland Foot Hospital. This was in marked contrast to England and Wales where the teaching hospitals were to be funded directly by the Ministry of Health and run separately from the district hospitals.

The Eastern District and Belvidere hospitals had previously been controlled by Glasgow Corporation. Belvidere, from its establishment by the Corporation in 1870, took patients with virulently infectious diseases, whose presence in a general hospital presented a considerable threat to other patients. Moreover, voluntary hospitals by their very nature could not cope with cyclical and irregular patterns of epidemics of infectious diseases, not least for financial reasons. To prevent the spread of infection in the community, the regime at Belvidere was strict. Patients were prohibited from bringing personal belongings into the hospital with the single exception of ration books. Visits could only be made to patients on the 'Dangerously Ill list' - otherwise information could be obtained from the ward sisters. Two years earlier the Scottish Hospitals Survey had described the buildings as obsolete and recommended the construction of a new hospital on another site in the east end of the city. The Eastern District or Duke Street Hospital had been built between 1902 and 1909 by the City and Barony Parish Councils which had merged in 1898. This was just one of three hospitals built at the time to cater for acute medical and surgical cases in the city. The largest was Stobhill Hospital to the north of the city with 1,700 beds, and Eastern District Hospital and

Oakbank Hospital in Cowcaddens originally had 500 beds between them. In 1930, following the abolition of the parish councils, responsibility for the hospitals was transferred to the Corporation. By 1948 the Eastern District Hospital had 300 beds, including a recently enlarged maternity unit. Apart from its in-patient facilities the hospital provided a casualty service and clinics for psychological medicine, ante-natal, post-natal and gynaecology, physiotherapy, and surgical appliances. The Glasgow and West of Scotland Foot Hospital, a voluntary organisation, was essentially a practical training school for chiropodists, whereas Bridgeton Orthopaedic, Rheumatic and Foot Clinic – also a voluntary body – provided a clinic in an area of the city where foot and lower limb problems were endemic, particularly among women textile workers.

Although the day-to-day management of the hospitals and clinics was, at least in the short term, to remain undisturbed, the Western Regional Hospital Board expected from the outset that there would be some rationalising and streamlining of services. The Bridgeton clinic was linked to the Orthopaedic Department at the Royal, with one of the specialists responsible for consultations there on one day each week. Greater integration was possible with the Eastern District, which was in some areas effectively merged with the Royal and designated a chronic rather than an acute hospital. The five medical wards were placed under the control of one of the five chief physicians at the Royal who, under the NHS, now had full time contracts. The two surgical wards were placed under the direction of an Assistant Surgeon at the Royal, with help from his juniors. The management of Maternity and Gynaecology and Psychiatry wards remained unchanged, but even in them there was a large turnover in personnel. While recognising that facilities at the Eastern District Hospital could be substantially improved, the Board of Management was prevented from taking immediate action by Government restrictions on new building. With no overlapping services, Belvidere was unaffected by these changes. Under the direction of Dr Thomas Archibald, the long-serving Physician-Superintendent, two empty wards at Belvidere were converted to take pulmonary tuberculosis cases to tackle this intractable problem which had been exacerbated by the war. The impression that the Royal had taken over rather than merged with the other units in the Board of Management was confirmed by the decision to give executive authority to A A McIver, the Royal's secretary and treasurer, and by the new building programme which was confined almost exclusively to the Royal. Work continued on the new Urological Department with three twelve-bed wards, two for men and one for women, and two operating theatres. Permission was also given for the construction of a new Radiotherapy Department, and a Hearing Aid Clinic, equipped with an audiometer, was inaugurated.

MANAGING THE NEW SERVICE

Despite the Government's intentions, there were the inevitable hic-coughs in implementing the new National Health Service, particularly in delivering free services for which there had previously been charges. The Ophthalmic Institution was overwhelmed with referrals by general prac-titioners of patients in search of free spectacles. There were other problems resulting in part from the protracted negotiations leading up to the Appointed Day. Although the outlines of the complex bureaucratic structure to oversee the new service were drawn, much of the detail still had to be filled in. Over the ensuing weeks the Board of Management of the Royal was inundated with a stream of circulars, spelling out how its various responsibilities were to be discharged. Towards the end of July 1948, for example, Circular Regional Health Boards (Scotland) (49)18 arrived along with a copy of Statutory Instrument 1948 No.1390(S.111) explaining how Medical and Dental Officers were to be appointed to the staffs of hospitals. On receipt, the secretariat had to prepare new full or part-time contracts for all consultant and specialist staff for two years in the first instance. At the same time, Statutory Instrument 1948 No.1388 (S.109) arrived, instructing the Regional Board to establish a Medical Education Committee. Following the amalgamation of St Mungo's College with the University Medical Faculty and the transfer of the College's property to the infirmary, the University Court was to be rep-resented on committees for all new appointments, along with representation of the Regional Board as the employing authority. There could be no doubt that, despite external appearances, the infirmary's room for manoeuvre would be severely circumscribed by the new bureau-cratic structure, which required constant reference to the Regional Board for permission for all types of expenditure and the appointment of staff, even registrars. In some cases where wider issues were involved—for example, in the case of secretarial support for consultants—the Regional

Board had to seek approval and guidance from the Department of Health for Scotland in Edinburgh. The resulting decisions taken to ensure uniformity in the system were not always in the Royal's best interest. The proposed reduction in the duration of nurses' training, from four years to the three years common in other hospitals, not only threatened the quality and reputation of the nursing education at the Royal but also deprived the infirmary of the services of between sixty and seventy fourth year students who worked on the wards as more or less fully qualified staff nurses.

For voluntary hospitals like the Royal the issue likely to give rise to the greatest friction between members of the Board of Management and representatives of the former Corporation hospitals, the Regional Board and the Department of Health for Scotland was the future use of endowment funds. The spirit of the Act suggested that these should be made available equitably across the whole system, but bequests had been made directly to the Royal or other voluntary hospitals, sometimes for a specific purpose. Shortly after the Appointed Day the endowment funds were transferred to the new Board of Management to administer, and bequests continued to be received, pending the appointment of a Hospital Endowments Commission for Scotland to resolve the question. Before the Commission's recommendations could be implemented, they needed to be ratified by the Secretary of State and submitted to Parliament. Given the sensitivity and complexity of proposals to redistribute endowments to unendowed hospitals, no progress was made for almost a year by the Department of Health for Scotland. It was not until the autumn of 1949 that the Commission was appointed and the Royal invited to submit information about their endowment capital and income. After much debate the Board of Management, as trustees for the time being of the endowments, suggested, in February 1950, that the income should be used largely for medical research at the Royal, for the social welfare of patients and for amenities for patients and staff. In the absence of decisions from the Commission the hospital boards in Scotland reached an understanding between themselves that endowment funds should continue to be used for the purposes for which they had been given. However, the Department insisted that endowments should not be used for augmenting salaries or for building projects. Although the Board of Management of the Royal had already begun to make disbursements to associated hospitals before this advice was received, fortunately the terms of one large bequest, the Sir Thomas Lipton Fund, allowed the income to be used for the sick poor of Glasgow and Cambuslang without restriction.

MAINTAINING THE MEDICAL SERVICE

Against the background of organisational upheaval the work of the infirmary in treating patients had to continue. There were new and exciting advances in medical therapy with the discovery of antibiotics which held out the possibility of a cure for some of the resistant forms of infection, notably tuberculosis. Towards the end of 1948 Dr A K Bowman of the Regional Board announced that supplies of the new drug streptomycin would be made available for use in the infirmary. There were all the usual stresses and strains of hospital life. Professor David Fyfe Anderson, Professor of Obstetrics and Gynaecology, and Dr Hugh Stirling, a Consultant Gynaecologist, were locked in a heated argument about the staffing of their wards. At the heart of their disagreement was the number of consultancies held by Dr Stirling who, while admitting that he probably had too many posts, was unwilling to relinquish any of them until the terms of his new sessional contract with the Royal had been properly ratified. A way out of the impasse was found through the proposed appointment of a further Assistant Gynaecologist. Just before the candidates were interviewed this expedient was sensibly vetoed by the Regional Board until a more general inquiry into gynaecological and obstetric services in the west of Scotland had been completed. The Board of Management of the Royal, having recently suffered a similar reverse in requests for equipment purchases to maintain the Royal's status as a premier teaching hospital, refused to be browbeaten and confirmed the appointment of Dr Robin Murdoch. The Regional Board, as the employing authority, hit back by announcing the amalgamation of the two gynaecological units in the Royal under Professor Anderson and transferring Dr Stirling to the Southern General. The Board of Management of the Royal, which had not been consulted, reacted angrily, rejecting the scheme outright. Under pressure the Regional Board backed off. Heartened by this victory the Royal staff were in no mood to brook further interference in the day-to-day running of the infirmary. When an encyclical letter from Dr A K Bowman, demanding the centralisation of admission procedures in January 1949 was received, it was rejected outright on grounds that it would lead to delays and 'upset the waiting lists for the various chiefs'. The Secretary, cheekily, asked the Regional Board how this instruction was to be implemented in a hospital as large as the Royal. Although the Regional Board made it clear informally that it did not intend to be gainsaid, no letter was received.

NEW BUILDING - OLD PROBLEM

Having tested their muscle the Board of Management of the Royal was sufficiently confident to explore urgently needed new building projects— a new nurses' home, pathological department, and the conversion of the Blind Asylum building as registrar, housemen and student accommodation, in collaboration with the University of Glasgow. The Regional Board refused to sanction the first two projects and the Professor of Pathology had to make do with minor alterations to provide additional space. To avoid further conflict with the Regional Board the Principal of the University, Sir Hector Hetherington, agreed to approach the Secretary of State for Scotland directly. In seeking approval for new building the Royal and the University could not have chosen a worse opportunity. The National Health Service was proving vastly more costly than had been projected. Such expenditure could only be sustained if the economy continued to grow, but early in 1949 exports sagged and the pound came under pressure in the foreign exchange markets. The Labour Government had no alternative but to prune spending. At first the Royal's maintenance budget was trimmed back and restrictions imposed on equipment purchases. As the financial crisis deepened the Regional Board cut back all capital expenditure. To ease the 'difficulty in providing sufficient Exchequer funds for projects which in themselves are not unreasonable' the Department of Health for Scotland allowed hospitals that had endowments to draw on them to make good any shortfalls. Believing that the country's financial difficulties were only temporary, the Board of Management pressed ahead with its building plans. In the autumn of 1949 the severity of the crisis was made clear. The Department of Health told all the Regional Boards to request the ranking of proposals to purchase all items of equipment over the value of £10. Furious at this seemingly unwarranted intrusion into their affairs, the Royal's Board protested vehemently to the Secretary of State, but to no avail. Early in 1950 the budget for the coming year was slashed from £996,500 to

£841,000, with capital expenditure and building maintenance bearing the brunt of the cuts. In the face of this return to an uncertain financial environment that the NHS was supposed to have finally dispelled, the Royal's Board had no alternative but to make maintenance and administrative staff redundant.

More serious was the prospect of a reduction in the number of medical staff, when it had for long been recognised that existing staffing levels were woefully inadequate if the infirmary was to maintain its reputation for teaching and research. By the end of 1950 the Department of Health was proposing, on the spurious grounds of ensuring adequate career paths, that the number of registrars and senior registrars should match the number of consultants' posts likely to become available each year. The implication of this policy was that the number of registrars in Scotland as a whole would be reduced from 260 to 200 and of senior registrars from 190 to ninety. Without any discussion of the likely effect on patient services the Regional Board, as the employing authority, began to act on this instruction, refusing to sanction any new appointments or to nominate representatives to appointment committees. The frustration and sense of betrayal amongst the medical staff was intense. The Royal's Board of Management, as it had done regularly since 1948, fought back by pressing ahead with the selection of suitable candidates for recommendation to the Regional Board. In the midst of this campaign the Regional Board launched a fresh assault by demanding economies in the number of domestic staff, even though staff over the age of seventy had been retired and efforts made where possible to introduce labour-saving equipment. The matron, Miss Manners, was incensed, stating categorically that cuts could only be made at the expense of patient care. She put down the higher staffing levels compared to other hospitals to the scale of the Royal's out-patient provision, which was largely due to environmental problems in the surrounding area with its chronically bad housing, serious social difficulties and the absence of an adequate general practitioner service. These assaults on staffing only served to exacerbate the already strained relations with the Regional Board, which appeared to those at the Royal wholly insensitive to the marked effects of different patterns of health provision inherited from the past. In fact, the Regional Board was grappling with other long-standing problems, particularly the shortcomings in hospital provision in much of Renfrewshire,

Dunbartonshire, Lanarkshire and North Ayrshire. There were simply not enough resources to meet all expectations of the fledgling NHS.

The Royal and the Regional Board clashed again in 1951 over the provision of a sixty to seventy bed unit for tuberculosis patients, which was urgently needed to cope with what was now an epidemic in the west of Scotland. As they had done in the past the staff and management remained implacably opposed to the admission of TB patients to the infirmary. Both the physicians and surgeons attacked the plan on the grounds that there was insufficient space, vigorously defending their pre-rogative to teach and research in their departments:

> It is submitted that, in the interests of humanity, economy and efficiency, it should be recognized that the proper function of these Units is the investigation and diagnosis of patients suf-fering from the more obscure type of disease and the treat-ment of such patients in cases where effective treatment is possible.

There was also concern that the knowledge that the Royal was admitting TB patients would make it difficult to recruit the better qualified student nurses or perhaps those from better homes. As a compromise the Board of Management volunteered to try to identify additional accommodation for TB patients at Belvidere. The Regional Board was not to be out-manoeuvred so easily and proposed that all student nurses, as part of their training, should have some experience of the management of TB patients, moving hospital if need be. Nevertheless, additional TB wards were located at Belvidere. There was, however, no problem in finding room in the infirmary for a Maxillo-Facial Unit with sixteen beds, oper-ating theatre, dental treatment room and associated facilities which opened in November 1951. The Unit, approved by the Department of Health to serve a wide area, added a new dimension to the Royal's port-folio of skills and saved patients the inconvenience of having to attend Ballochmyle Hospital in Ayrshire, where the principal plastic surgery beds were located.

ENDOWMENTS AND RESOURCES

In June 1951 the Hospital Endowment Commission made tentative pro-posals for the pooling of endowments for research purposes on a regional basis. This was the reverse of the scheme implemented in England and Wales which left endowments in the control of the hospital boards of management, principally with the old voluntary teaching hospitals. As a major teaching hospital and the oldest voluntary hospital in the west of Scotland with the largest endowments, the Royal condemned the plan as unjust. Turning a deaf ear, the Commission came forward with a suggested division of the Royal's endowments – then valued at roughly £1 million. Although the Royal's Board of Management was to be allowed to continue to manage some of the funds, forty per cent was to be expropriated for research purposes and a further twenty per cent to provide endowments for the Board of Management for Glasgow North Eastern Mental Hospitals, and Motherwell, Hamilton and District Hospitals. The Royal medical and nursing staff had no quarrel with the suggested division, but were opposed to losing direct control of the funds. The Commission accepted that administration of research funds by the Regional Board was, perhaps, not appropriate and, instead, recommended the establishment of a central Scottish Hospital Endowments Research Trust with less than the forty per cent of total endowments originally proposed. The Trust's capital was pruned because the Commission was anxious to ensure that every Board of Management could count on an endowment of £2 for each bed. The necessary legislation was passed in 1953, but the National Health Service (Glasgow Royal Infirmary and Associated Hospitals Endowment Scheme) Approval Order was not submitted to Parliament until early in 1955. Under its terms, as well as endowing the Scottish Hospital Endowments Research Trust, the Royal provided support for four other boards of management and the Western Regional Hospital Board. After these transactions had been made the Royal was still left with over £600,000 in endowment funds, along with a remarkable £345,000 donated since the formation of the NHS and excluded from the scheme. However, even expenditure from these funds of more than £1,000 on research or any item of equipment had to be approved by the Regional Board.

No sooner had the Royal come to terms with this loss of autonomy than the Conservative Secretary of State for Scotland, James Stuart, and the Minister of Health for England and Wales, Iain McLeod, appointed an independent committee under the chairmanship of the Cambridge economist, Claude W Guillebaud, ominously to 'review the present and prospective cost of the National Health Service, to suggest means whether by modifications in organization or otherwise, of ensuring the most effective control and efficient use of such Exchequer funds as may be made available...' The Scottish representative on the Committee was Professor J W Cook, a Glasgow chemist. Despite the pressing problems of financing the service, the Committee proceeded at a leisurely pace, making it clear that they had no intention of rubber-stamping draconian cuts in the infant NHS. This at least was good news for boards of management like the Royal's, frustrated by the petty restrictions on expenditure, encouraging them to press their case for better facilities. The Royal's Board of Management protested in midsummer 1953 to the Department of Health for Scotland at the failure of progress in negotiations to improve accommodation in any of their hospitals, particularly the surgical wards in the infirmary. A sub-committee of the Royal's Board of Management was established to prepare a coherent development strategy prioritising projects. The sub-committee was also instructed to consider the difficulty the Royal was facing in attracting high-calibre university-trained junior doctors which, it was believed, was due to the uncertainty and lack of security caused by the staffing policies pursued by the Department of Health and the Regional Board. The resident medical staff themselves were irritated by the summary discontinuation of their free supplies of beer, stout and cider.

Despite the determination of the Royal's Board of Management to chart a way forward it took months to arrange a meeting with the Regional Board to discuss the principal issues of contention. This lack of progress and absence of clear policy was immensely frustrating for medical, nursing and technical staff alike, inevitably leading to acrimony and recriminations, with everyone developing their own blueprints for the future. The Regional Board misinterpreted these disagreements and attempted to exploit them to its own advantage. A A MacIver, Secretary of the Royal's Board of Management, deplored this lack of understanding and failure of the infirmary staff at all levels to recognise the Regional Board's wider responsibilities. Thanks to the conciliatory tone set by the Regional Board's chairman, Sir Alexander Macgregor, it proved possible to reach an understanding in principle on most of the questions, notably the designation of the Orthopaedic Department's ward for cardiac surgery, the transfer of three surgical wards to the Orthopaedic

Department, and the appointment of a consultant General Surgeon to take charge of the Casualty Department. This thawing in relations with the Regional Board coincided with the loss of four of the Royal's old style chiefs - Professor 'Pop' J A G Burton, George Henry Stevenson and George Carson Swanson retired, and Alfred Mackenzie Clark died suddenly. Of these four distinguished members of the infirmary's staff, Pop Burton was the most colourful. He was a man of no pretension, always ready to deflate, with a ready wit, those whom he thought were overbearing and pretentious. He was succeeded as first full-time Professor of Surgery by W Arthur Mackey - only the second full-time professorial appointment.

The Guillebaud Committee reported in January 1956, recommending that, to allow the management of the NHS to find its feet, there should be no fundamental changes and proposing that the funding for capital projects should be sharply increased to bring it back into line with the pre-war level. The Treasury was not best pleased, but Health Board managers and doctors were delighted. The Royal's Board of Management had already made common cause with the Western Infirmary, the Edinburgh Royal Infirmary and the Aberdeen Royal Infirmary in requesting an urgent meeting with the Secretary of the Department of Health for Scotland to discuss the inadequacies of the budgets for capital and equipment expenditure. Although a meeting was refused the action of the four hospitals won the approval of the Regional Board which, in turn, approached the Secretary of State over the head of the Department. In the meantime the Royal's sub-committee on development strategy had been hard at work reviewing building projects and drawing up lists of badly needed new equipment, particularly for in-patient X-ray and radiotherapy and for cardio-vascular procedures being pioneered by Professor Mackey, keen to justify his full-time appointment, and Dr Joe Wright, the consultant cardiologist. The Regional Board did make a little extra cash available in 1955-6, including funds for some of the electrocardiograph equipment, yet there were still endless irritations. For example, Professor Mackey found he had to share his office with his secretary, who had to leave the room every time he wanted a private consultation. Despite repeated requests it proved impossible to secure sanction from the Regional Board to create a separate office. Similar difficulties occurred in attempts to form a medical art and photography department;

and, more seriously, over proposals to create a regional radiotherapeutic centre which were abandoned without any consultation. There was common ground, however, on the formation of a Regional Physics Centre under Dr John Lenihan—despite the fact that the Royal's own physicist, Walter Jackson, was reluctant to join the venture.

RESEARCH EXCELLENCE AND INNOVATION

Notwithstanding this seemingly endless struggle for resources, the medical and nursing staff made every effort to maintain and develop the Royal's reputation as an international centre for research. In medicine, Professor Leslie Davis headed a team investigating various haematological problems, winning recognition as the regional centre for the treatment of haemophilia. Dr Edward McGirr was pioneering techniques using radioactive isotopes in the diagnosis and treatment of thyroid problems and of polyeythaemia vera. In cardiology Dr Joe Wright had a team studying 400 patients with mitral valve diseases and 100 with congenital heart problems, developing new procedures for diagnosis and relief of pain. He collaborated with Professor Mackey, who was experimenting with the potential of open-heart surgery for the treatment of congenital and acquired diseases of the heart and large blood vessels. As part of this work efforts were being made to construct a mechanised heart-lung pump oxygenerator machine with total heart-lung bypass at the University's new Veterinary Hospital at Garscube by Professor (later Sir) William Weipers. There were other joint research projects with the Veterinary School, notably in bacteriology into leptospiral infections in animals and humans. In plastic surgery and the treatment of burns the Royal was acknowledged as a world leader. During 1956 Mr Tom Gibson won first prize in an international competition for a short coloured film on an operative technique evolved for the treatment of lymphoedema of the legs.

Every month the Board of Management was asked to support this vibrant research activity by making small grants from endowments for equipment and travelling expenses, and giving leave of absence for staff to study abroad. Often research was handicapped by the bureaucracy surrounding the purchase of equipment, requiring permission from the Regional Board. For example, advances in the treatment of peripheral vascular disease were delayed by the lack of a Norton Victor Serial cassette charger for abdominal aortography. Overall supervision of the medical work of the infirmary was in the hands of the talented Medical Superintendent, Dr Thomas Bryson, who died prematurely at the end of October 1956, to be succeeded by his deputy, Dr J Killoch Anderson. In paying tribute to Dr Bryson, Colonel Denholm, the deputy chairman, recorded, 'His accessibility to the layman, his readiness to listen to and discuss our ideas on the hospital, made him the ideal liaison officer between us and the medical side of the administration.'

Following the release of the Nuffield Report (Job Analysis of the Work of Nurses in Hospital Wards) in 1953, the nursing staff at the Royal had been looking at ways of improving nursing education. The report had been critical of the lack of integration of theoretical and practical instruction and inadequate professional education. With financial support from the Department of Health for Scotland and the Nuffield Provincial Hospitals Trust, the Royal inaugurated in 1956 an experimental three year training course. The experiment was to be assessed after five years. Three adjacent houses were purchased in Clevelden Road in the west end of the city well away from the infirmary, to provide accommodation and classrooms. There were to be three annual intakes of twenty-five students for the duration of the experiment. In keeping with the report, the emphasis of the course was on integration, with students attending wards and visiting other health-related institutions from the beginning of their studies. As time went on they spent more and more time in the wards. After two years the students sat their final exams, spending their third year of training as staff nurses on the wards of either the Royal or approved hospitals. The scheme was evaluated by a committee chaired by Professor Brotherston of the University of Edinburgh at the end of the first five years. It was considered so successful that the General Nursing Council recognised the course formally as an Alternative Scheme of Training from September 1961.

BUILDING ON STRENGTHS

During 1956 the Royal medical staff, heartened by the Guillebaud Report, worked upon a number of proposals for new construction based on areas of excellence. Professor Mackey planned the conversion of Ward 47 from an Orthopaedic Department into a Cardiac Surgery Unit at a cost of £21,000. He also slipped in an office for his long-suffering secretary. It was hoped that a regional radio-therapeutic centre might be built at Belvidere. There was reason to be optimistic. The Department of Health gave approval in principle for a Regional Steroid Laboratory in the old Post Office at Castle Street and for the development of the Island site (see plan on page 000). The Board of Management envisaged the Island site as offering the potential for the Royal to maintain its position as a leading teaching and research hospital, providing new suites of lecture theatres, staff and student canteen and dining-room facilities, the reloca-tion of the Eye Department from the Ophthalmic Institute, two new wards and an operating theatre for the Professor of Gynaecology, and offices and research laboratories for the Professor of Medicine. With no immediate prospect of finance being forthcoming, the need for better student accommodation was so pressing, following the General Medical Council's recommendation that students should spend at least one month in hospital residence, that a number of temporary solutions were investi-gated. This included the modernisation of parts of the old St Mungo's College building, the erection of a temporary building in the quadrangle next to the Out-Patient Department, and the use of the Cathedral Halls, which belonged to the infirmary, as a new student and staff canteen and reading room. The Royal was unsuccessful in securing sufficient financial support for additional accommodation for teaching and housing the larger number of student nurses following the reduction, against the staff's bet-ter judgement, of the training from four to three years. The Regional Board only contributed £2,000 out of an estimated budget of £7,000. Moreover, Glasgow Corporation wanted the site for the proposed new nurses' home, opposite the infirmary, to improve the approach to the Cathedral. There were other minor continuing building projects on the Board's agenda, including the provision of bedside lockers for all patients' beds and the fitting out of a photographic department.

In March 1957 the Department of Health made it known that it would not be possible for any major extension of the infirmary to com-mence for at least three years. The Regional Board, however, did promise that the development of the Royal would be assigned the high-est priority and encouraged the medical and nursing staff to work up a detailed schedule of requirements to be fed into the planning process but not to commission any detailed drawings or go out to tender. The medi-cal and nursing staff responded typically to this invitation, commissioning drawings for a building in Vicar's Alley intended for a Medical Art and

Photography Department which was to be enlarged to include radio-active isotope and electro-encephalography departments. This building, along with a new administrative block and audiology department, was completed in 1959. The medical staff were not going to be deterred from their quest for improved facilities for teaching, research and patient care, particularly for an innovative artificial kidney unit and Professor Mackey's exciting developments in cardiac surgery. There was also an urgent need to modernise the operating theatres, not least because the electrical wiring was unsafe and there was a high risk of infection from faulty plumbing. As an interim measure an anti-infection sub-committee was appointed which was forced to halt 'clean' surgery in the spring of 1958 because of a serious increase in staphylococcal infection. The Universities Grants Committee issued new instructions in June about the provision of teaching and research facilities in teaching hospitals, which in future were to be financed by an additional grant on the Universities and Colleges vote, subject to specific Treasury approval for expenditure of over £10,000. The UGC was only prepared to fund schemes where the facilities complemented NHS-resourced new building projects. No sooner had this alternative avenue for capital funding been opened than the Regional Board, in response to Government pressure, began to investigate staff and consumable costs in different units, calling in outside consultants to provide independent advice. Boards of Management were told to ensure economy. Regardless, the Royal Board pressed on with development plans, winning approval from the Regional Board for the setting up of a Joint Planning Committee in January 1958. Later in the year Dr Arthur Jacobs of the Urology Department secured endowment funds to pay for the purchase of an artificial kidney machine, on the understanding that the Board would fund the alteration of the building. This still meant that one of the physicians, Dr Arthur Kennedy, had to wash and clean the dialysis machine himself.

CLOSING THE DOOR AND CUTTING COSTS

It was not until June 1959 that the Joint Planning Committee had the confidence to propose that the new building should include a Biochemistry Department, equipped with the latest electron microscopes for bacteriological and biochemical investigations, as well as an Institute of Research to maintain the Royal's lead as an international teaching hospital. One consequence of the decision to seek this centre of excellence status for the Royal was a petition to terminate finally the open door policy that had been a hallmark of the infirmary since its inception. In particular the surgical chiefs were anxious that the Regional Board should make 'better provision [elsewhere] for the disposal of frankly geriatric cases'. Before the Regional Board could respond the Royal hurried on with its plans, appointing Basil Spence & Partners as architects in direct contravention of the Regional Board's instructions not to do so. At this juncture the Department of Health intervened by informing the Board of Management of the Royal that the proposed redevelopment would take the hospital well above the ceiling of 800 beds that was considered desirable if good staff relations were to be maintained. While recognising the historic reasons for the Royal's size, the Department made it clear that any further increase could only be a temporary expedient, pending a radical restructuring of hospital services in Glasgow for which plans were at an early stage. The medical and nursing staff at the Royal took comfort from the fact that the Department was taking a very long view and when it came to rebuilding the infirmary completely in fifty years' time, after their retirement, there would be no difficulty in reducing the number of beds to 800. The Regional Board, irritated by interference from Edinburgh, backed the Royal, which pressed on with its plans.

Nevertheless, the Regional Board was not willing to allow the Royal to over-run its annual budget to achieve international recognition. In September 1960 they questioned why the running costs had exceeded the annual allocation by £23,000, about 1.5 per cent, and on the capital account, some £13,000, over 17 per cent. This was a period of economic restraint following the Conservative Government's spending spree prior to the 1959 election. As well as exploring the reasons for these over-spends, and apparently higher costs than other hospitals, the infirmary, like other hospitals elsewhere in Britain, had to achieve a one per cent saving across the board. The finger was pointed at the surgical wards, which had lower than average occupancy rates. Professor Mackey reacted angrily, stating categorically that the Royal was being starved of funds. Even the members of the Board of Management were taken aback at the vehemence of his onslaught and felt obliged to draw attention to the considerable sums that had been made available by the Regional Board. However they did agree that, in the provision of new equipment, necessary for advances in surgical technique, the Royal had been ill-served. Professor Mackey had an ulterior motive: to secure an innovative, well-founded cardio-pulmonary unit in the Royal, with the support of the Department of Health. A meeting between representatives of the infirmary, the Regional Board and the Department of Health in late December was sufficiently encouraging to persuade the Royal Board to set up a steering committee, chaired by Professor Davis. There followed almost a year of further frustrating negotiations against a background of even more stringent public-expenditure control, accompanied by the employment of external consultants by the Department of Health in the quest for economies. In the midst of the impasse Professor Davis retired; the first full-time clinician and teacher to work in the infirmary. He was succeeded by his young assistant, Professor Edward McGirr, who was determined to keep up the pressure on the Regional Board and the Department of Health for better facilities.

A NEW INFIRMARY

At last, in November 1961, the Department of Health indicated that it was sympathetic to a major building project involving not only the long discussed development on the Island site, but also new accommodation for the Out-Patient and Accident departments. This was part and parcel of a review of accident and emergency services by the Regional Board which, it was estimated, would require a further 120 beds for the Royal. This news had one unwelcome drawback—the Regional Board demanded that the Board of Management should prepare yet another long-term development plan. Refusing to be cynical about the Department of Health's motives in providing no guaranteed commitment, Professor Mackey, Professor McGirr and Dr Killoch Anderson worked at break-neck speed to reconsider the infirmary's building programme in this wider context. Within days they had defined their priorities, reciting well-rehearsed arguments. The immediate needs were for improvement to the gatehouse, temporary accommodation for biochemistry, reorganization of the pharmacy, improvement of the pathology building and, above all, the development of the Island site along with the Accident and Out-Patient departments. The urgently needed major projects were defined—a new nurses' home and residential accommodation for junior medical staff, visitors, postgraduate and under-

213

graduate students and research workers. The longer-term developments were not far behind: a new operating theatre suite, a new laboratory building, kitchens, canteens and administrative offices, and a new ward block. There was an atmosphere of excitement that at last action would be taken. Professor McGirr enthusiastically sought to involve the junior medical staff—mostly his contemporaries—in the planning process, launching a project in collaboration with Professor Symington to create a badly needed integrated haematology and anti-coagulant service. This move appears to have been in response to the Platt Report on the Medical Staffing Structure in the Hospital Service which proposed a radical shift away from the hierarchical management of units towards a flatter profile, where each consultant had a prescriptive right to beds. At the same time the Regional Board announced a strategy for a proper geriatric service that would relieve pressure and free beds. The tentative suggestion was that the Royal's Board of Management should take over the 100-bed Lightburn Hospital in Lanarkshire, which would be refurbished and enlarged for the purpose.

As might have been anticipated from all the false starts and trials of the previous decade, the enthusiasm was misplaced. The Regional Board approved the concept of the haematology and anti-coagulant service, but failed to make any funds available for the necessary staff. There was no money to carry out any work at Lightburn and the scheme was put on ice, and even discussion of the proposed geriatric service ceased, despite the growing scale of the problem as more and more people were living longer. Eventually the Royal's Board of Management told the Regional Board that they were not prepared to reopen the question unless there was a real commitment to fund refurbishment. Because of delays in reaching agreement about building on the Island, now known as Phase 1 of the redevelopment of the Royal, temporary accommodation had to be found for the major accident centre which was to serve the whole east side of the city. Likewise, there was no sign of any funds being forthcoming for a nurses' home and the Royal's Board of Management was forced to patch up the existing accommodation and identify suitable digs in an effort to attract pupils of a high standard. The decline in the social fabric of the east end was making the infirmary a more dangerous place to work, with regular attacks on the nursing staff by drunk emergency patients. In addition, with all the proposed new services, the infirmary would need to find at least another seventy nursing students.

Planning and Planners

By the autumn of 1962 the Department of Health was prepared to 'face up to the entire re-development of Glasgow Royal Infirmary'. The small Working Party, which had ceased to meet after the completion of the previous plan, was at once called back to action. With so much at stake these busy research clinicians had no alternative but to proceed with the laborious task of trying to ensure that the facilities of every unit and University department in the 'new' hospital would at least be on a par with other teaching hospitals. Immediately this more ambitious scheme ran into difficulties when the Glasgow Corporation Town Planning Committee made it known that there was little prospect of making ground available by rehousing and demolishing the homes of 200 families in Alexandra Parade. This news gave the Regional Board and the Department of Health the opportunity to refuse to participate in further discussions until the matter was resolved. At the end of their tether, the infirmary invited the Town Planning Committee to understand 'that Glasgow without the Royal Infirmary was unthinkable'. Wisely, the Board of Management left it to the Regional Board to register a formal protest on Christmas Eve. In this impasse the Working Party felt unable to discuss anything more than generalities, rather than devoting more time to preparing a long-term plan. The despondency of the staff was not helped by the receipt of a massive questionnaire from a committee appointed by the new Scottish Health Service Council to inquire into 'the administrative practice of hospital boards' and chaired by William Farquharson-Lang, chairman of the North Eastern Regional Hospital Board.

As worrying for the staff was another overspend in the budget, leading to more tightening of budgets and investigation of the cause of the losses. The only area in which there was any progress in the opening months of 1963 was in the detailed planning of the accident service, but again this was largely concerned with procedures and not with the practicalities of providing the required accommodation. The Staff Association quickly made it clear that they considered it fruitless to create a management structure for the service, let alone inaugurate it, without financial guarantees from the Regional Board for extra staff and premises. As a way

215

forward the Board of Management suggested an interim compromise service, co-ordinating the different specialities involved through the creation of a small forty-bed unit until additional funds were forthcoming. Even this plan failed to win support, due largely to an intense argument with the orthopaedic department about the treatment of fractures.

It was not until late May that the Corporation finally relented and indicated that designated land to the east of the infirmary could be made available. Another month passed before a Joint Planning Committee with the Regional Board was set up. Not surprisingly, the agenda was changed once again, with the additional proposal that the Glasgow Dental Hospital in Garnethill could be relocated on the site. This suggestion required another round of negotiations with staff and also with the Corporation, as it was intended to build the new Dental Hospital on ground that had not been designated in the recent concord. In the meantime, Basil Spence & Partners were preparing a series of design proposals for outline planning approval by the Corporation. On 21 November 1963 a Provisional Regional Building Programme for 1964 to 1971 was announced by the Regional Board. To the dismay of the Royal, no allocations were to be made in 1964–5 and in the following two years the only mention of the infirmary was the conversion of the radiotherapy department for casualty use at a modest £20,000. However, in the expectation that redevelopment would be funded directly by the Scottish Office, the Joint Planning Committee was hard at work putting specifications together for what was now, in fact, a new hospital of between 800 and 1,000 beds; a long way from the original plan to redevelop the Island site to meet urgent accommodation problems. Sensible as such a bold initiative might be, no progress on any minor improvements could now be made until the whole 'Major Development Scheme' had been worked up. There was concrete news at the end of the year with the announcement that the management of Lightburn Hospital would finally be transferred to the Royal in the spring of 1964, with approval to build two sixty-bed geriatric units. In addition, the Royal was to have access to geriatric beds at Robroyston and Foresthall.

By midsummer the outline of the new Royal was beginning to take shape. A model was presented to the Board of Management and staff, with an explanation from the Regional Board that the recently re-christened Scottish Home and Health Department could only identify funds to allow development to take place in three distinct phases. It was hoped that the first two phases would take place almost immediately one after another, with Phase 3 some way off. Remarkably, all the local parties, including the University of Glasgow and the Regional Board, supported the scheme and it only waited sanction from the Scottish Office. Once again the staff were to be disappointed, the Under-Secretary of State in the Conservative Government was only able to guarantee funds in 1968–71 for Phase 1—the reconstruction of the Out-Patient Department and temporary accommodation for the Accident and Emergency Service. This fell far short of the Royal's pressing needs if it was to maintain its status as a national centre of teaching and research. There seemed little prospect of Phase 2 being completed before 1977–8—almost thirty years after the development had first been mooted.

Tongue in cheek, Dr Donald Campbell of the Anaesthetics Department penned a poem 'On Planning 1995 to 2965' - with apologies to almost all poets:

It's no go Re-building, it's no go for the Sick.
All they want are some Clover-leaves.
Four-leafed should do the trick.

It's no go for Surgery, it's no go for Medicine.
All they want is a new Ring Road.
And a lay-by to put the beds in.

It's no go the G.R.I., it's no go for Lister,
All they want is to do Phase I
And to let the Phase II fester.

It's no go the new Gatehouse, it's no go new Scenery.
All they want is a Necropolis
Until the next Centenary.

In October 1964 the election of a Labour Government dispelled some of this disillusion, arousing fresh hopes of an accelerated programme of capital expenditure. There was now another compelling reason for swift action as the Government was committed to a massive expansion of higher education which held out the prospect of additional full-time professorial appointments at the infirmary if suitable accommodation could be provided. The Labour Government at once breathed life into the

Hospital Plan for Scotland, initiated by the Conservatives, which was attempting to provide a structure and timetable for development. Each Regional Board was asked to review their hospital provision on the basis of four acute beds rather than the previous 3.6 per 1,000 of the population. The Western Regional Hospital Board included the redevelopment of the Royal in their plans and successfully persuaded the Department of Health for Scotland to waive the 800-bed ceiling. The new Royal was to have 1,050 beds on the grounds that obstetric and paediatric patients were to be treated in future.

DRAWING BOARDS

The medical and nursing staff were more determined than ever to turn this commitment to the Royal's future into bricks and mortar at a time when medical procedures were advancing rapidly. In March 1965 Professor McGirr led a campaign for the extension of the novel Intensive Care Unit, opened two years before, to meet the needs of the whole hospital—a model adopted by major teaching hospitals in England. The idea was that the enlarged Unit would provide eight beds for intensive care and eight for seriously injured accident patients. Like the Accident and Emergency service, this innovation demanded co-operation between different specialities—particularly physicians, anaesthetists and cardiologists. In the short run, the proposal was held up by the practical difficulties of decanting Surgery, including cardiac services, the Out-patient Department and Urology, to allow work on Phase 1 to begin. It was essential that none of these services should be disrupted or patients might be lost to other hospitals. Professor Mackey was reluctant to accept cardio-surgery beds at Mearnskirk Hospital where most of the Regional Board's facilities were located, for fear it might become a permanent arrangement which would be regrettable at the very moment that a new privately endowed chair in medical cardiology had been established to mark the imminent retiral of Dr Joe Wright. With the prospect of major upheavals in the daily work of the whole infirmary and the consequent potential for friction and disagreement when building work began in earnest, a series of meetings was held in the winter of 1964–5 in an effort to improve communications with staff, seek their advice and win their co-operation. One outcome was the establishment of an operating theatres sub-committee.

218

It was not until December that Judith Hart, the Labour Government's Under-Secretary in the Scottish Home and Health Department, formally announced a timetable for redevelopment. Phase 1 was now not to commence until early in 1967 and only a possibility was held out that Phase 2 would begin in 1973–4 and could be expected to be completed 'by about 1980'. The only good news for the infirmary was confirmation that the Labour Government had rejected the idea of rebuilding the Royal on a completely new site somewhere else in the city as had been mooted in the first draft of the Hospital Plan for Scotland. The Joint Planning Committee, well aware that there was no prospect of Phase 3 being launched for at least thirty years, urgently reviewed the redevelopment plans. They made it clear that the Minister's announcement appeared to overlook the need for a new Accident and Emergency Department and the growing obsolescence of the infirmary's operating theatres. Moreover, there had been no announcement from the UGC about new building for University departments at the Royal. There was no alternative but to return to the drawing board and work up new plans that would incorporate the buildings erected in 1907–14 as part of an integrated and reshaped hospital. It seemed that after twenty years of negotiations the Royal was back almost to where it had started on the assumption that the existing infirmary had a fifty-year life expectancy! It took another three months for the architects to develop this alternative scheme. It was discussed with the Regional Board, the Scottish Home and Health Department and the University in April 1966. The Department's representatives were completely unhelpful, endlessly harping back to questions of cost. Exasperated, the delegations from the Royal's Board of Management, the staff and the University stormed out in 'high dudgeon', demanding a meeting with the Minister. This show of solidarity had the desired effect and within a month the Department, with a few minor alterations, had accepted the new plan. This encounter made a strong impression on Dr Alexander Bowman, the Regional Board's Senior Administrative Medical Officer, who condemned in print the 'reluctant, die-hard outlook' of the former voluntary hospitals.

CHANGING STRUCTURES

While the staff at the Royal were coming to terms with the implications of Judith Hart's announcement, the Board of Management was asked to respond to the Farquharson-Lang Report on the Administrative Practice of Hospital Boards in Scotland. The report called for greater delegation of authority and the reappraisal of the functions of the Boards and their committees. It recommended the abolition of house committees and all ad hoc committees and the retention of only three functional committees to be responsible for the supervision of medical and allied services and patient care, the financial control of expenditure, and the supervision of buildings, services and equipment. Although the Royal's Board of Management undertook to change procedures in an attempt to delegate authority, there was no enthusiasm for altering the committee structure, particularly as the recently published Salmon Report on Nurse Staffing would inevitably lead to a reorganisation of nursing services and training.

The Royal's Board of Management elected to be a pilot site for the staffing structure proposed by Salmon. This it was ideally placed to do as the majority of matrons in the Royal Board's hospitals were about to retire and the transition to the new grades of Chief Nursing Officer, Principal Nursing Officers, and Senior Nursing Officers, would be relatively painless. Yet again, the Royal was destined to be frustrated as the Minister could not grant approval until the Report itself had been accepted by the Government, which it was thought would not be much before the close of the year. However, the Royal was encouraged to persevere with its plans, particularly the preparation of a course for senior nurses eligible for top management appointments early in 1967. At the same time a report of the committee chaired by Sir John Brotherston, on the Organisation of Medical Work and Health Service in Scotland, was published. This called for the creation of Divisions covering the main disciplinary areas, medicine, surgery and so on, and the abolition of units. After the experience of bitter demarcation disputes over areas of competence of new services, like Accident and Emergency, the Royal's Board of Management was quick to see the advantage of adopting these recommendations. Six divisions were established—Medical, Surgical, Anaesthetic, Accident, Orthopaedic and Medical Laboratory—each with its own chairman and committee reporting to the Medical Staff Advisory Committee.

A FULL DEVELOPMENT PLAN!

In the meantime, the revised plans for Phase 1 had been completed and were ready to be made public directly formal approval by the Scottish Home and Health Department was notified. The Royal prepared the ground well, inviting five of Glasgow's Members of Parliament to view the infirmary and inspect the plans in September 1966. By the end of the year the UGC had given its approval in principle for the construction of a University Block in Phase 1 as originally conceived in the development of the Island site. Meanwhile, two new University professors, Professor Gemmell Morgan in Biochemistry and Professor Thomas Lawrie in Medical Cardiology, were pushing hard for better staffing and accommodation. Professor Lawrie, immediately after he arrived, complained that he had only one lecturer to help him, Dr A Ross Lorimer, and no chief technician in the Electro-Cardiogram Department. Professor Gemmell Morgan requested a budget of £11,000 for urgently needed equipment, pointing out that no new equipment had been purchased for over a year and no increase in staff to help cope with a 70 per cent increase in the workload in the last two years. These requests were received sympathetically by the Royal's Board of Management which could do little more than lay them before the Regional Board which, in turn, could find no justification for providing any help.

On 10 January 1967 the Secretary of State for Scotland gave his final approval for Phase 1 to the delight of the Board. Work would begin in 1970–71. Detailed planning work began at once to prepare an operational policy for the architects. At the same time the infirmary was given authority to implement the Salmon Report proposals. It was also decided to disband the Medical Committee and replace it with a Patient Care and Staffing Committee following the Farquharson-Lang recommendations. No sooner had these changes taken place than the General Nursing Council came to inspect the hospital and scrutinise the training provided. Although the courses were approved, the delegation added its voice to the clamour for better accommodation by condemning the working conditions and accommodation of the nursing staff. Fuel was added to the controversy in a letter to the medical magazine, Lancet, written by Professor J. Norman Davidson of the Department of Biochemistry at the University of Glasgow and a long-time member of the Royal's Board of

Management. In it he demonstrated that the cost of teaching medical students in Scotland was markedly lower than in English provincial hospitals and much lower than in the major London hospitals. The inference of his letter was that English teaching hospitals were far better resourced than their counterparts in Scotland. The chairman of the Board of Management, now a local businessman, William McKinlay, tried to counter Professor Davidson's argument by quoting figures that purported to show that Scotland was far better provided than England and had higher hospital running costs. To his embarrassment, these subsequently proved to be wholly inaccurate. Such interventions, however well meant, could do little to expedite the tedious business of fleshing out the details of Phase 1. At every stage, approval had to be won from the Regional Board and on some occasions from the Scottish Home and Health Department itself. Anything that affected the profile or layout of the building had also to be approved by the Corporation Planning Department.

Given that the existing ward blocks would remain in service, at least until the end of the century, the staff turned their attention to what needed to be done to modernise them. The most serious defects were inadequate sanitary arrangements, poor ventilation and the cramped accommodation for the nursing staff. There were other more general problems, including outdated operating theatres, a poorly resourced haematology and blood transfusion service, and little space for offices. These were badly needed for the Anaesthetic Department with a newly created University Chair, the Social Work Department, and Nursing Administration—now centralised for the Royal's Board of Management following the implementation of the Salmon recommendations. As with the redevelopment, a planning team was set up to prepare a phased programme of modernisation. Inevitably, the two development programmes fused, as the one was contingent on the other. This resulted in further delays as the Royal's Board of Management were anxious that any new development on the Royal site would not prejudice the infirmary's future as a major teaching and research centre. The Board of Management and the staff were particularly anxious to hear more from the Regional Board about the possible replacement of the Eastern District by a new general hospital at Rutherglen. To this end a full 'Development Plan' was commissioned to 'cover the period from the present until the completion of the final phase of the new hospital'. By January 1968 the Corporation had given formal approval for the rehousing of 200 families from the site of Phase 1, which would enable building to commence in March 1972, five years later than Judith Hart had predicted. The projected cost of Phase 1 was now put at some £7 million, greatly in excess of previous estimates. This made a start on construction before 1972 impossible because of the Scottish Home and Health Department's commitment to the rebuilding of the Glasgow Royal Hospital for Sick Children and Ninewells Hospital at Dundee. This was little comfort to the hard-pressed staff at the Royal, desperate for better facilities.

At the end of their tethers, Professor Mackey and Professor A C Forrester, the newly appointed Professor of Anaesthetics, pleaded for extra space to be made available for research and the treatment of patients in the existing building when major advances in surgical techniques were taking place all the time. There was a particular need for the Royal to develop a kidney transplant unit, bringing together a number of different specialities, and to improve intensive care for patients who had suffered acute heart attacks and strokes. In the circumstances the Board had no alternative but to agree to providing further makeshift accommodation. The final plans of the revised Phase 1 were made public in April and were welcomed, apart from some adverse comments about the size of the reception, recovery and intensive therapy areas in the operating theatre suite. However the staff at the Royal still wished to be reassured by the Regional Board that the existing ward block and operating theatres would be improved before work began. Despite regular reminders, nothing was heard from the Regional Board until September, when all too familiarly, the Royal staff was told to prepare a detailed five-year plan for consideration. Not surprisingly, the list of priorities in November were more or less identical with those outlined earlier in the year, but with the addition of other less essential requests. Almost none of these proposals were accepted in the coming three years' expenditure plan. Meanwhile, in a period of rising inflation, the cost of Phase 1 had climbed to over £8.5 million.

REORGANISING THE SERVICE—CUTS AGAIN

At this juncture the Home and Health Department published a review of the Health Service Structure in Scotland, which recommended radical reorganisation: the abolition of the Regional Board and Boards of

Management and their replacement by single-tier Area Health Boards. This would bring to an end the system of management of the Royal, with representatives of local authorities, the University of Glasgow and the community, that had commenced in the 1790s and been continued on nationalisation in 1948. It was not clear if these changes would disturb the timetable for redevelopment. In February 1969 the Regional Hospital Board confirmed these fears by announcing a postponement in start dates due to cuts in Government expenditure and overspend on existing projects and day-to-day running costs. The new hospitals, which were proving to be far more expensive than anticipated, were the Gartnavel General Hospital and the replacement for the Royal Hospital for Sick Children. The Royal had consistently over-run its annual budget, but little consideration had been given in arriving at standard costs for the type of cases treated or the appalling social conditions from which many of the patients came. The only definite news was that in Glasgow, the Western Infirmary—Phase 1—would be delayed for nine months and a decision about the Royal would have to wait until the budget for 1971–2 was finalised. Everyone at the infirmary had by now had enough and when a call was received from the Regional Board for further financial discipline, the Board of Management rebelled—'This Board has had insufficient allocations for normal maintenance for twenty years. Obviously, therefore, the Regional Board must be financially over-extended and the time has come for joint consultation to reduce their commitment to end this recurring problem of over-expenditure caused in the past two years by operational needs.' The Royal's Board of Management saw one way out of their difficulties as raising the profile of the Royal in the community by celebrating the 175th anniversary of the reception of the first patients on 8 December 1794, with a service in the cathedral and public lecture by Sir John Brotherston, Chief Medical Officer in the SHHD, appropriately on the 'Teaching Hospitals' place in the Community'.

Thoroughly disgruntled, the staff were in no mood to respond sympathetically to a request to co-operate in cutting expenditure, telling the Regional Board it was their responsibility to make strategic decisions about the withdrawal of patient services. The problems in the hospital were now acute. A gift from Tenovus-Scotland, the medical charity, to establish a renal transplant unit, had foundered because of the lack of suitable accommodation and the use of Ward 47 for cardiac surgery had been deemed to be unsafe because of fire hazards. The renal transplant unit found a home at the Western Infirmary, leaving the Royal to concentrate on its existing strength of kidney diseases. However, even this proposal ran into serious accommodation problems, leading Tenovus-Scotland to seek to revoke the offer of funds. It also seemed likely that cardiac surgery would, after all, be absorbed into the unit at Mearnskirk or alternatively transferred to Stobhill. The University intervened to veto this decision, persuading the Board to identify alternative accommodation within the infirmary. When this could not be found, the unit was temporarily relocated at Stobhill. There were similar difficulties in the biochemistry department, where the number of analyses had climbed from 12,600 in 1953 to 407,000 in 1968, and were estimated to rise to 1.25 million in 1973. Yet the department was hopelessly under-staffed and badly housed. Equally hard-pressed were the departments of surgery and anaesthesia, where additional accommodation was desperately needed. Professor Forrester even went so far as to suggest that 'from the funds available to his department one or two caravans might be purchased'. The operating theatres were by now obsolete and could not be used in very cold or hot weather because of lack of adequate ventilation.

PHASE 1 AT LAST

A visit by the Regional Nurse Training Committee in June 1969 repeated the General Nursing Council's criticism of the poor offices and inadequate housing for the nurses at the infirmary. The new University of Strathclyde came to the rescue with the offer of hostels for student nurses and even suggested housing the biochemistry department. The catalogue of overcrowding and overwork was endless, resulting entirely from the indecision about new building since the inception of the National Health Service. In June the Regional Board tentatively held out the possibility of the partial refurbishing of the existing wards and operating theatres in the quinquennium 1972–7. The Medical Staff Advisory Committee was too experienced to accept such nebulous carrots and dismissed the offer out of hand, demanding an urgent meeting with the Regional Board. By this time the Regional Board was not enthusiastic about having any meetings with the Royal. The Board also told the Regional Board that any proposal to house the biochemistry department at a distance from the Royal was totally unacceptable and a new building had to be provided. The response from the Regional Board was complete silence. It was not until the end of 1969, after constant badgering by Professor Gemmell Morgan, that the Regional Board was prepared to consider a new building for the biochemistry department. Well aware of the tactic of asking for a detailed proposal, he had one ready directly the letter was received. To everyone's surprise, this was accepted and a site identified adjacent to the proposed Phase 1. With so little progress in securing better facilities, it is not surprising that the Royal lost some of its best staff. In 1970 Professor Tom Symington of Pathology left to take up the prestigious post of Director of the British Institute of Cancer Research in London and Professor Stuart Douglas, the Consultant Physician in Administrative Charge of Wards, accepted the appointment of Regius Professor of Medicine at Aberdeen.

The public-expenditure announcement in April 1970 included a definite start date for work on Phase 1 in 1973 at an estimated cost now of £10.4 million. As well, the Regional Board included most of the other urgent projects in its expenditure plans for the period up to 1975. This included the extensions to the anaesthetics and surgery departments, which were expected to commence in the spring of 1971. As well, an understanding had been reached for the location of the Renal Investigation Unit in accommodation acceptable to Tenovus-Scotland. The unit, under the direction of Professor Arthur Kennedy, was to form part of an integrated Renal Service in conjunction with the transplant service at the Western Infirmary. In more confident mood, Professor Mackey re-opened the question of the future of cardiac surgery at the Royal, which he firmly believed was a necessary counterpart to an expanded cardiology department that was already being constructed. One of his reasons for raising the matter was that there was a shortage of cardiac beds in the city because the contractor, who was completing the cardiac unit at Mearnskirk Hospital, had become bankrupt. Moreover, the University was anxious to create a Chair of Cardiac Surgery based at the Royal. The Royal's Board trod cautiously, not wanting to irritate the Regional Board any further at this critical juncture and, at the same time, reluctant to see that flagship speciality move to Stobhill Hospital. Fortuitously, the Regional Board had already decided against the move to Stobhill and was now quite contrarily keen to see the unit stay at the Royal. Delighted, the Board identified Wards 31 and 17 in the Centre Block as suitable. Financial constraints, however, prevented this course of action and the Board of Management was forced, reluctantly, to accept beds at Mearnskirk on the strict understanding that cardiac surgery would return to the Royal as soon as Phase 1 was completed. As it turned out, this was just a threat by the Regional Board, and after further posturing by the Royal to win resources, the move to Mearnskirk proved unnecessary. In the meantime the planning of the upgrading of the existing ward blocks and operating theatres was proceeding swiftly, including a more rational re-allocation of space to departments. Professor Gemmell Morgan

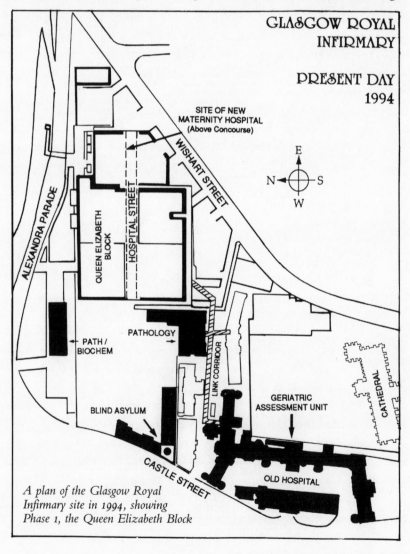

GLASGOW ROYAL
INFIRMARY

PRESENT DAY
1994

SITE OF NEW
MATERNITY HOSPITAL
(Above Concourse)

WISHART STREET

ALEXANDRA PARADE

QUEEN ELIZABETH BLOCK

HOSPITAL STREET

PATHOLOGY

PATH /
BIOCHEM

LINK CORRIDOR

BLIND ASYLUM

GERIATRIC
ASSESSMENT UNIT

CATHEDRAL

CASTLE STREET

OLD HOSPITAL

A plan of the Glasgow Royal Infirmary site in 1994, showing Phase 1, the Queen Elizabeth Block

had also agreed the schedule of accommodation for the Biochemistry Laboratory as a component of the overall Phase 1 development.

LOSING MORE ENDOWMENTS—NEW APPROACHES TO HOSPITAL MEDICINE

The generally good news about the building programme was tempered by the new Hospital Endowment (Scotland) Act 1971, passed by the Conservative Government of Edward Heath, which effectively confiscated the pre-1948 endowments. Under the terms of the new legislation, investments of £423,000 (with market value of £506,000) together with £20,000 of net current assets, were handed over to the Scottish Hospital Trust. The legislation overrode the wishes of benefactors, except for very specific clauses, like the maintenance of graveyards or the awards of prizes and medals. Under the new scheme the infirmary was entitled to receive a fixed quota of £3 per bed a year plus an additional payment which, the Board claimed, would reduce the income from the pre-1948 endowment by £10,000 to about £14,000 a year. As a result, the Board was forced to abandon the infirmary's research scholarship programme and its subventions to University fellowships and curtail the purchase of equipment for research purposes, severely damaging the Royal's research capability. As in 1954, endowments received since 1948, which now totalled over £480,000, were exempt from the scheme. In the face of a Parliamentary decision there was nothing the Royal staff could do but register a muted dissent.

Apart from the suggested administrative restructuring of the health service in Scotland there were other changes under discussion that might threaten the whole concept of reconstructing a traditional hospital. The Royal's Board of Management had already set its face against day hospital facilities, probably because of the long experience of catering for the needs of patients who came from socially deprived backgrounds where homes afforded little possibility of successful convalescence. There were some consultants who were prepared to experiment following a report by the King Edward's Hospital Fund which showed that of 196 geriatric units in the United Kingdom, 90 had a day hospital and a further twenty-nine were planned for the immediate future. Dr B Isaacs of the department of geriatrics was keen to explore the potential of such facilities, beginning at Lightburn. The Home and Health Department was also pressing for a much more 'active rehabilitative approach' to encourage patients back into the community. There were other proposals for a new, more interventionist approach to what amounted to social engineering through the restriction of family size by means of birth control. Professor Malcolm Macnaughton, who had succeeded Professor Fyfe Anderson in the Chair of Obstetrics and Gynaecology, was an enthusiastic advocate of the infirmary becoming directly involved through the provision of family planning clinics, with the support of a referral service on the spot for any patients with special problems. He had become convinced that family size was one of the underlying causes of much of the deprivation and many of the obstetric complaints in the Royal's immediate catchment area. Others doubted the wisdom of the hospital service assuming responsibility for what was perceived as a local authority or even voluntary sector matter. Nevertheless, the outcome of widespread use of contraception would be fewer children and, therefore, a declining, if ageing, population with which the existing hospital service was not well equipped to cope. Professor Macnaughton was not to be gainsaid and eventually won approval for a clinic in association with the Family Planning Association.

THE LAST DAYS OF THE BOARD

As the start date for work on Phase 1 drew nearer the very detailed planning for the maintenance of service with the minimum of disruption became more intense. This ranged from consideration of how the pile driving on the new site was likely to affect both staff and patients to investigation of the plumbing in the existing wards. Committees were inundated with reports and suggestions, often becoming involved in complex and delicate adjudication between competing specialists. At no time was there any real indication of what type of service or areas of specialisation the Regional Board or the Home and Health Department wanted for the Royal. It was left to the Board of Management in what was, after all, a planning vacuum because of the imminent reorganisation of the health service to make its own policy as it had done in the days of the old voluntary hospitals. Even though it was about to be swept away, the members of the Board, led by William MacKinlay, remained deeply committed to the Royal and its future as a major teaching hospital. In the autumn of 1971 the Scottish Home and Health Department announced a £1 million supplementary award for upgrading the existing ward blocks.

By the spring of 1972 the legislation to reorganise the health service in Scotland was completing its progress through Parliament. The Scottish Home and Health Department was preparing for the fundamental changes that would result by issuing a spate of circulars reminiscent of the period around the formation of the NHS. As then, the Board was in financial trouble with an overspend for the fiscal year 1971–2 of about £250,000. The Scottish Home and Health Department did not have things entirely its own way, facing a barrage of criticism over the transfer of building and construction work to the Common Services Agency. On the whole, there was nothing much the Royal's Board of Management or staff could do but acquiesce to the changes, not least as their experience of dealing with the existing NHS structure had not been particularly happy. Despite the certain knowledge that the existing administrative structure would be swept away in two years, the Royal's Board of Management had to preserve the appearance of business as usual, if nothing else but to guarantee the commencement of Phase 1. A joint co-ordination committee with the Regional Board and the Home and Health Department was formed 'to consider the organisation, method of equipping and bringing into use of Phase 1'. Nevertheless there was an all-pervading sense of change and hiatus. When Professor J Norman Davidson, who had been a member of the Board since its inception, representing the Regional Board, died suddenly, he was not replaced. Professor Arthur Mackey, who had struggled tirelessly for better surgical facilities, retired within sight of the promised land but destined never to enjoy the fruits of his labours. To the relief of everyone at the Royal the redevelopment of the existing ward blocks was included in the construction plans for the Regional Board's last year of operation. On 2 February 1973 Phase 1 went out to tender. Piling work started in the autumn and building work at the end of March 1974, the very month the Royal's Board of Management demitted office.

The 1973 annual report appeared in 1975 with a valedictory review of the Royal Infirmary Board's stewardship since the formation of the National Health Service twenty-five years earlier. The most remarkable achievement of the Royal during these years was the high standard of service and research it had been able to deliver in the face of what must have appeared, at times, to be insuperable odds. With no prospect of funds to build a new ward block, the staff in all departments made every effort to reduce the length of the stay to cope with what seemed an inexorable rise in the number of patients.

> For example, in 1948 in Glasgow Royal Infirmary there were a total number of 18,467 patients under treatment. The average residence was 16.1 days. In 1972 the number of patients under treatment was 30,230 and the average length of stay of patients within the infirmary was 7.6 days, less than half of the length of stay in 1948. It has meant an increase in the number of patients of 63 per cent, the equivalent of a hospital, based on 1948 figures of between 500 and 600 beds.

Every year there was a steady flow of research grants to and publications from every department. New medical and surgical techniques were introduced, often in the most makeshift accommodation. It is testimony to the loyalty of the staff at all levels to the infirmary and their commitment to the patients that the frustrations of having to devote so much time to winning better buildings and facilities never turned to despair and only rarely to open rebellion against the Regional Board. There was no doubt that by 1974 an administrative reorganisation was overdue which would allow far more coherent strategic planning—something the Home and Health Department and the Regional Board had singularly failed to achieve. What was not clear was how major teaching and research hospitals, dependent as they were on a mix of funding from the Home and Health Department and the Universities Grants Committee, would fit into the new structure. It seemed inevitable that they would lose much of their long-cherished independence. Close relations with local communities, through the lay members of their boards of management who gave their services entirely voluntarily, also seemed to be threatened.

7 GOING THE EXTRA MILE, 1974–92

From Simshill in Cathcart, where Laidlaw lived, to the Royal Infirmary in Cathedral Street was a short trip but a big distance. Fortunately, the architecture changed in stages, like decompression chambers, so that you didn't get the bends.
One half of the first gate was open yet and he drove in. A lot of cars were in the parking area but there was plenty of room. Locking the car, he was struck again by the size of the place, three huge linked units, each with its own imposing dome. It seemed to him a castle of black stone. It made illness appear not a leveller but an accolade that admitted you to a Gothic aristocracy.

William McIlvaney, *The Papers of Tony Veitch*, 1977

GOING EAST

In keeping with the spirit of efficient management redolent of the reorganisation of the National Health Service, the rather grandly named Eastern District Executive Group of the Greater Glasgow Health Board (GGHB) met for the first time on 20 March 1974. The members were the District Nursing Officer, Miss M I W Thomson, the District Medical Officer, Dr J Killoch Anderson, the District Administrator, Ian Dorward and Mr W Storm, the District Finance Officer. Despite the impression that was given that reorganisation would lead to a more modern and professional approach, the minutes of the first meeting suggest that the District got off on the wrong foot. The members took themselves and their new responsibilities very seriously, referring to themselves, self-importantly, by their titles. Unlike the Board of Management of the Royal Infirmary and associated hospitals, the Eastern District was a larger grouping of all the hospitals in the east of Glasgow—the Royal Infirmary, the Eastern District and Lightburn Hospitals, Canniesburn, the Royal Maternity Hospital in Rottenrow, the Glasgow Dental Hospital and School, and Gartloch Hospital for mental patients. To distance themselves from the interests of any one hospital, the Group chose offices at 13 Bath Street in the city centre well away from any of the facilities for which the District was responsible. As in 1948, little detailed preparation had been made for what was in effect a much greater upheaval than the 'Appointed Day' a quarter of a century earlier. For the time being, the separate 'institutional committees' were left undisturbed, reporting to the District Executive Group instead of their respective boards of management. For administrative staff there followed early retirements of those approaching the end of their careers and then a complicated game of musical chairs for others as they were assigned posts in the five districts that made up the GGHB—the Northern, Eastern, South Eastern, South Western and Western districts. At the same time, with the transfer of public health responsibilities from the local authorities to the new health boards, staff from the old Medical Officer of Health Department had to be found a home in what were already overcrowded offices.

The first full meeting of the District Executive Group took place on 8 April when the Executives were joined by Professor Arthur Kennedy and Dr J McGlone as chairman and vice-chairman of the District Medical Committee and a representative of the University was invited to attend. From the outset, the Executive Group was determined to improve the use of resources, particularly by responding rapidly to issues raised in individual hospitals. To this end, an operational research project based in Professor McGirr's unit was launched to explore the factors on which clinical judgements in the wards were based. The Royal was quick to seek a solution for the overloaded Accident and Emergency Service. The Casualty Department serving an area with one of the highest rates of multiple deprivation in Europe was attending to 81,000 new patients a year—over 200 a day with a staff of one consultant and six senior house officers. As a matter of urgency the Royal requested another consultant, a senior registrar, two registrars and two additional senior house officers who were taking part in the general practitioner vocational training scheme. It was recognised that high calibre candidates would only be attracted to these posts if the casualty service was combined with other emergency services, like respiratory intensive care and burns, which offered scope for innovation and research. Part and parcel of this proposal was a response to a Government report calling for much greater contact between general practitioners and their local hospitals, particularly opportunities for continuing vocational training. The swelling tide of new casualty patients was also putting pressure on the accident and orthopaedic wards which were full to overflowing. In the time-honoured tradition, the Royal sought to offload the less demanding orthopaedic patients onto another hospital—this time Stobhill. No relief was forthcoming as Stobhill's second orthopaedic ward was closed as the building was in danger of collapse. Keeping to its word, the District Executive Group energetically brought these problems to the attention of the GGHB, pressing for an early solution.

KEEPING PACE WITH CHANGE

Despite these problems, and the disruption caused by the start of work on Phase 1, the Royal's programme of research was maintained. Dr J F Winchester and Professor Kennedy were engaged in studying the effects of haemoperfusion on dialysis patients and those suffering from drug overdoses. Professor T D V Lawrie and Dr Ross Lorimer were examining the effects of a new centrally active anti-hypertensive agent with patients taking part being described by one of the study's assessors as the 'equivalent of guinea pigs'. A team led by Dr I G Stothers was looking at the incidence of deep-vein thrombosis and methods of prevention in patients undergoing minor foot surgery. Another group under Dr F Moran was measuring the effect of doxipram on cardiac output and pulmonary vascular resistance in order to assess its safety for use in patients with respiratory failure. Dr G H Beastall of the Steroid Biochemistry Department won a grant from the Medical Research Council to investigate the uptake of zinc and biosynthesis of citric acid in the prostate gland. All such projects had now to be scrutinised by assessors, usually other clinicians in the District, and approved by a District Ethical Committee to ensure there was negligible risk to patients and potential benefit to them and others.

The medical staff may have been willing to press on with research, accepting the long hours of work and overstretched services as normal in any hospital; the nurses and technicians were not. Within weeks of taking office the District was locked in dispute with them over working and living conditions which once again had been heavily criticised during a visit by members of the General Nursing Council. Nurses worked to rule, refusing to carry out non-nursing duties, and radiographers took one-day strike action in an effort to improve working conditions and secure a pay settlement above that proposed by the Conservative Government of Edward Heath, defeated at the polls in February over the issue of miners' pay. The incoming Labour Government quickly settled with the miners and the other public sector workers affected by the pay freeze, including an interim award to nurses and auxiliaries in the hospital service. The settlement ended the industrial action but left unanswered the questions of terms and conditions of service and pay differentials between grades. The Secretary of State for Social Security appointed Lord Halsbury to conduct an independent inquiry which would be binding on the Government. His report, published in October, abolished the different scales for midwives and nurses, streamlined the pay and grading structure, and recommended substantial pay increases and more generous holiday entitlement. Following a separate inquiry chaired by Asa Briggs, Vice Chancellor of the University of Sussex, into nursing education, sister tutors were no longer to double as ward sisters, but be entirely separate. These welcome changes put further pressure on the already overstretched wards in the Royal which lacked sufficient auxiliary staff.

IN SICKNESS AND IN POVERTY

One of the challenges for the Royal was the number of patients who used the casualty department as a general practitioner surgery or, in the deprived east end with an increasing problem of drug and alcohol abuse, as a place to escape the cold. Before reorganisation the Royal's Board of Management had been in discussion with the Scottish Home and Health Department about the possibility of establishing a health centre in Townhead. Under the previous arrangements the management of Health Centres was an SHHD responsibility and no local agreements were necessary to allow work to begin on the Townhead site in 1974. On learning this, the Eastern District urged that discussions should take place with the general practitioners and dentists who had indicated a willingness to use the Centre when it was scheduled for completion in 1979. As part of the reorganisation of health services the planning of health centres was at the time being transferred from SHHD to the Greater Glasgow Health Board. Both were committed to health centres as a means of taking pressure off expensive hospital facilities. The GGHB informed the Eastern District that work on a health centre at Bridgeton would begin in eighteen months. Encouraged by the news that money would not be an obstacle, the Eastern District pressed for centres in the most deprived areas of the east end, where housing conditions were appalling, at Baillieston, Shettleston, Parkhead, Blackhill, Garthamlock, Rogerfield and Easterhouse. The GGHB was very receptive to these proposals and hurried ahead in holding discussions with all the interested parties.

Such plans could offer no immediate respite to the crowded casualty department at the Royal. One practical step was to establish procedures with the Social Work Department of the newly formed Strathclyde Region for tackling the problem of the homeless using the infirmary as a place of shelter. It was recognised that such people, who usually required no hospital treatment, presented junior doctors with special problems. Early in 1975 the Region appointed Miss M M Leitch, previously the Royal Group of Hospitals' Medical Social Worker, as Assistant Director of Social Work with particular responsibility for social work in the health service. There was a long delay in her taking up the appointment; but when she did she rapidly addressed the particular social problems affecting the Royal. In collaboration with A M Murray of the Royal's Accident and Emergency Department, a pro forma was introduced for referring 'homeless and vagrant' persons to an emergency social work team for accommodation and practical assistance. She also helped the Royal's own social workers establish a follow-up scheme for discharged patients receiving community care with the support of volunteers and funds from the Dorcas Society. The first patients to be supported in this way were those discharged by the Centre for Rheumatic Diseases because the majority only ever attended as out-patients.

The Royal's Tradition

As the new structure rapidly evolved, the Royal had strenuously to defend its traditions and position as the city's oldest teaching hospital. Although the battle was lost to continue publishing an independent annual report, the infirmary succeeded in winning permission to grant distinguished retired consultants the titles of honorary physician or honorary surgeon to the Royal Infirmary. More difficult was to challenge the Scottish Home and Health Department's decision that there was no longer any need to retain the posts of consultants in administrative charge of wards. The Accident and Orthopaedic and the Anaesthetic divisions at the Royal did not believe this was a battle worth fighting, but the Surgical and Medical divisions disagreed, arguing that its size and complexity of the procedures carried out required that this grade be continued. This opinion was shared by the Medical Faculty of the University of Glasgow, which was 'firmly of the view that the present practice of its professorial heads of departments being in charge should continue; this applied both to clinical and para-clinical professors'— largely to protect the interests of sub-specialities within a division, such as peripheral vascular surgery in the surgical division. In the face of these representations, the Eastern District accepted the need to continue to make such appointments, which would have to be done in the very near future with the retirement of John Hutchison, consultant in administrative charge of the cardio-thoracic surgical unit, A M Murray, consultant in administrative charge of the accident and emergency unit, and William Reid, consultant in administrative charge of peripheral vascular surgery. Without further reference to the SHHD, the GGHB filled these posts either in the Royal or at another hospital.

The foundation stone of Phase 1 of the new Royal was laid in May 1974 and the new building began to take shape under the supervision of the Common Services Agency. With the GGHB having no direct involvement in building projects, the District Medical Committee formed a separate Commissioning/Co-ordinating Team to discuss the details of the commissioning of Phase 1 with CSA. The team was concerned that in Phase 1 and the biochemistry building, the air-conditioning plant should not be left lying about before installation as had occurred in other new hospitals in Glasgow with the attendant risk of bacterial infection when finally commissioned. At the same time the Royal, supported by the District, was pressing for the upgrading of the existing building which it was expected would remain in use well beyond the bicentenary in 1994. There was annoyance that the £1.4 million budget allocated by SHHD for this purpose in the closing months of the Western Regional Hospital Board had been diverted to fire prevention and precaution and to the installation of a new telephone system. Such building work as was in hand fell far short of what was required to bring the infirmary up to an acceptable standard for a modern teaching hospital; most urgently, the drains needed to be renewed. It was reckoned, conservatively, that an additional budget of £1.6 million was required.

A petition to SHHD could not have come at a worse time. The Labour Government was plunged in a serious financial crisis due to the unparalleled inflation since the election. As a result the Eastern District was overspent by almost £400,000 at the end of the financial year. The Government imposed strict spending limits for the coming year which were recognised to be less than adequate, and called on the public service to tighten its grip on management. The Royal was affected at once. Professor Philip Caves, who had succeeded John Hutchison as consultant in administrative charge of the cardio-thoracic surgical unit, was told that the District could not afford equipment costing only £10,500 to enable him to increase the number of open-heart operations from six to twelve a month. This was followed early in 1976 by efforts to rationalise services between hospitals in an attempt to prune expenditure. Undaunted by the cuts, Professor Caves told GGHB he needed a further £84,000 a year and a non-recurring budget of £22,500 for equipment to be able to conduct each week seven cardiac by-pass operations (for which there was much demand). GGHB replied by calling for the views of the districts on how they envisaged their services developing—should they in the long run offer an integrated service covering all aspects of clinical treatment and investigation? The Royal had no doubt that this was impractical and proposed that some hospital services would be common to all hospitals, but others, like cardio-thoracic surgery or renal transplantation, would be concentrated in a few hospitals and occasionally in just one hospital. Consultations were inconclusive, Professor Caves' requests for funds were turned down and he was told to cut his list. Nevertheless, SHHD found £50,000 to make a start on improving the sanitary arrangements in two wards of the main building.

An infirmary for the community

As work on Phase 1 progressed, the physical appearance of the whole of Glasgow was changing dramatically. Much of the old tenement property in the inner city was being swept away and enthusiastically replaced by concrete high-rise developments, reminiscent of the slum clearances in the 1920s and 1930s. Much the largest scheme in the vicinity of the Royal was in Calton, adjacent to Tennents Brewery—the Wellpark Housing Project. This new housing, conceived as New Jerusalems, quickly created its own social and health problems described by the

Glasgow song writer, Adam McNaughton, in his 'Jelly Piece Song':

> *I'm a skyscraper wean, I live on the nineteenth flair*
> *An I'm no gaun oot tae play any mair,*
> *For since we moved tae oor new hoose, I'm wastin' away*
> *'Cos I'm gettin wan less meal ev'ry day*
> *Oh ye canna fling a piece frae a 20 storey flat*
> *700 hungry weans'll testify tae that.*

This song soon became a rallying cry for those who were appalled at the wholesale destruction of the heartland of old Glasgow. Amongst these was Matt McGinn from Calton, also a poet and folksinger, who condemned the so-called developments as 'bloody great concrete jungles and deserts'. At about this time he immortalised the Royal in his song 'Big Willie's Blues':

> *I went up to the Royal Infirmary, to see Big Willie there,*
> *I stepped up to his bedside and sat down on his chair.*
>
> *He didn't look too cheerful, his face was turning blue,*
> *I asked him how his health was, but all that Willie said was 'Oooooh...'*
>
> *I spoke to him about racing, football and politics too,*
> *I asked his opinion of the weather, but all that Willie said was 'Oooooh...'*
>
> *From the table he snatched up a notebook, from my pocket he picked out a pen,*
> *He began to scribble something and he lay down peacefully then.*
>
> *The sister she came running, she said Big Willie was dead,*
> *I pointed to that paper, I said 'Those are the last words he said.'*
>
> *The sister read that message, and I found I'd made a boob,*
> *It said 'Ya stupid lookin' clown ye, you're sittin' on ma oxygen tube.'*

With its very humour, the poem captured the affection in which the Royal was held by the local communities threatened by redevelopment.

Cases like Big Willie's were high on the agenda of the infirmary which was pressing for a resolution of the request from Philip Caves for additional staff for cardiac surgery, particularly the appointment of another anaesthetist. The medical staff were also keen to restate the role of hospitals in preventive services in the community to keep people from becoming patients. Such a vision of the Royal's work flew in the face of an SHHD memorandum 'The Health Service in Scotland – the Way Ahead', which unhelpfully drew a distinction between hospitals and community services. The Eastern District Medical Committee, chaired by Professor Arthur Kennedy, was convinced of the error of separating 'health and welfare services'. The Royal was having difficulty in maintaining good relations with the local community because the financial cuts made it impossible to maintain out-patient clinics over the summer holiday period and the accident and emergency service was still hopelessly overcrowded and overworked The medical and nursing staff at the infirmary insisted that the Health Board should explain publicly that the cause of the difficulties was the Government's restrictions on spending.

THE GOVERNMENT WIELDS THE SURGEON'S KNIFE

When the Eastern District's budget was fixed in July 1976 for the coming year, an effort was made to ease the Royal's chronic shortage of running costs in providing health care for a catchment area with such persistent social problems. However, in a period of advancing inflation and continuing Government economies, this soon proved inadequate. Hard-pressed staff received no support from members of the Labour Government, who regularly wanted to know why constituents had to wait so long for consultations and treatment. Worse still, the Scottish Home and Health Department notified the Greater Glasgow Health Board that:

> funds for growth in the National Health Service were severely restricted to the extent that no additional finance was likely to be available for any development or expansion of the service in Glasgow in the foreseeable future: if a District Health Board could not find funds from its own resources by reorganising its services to divert money from less hard-pressed to more hard-pressed specialities, even the most necessary developments could not proceed. Glasgow was at present over provided with health service resource and would be forced to reduce expenditure considerably in line with falling population and the drawing off of patients by the provision of health services in neighbouring areas.

This was bitter news for the Royal Infirmary on the eve of the commissioning of Phase 1 of the new hospital and at the very moment when the upgraded medical ward blocks were ready for use. An immediate consequence was an across the board cut of 10 per cent in the supplies and services budget and the careful scrutiny of medical and nursing positions as they fell vacant. Room for financial manoeuvre was further circumscribed by the Government's decision to phase out private beds in the NHS. By the end of November 1976, with five months of the financial year still to go, the Eastern District had a projected overspend of £600,000. Despite the economic constraints staff at every level remained deeply committed to the future of the infirmary as a centre of excellent health care.

Against this gloomy background the Phase 1 Commissioning Team, led by Mr Tom Gibson, began its work. They were handicapped in making any detailed plans by the Health Board's refusal to allocate beds and functions until the revenue implications had been fully explored in the light of a progressively contracting budget. The District Medical Committee, however, pressed ahead with the preparation of its own plan of action. This took almost a year of negotiation and debate to complete. It was finally decided, subject to Health Board approval, that 78 per cent of the beds in Phase 1 would be allocated to surgery as near as practical to the new operating theatres. There were also to be a number of intensive therapy units in the new hospital, including acute surgical and medical admissions, and coronary and renal care. Although opthalmology beds were to be included, the District looked to the Health Board to conduct a wider review. The physicians were not enthusiastic about these proposals as they would disadvantage the University's Department of Medicine which would be seeking to fill the Muirhead Chair at about the time Phase 1 opened. The Dean of Medicine at the University supported the objection by stating that it had been understood from the inception of the NHS that clinical teaching wards should not be far removed from University departments, which they would be under the suggested disposition of beds. Professor Rab Goudie, the University's representative on the District Medical Committee, put the case forcibly for wards to be 'functionally related', by which he meant on the same floor of Phase 1 as the departments in the new university block. After an intense discussion the decision was ratified on the understanding that this was as an interim arrangement until Phases 2 and 3 were completed. In making recommendations the District Medical Committee and the Commissioning Team were careful not to make commitments that might have additional budgetary implications; for example by extending the procedures offered to cardiac patients. Above all, unambiguous guidance was needed from both the Health Board and the Scottish Home and Health Department.

LOSING PATIENCE

By the opening months of 1977 the continuing financial constraints were beginning to test everyone's patience; particularly irksome was the persistent belief by the Scottish Home and Health Department and the Department of Health in London that hospital costs could be compared across the whole United Kingdom. The focus of most of the discontent in the east end of Glasgow was the Centre for Rheumatic Diseases in Baird Street - directed by Professor Watson Buchanan - which had borne the brunt of criticism from MPs and Government ministers about long waiting lists. Under pressure from a decision to restrict patient services in holiday periods, Professor Buchanan went directly to the press and in so doing lost the goodwill of some of his equally hard-pressed medical colleagues. Part of the problem was the lack of direct support from other departments with overlapping interests and the Health Board decided, without consulting the District, to transfer the Centre into Phase 1 of the Royal as soon as possible. This upset the allocation of beds agreed by the District and the Commissioning Team. To help improve public understanding, an Open Day was arranged at the Centre of Rheumatic Diseases later in the year.

The other area of pressing concern to the infirmary was the Accident and Emergency Service, where a successor to Mr Murray had still not been found. The overcrowded, old-fashioned, short-staffed casualty department was well described by William McIlvaney's Inspector Laidlaw in *The Papers of Tony Veitch*:

> Across the courtyard was the single-storey Casualty Department like a gatehouse where they examined your credentials. He went in. It was after eleven.
>
> Starting opposite the treatment room is a row of cubicles. They presented Laidlaw, as he went, with a succession of tableaux that might have come from a contemporary mystery play. A girl whose eyes were still in shock was holding a bloodstained bedspread, waiting for someone or something. There was a young man with a left eye like a piece of bad fruit. He was protesting hysterically about injustice while a doctor attended him. A woman was crying while her arm was being bandaged. 'He gives me some awfu' kickings,' she was saying. A middle-aged man was explaining to a nurse, 'It's a kinda shifting pain,' while two young policemen looked on.

Laidlaw recognised a familiar art, that of postponing arrest by young policemen through the contraction of sudden, mysterious maladies.

It was not surprising that there should have been a fatal mis-diagnosis in the department on one very busy Saturday night in February 1977 when, as Inspector Laidlaw had witnessed, some patients were drunk. Alexander Brown was transferred from police cells where he had been taken for being drunk and disorderly when his fellow inmates noticed blood pouring from his nose. On arrival at the Royal's casualty department, which was known to be the busiest in Europe, he was treated as just another victim of Saturday night over-indulgence. Only later was it discovered he had a multiple fracture of the skull. He soon lost consciousness and died. The Fatal Accident Enquiry was highly critical of the admission procedures for accident and emergency patients at the Royal. The executives of the Eastern District placed the onus squarely on the Health Board, which was blamed for the 'physical and staffing shortcomings of the Accident and Emergency Department'. The Health Board disagreed, calling for improved admission procedures, but, in the circumstances, was willing to discuss modest improvements to premises and additional space once Phase 1 was completed. Wherever the responsibility resided, the incident only served to exacerbate an already highly charged atmosphere in the Royal, which urgently needed to be defused.

CHARTING A COURSE IN TREACHEROUS WATERS

At its meeting in May the District Executive Group tried to find a way forward by using the deteriorating financial position as a catalyst for a review of the provision of health services in the whole of the Eastern District by the District Medical Committee. The review was both to investigate the impact of the cuts while, at the same time, exploring desirable new developments in patient care and, as important, preventive medicine in the community. The plan was that new projects and schemes would be implemented as funds permitted. In fact, some development was now possible as the infirmary had remarkably achieved an underspend for the year due almost entirely to the enormous difficulty of finding suitable recruits for nursing positions. The first project to be approved affecting the Royal was in the new biochemistry building and was designed for biochemical screening in relation to toxic metals chronic health hazards. It was also possible to release funds for the purchase of new equipment. At the same time it was learned that the infirmary would continue to be a major centre for cardiac surgery in Scotland. There was concern that, without the additional financial support Professor Caves had been seeking from the Scottish Home and Health Department, this would be at the expense of other surgical specialities. It was also unclear as to how cardiac surgery would relate to medical cardiological investigation—a necessary precursor of any invasive procedure. The same concern was mirrored in the reflection of a request to increase the number of daily kidney dialyses undertaken at the Royal. The District Executive Group was in the same uncomfortable position between the Royal and the Health Board as the former Royal Board of Management, but with no lay non-executive members to turn to for support and guidance. Consequently the Executive Group had no alternative but to represent the views of the medical staff at the infirmary in the absence of clear decisions from the Health Board which was responsible for taking a broader view of the distribution of beds and services.

The Health Board's response was to encourage rather than stamp out competition. Other cardiac units were asked to submit papers which were inevitably partisan. When a whole body scanner became available early in 1978, the Royal was invited to bid against the Western on the basis of a previous submission prepared by Professor Blumgart of the Department of Surgery. The Royal was successful, but was required to meet the full running costs out of existing resources and allow 'reasonable access' to staff from the other districts. Later, the Scottish Home and Health Department volunteered to provide 50 per cent of the running costs for the first year on condition that the evaluation programme was under its control. Such a tactic only served to fuel suspicion amongst the medical and nursing staff at the Royal that the Health Board and the Scottish Home and Health Department had a hidden agenda, particularly as a stream of policy recommendations in the shape of reports was being distributed for consideration by Area and District Medical Committees. One of these reports, entitled SHARE, Scottish Health Authorities Revenue Equalisation, from the Chief Administrative Medical Officer, suggested that, in future, revenue calculations would be based on workload and throughput and financial allocations to take account of the cross-boundary flow of patients on statistics derived from the Scottish Medical Registration 1 (SMR1) forms. To the alarm of the Royal, it appeared that these had not been completed for at least 6 per cent of patients and much of the information on those that had been returned was imperfect. This could well affect decisions about the requirements of individual units in Phase 1, now due to open in 1980. The Health Board, recognising this problem, did not let it impede progress with the complex negotiations for apportioning space in Phase 1. Reluctantly, the Department of Medicine accepted that it was impossible to meet all its requirements in Phase 1 or even, for that matter, on the infirmary site. Other divisions, taking their cue, conceded that there would have to be sacrifices and compromises if the Commissioning Team was to make progress with detailed planning.

Still unresolved was the staffing and accommodation of the Accident and Emergency Department, although a replacement for Mr Murray, Mr R G Simpson, had now been in post for some months. The situation was reviewed at a meeting with the chairman of the Health Board in September 1978 when it was agreed to redevelop the department on its existing site rather than incorporate it within Phase 2, which might not be built for a further fifteen or twenty years. Work began at once on the preparation of alternative schemes. The Health Board indicated that, in the prevailing economic conditions, there would inevitably be a considerable gap between the drawing board and the start of work on the ground and, in the meantime, the staff of the service would have to make do in much the same way as they had done in the past. This was unacceptable to the Executive Group of the Eastern District, which sought assurances that the work to upgrade the department, working as it was at the coalface of deprivation, would be given the highest priority. Mindful of the censure in the fatal accident inquiry and aware of the growing problem of drug—as well as alcohol-related emergency admissions, the Board was not unsympathetic and in turn requested guidance from the Scottish Home and Health Department. In the meantime the nursing, medical, technical and administrative staff pressed on with the preparation of a draft plan for the new department, which was ready to be sent out for appraisal and feasibility studies by March 1979. At the end of that month the Special Advisory Committee on Accident and Emergency Services visited the infirmary and was appalled at the conditions in the department, threatening to withdraw recognition of it as a suitable place for training postgraduate students. Acting with the Dean of Post-Graduate Medicine at the University, the Royal won a year's grace from the Joint Committee on Higher Medical Training for improvements to be made. Despite the obvious urgency, it was not until the end of June that representatives of the Scottish Home and Health Department visited the infirmary and recommended to the Health Board an immediate short-term upgrade of the existing department at an estimated cost of £300,000 pending an entirely new building some time between 1990 and 1995. The Executive Group and the Accident and Emergency staff were not best pleased at not being invited to the meeting between the SHHD and the Health Board when this proposal had been accepted. Presented with a fait accompli, the other surgical wards could do nothing but agree to find space for accident and emergency patients during the upgrading.

WHERE HAVE ALL THE STAFF AND MONEY GONE...?

During 1978 the Royal suffered a haemorrhage of senior staff through retiral, death and resignation. Professor Edward McGirr, Muirhead Professor of Medicine and for some time Administrative Dean of the Medical School, retired and was succeeded by Professor Arthur Kennedy. In June 1978 Professor Philip Caves, widely recognised as a brilliant young cardiac surgeon, died suddenly due, it was reported, to a workload that would have daunted most ordinary men. In January 1979 Mr J Kennedy Watt, who had made pioneering advances in peripheral vascular surgery, collapsed and died. The following April, Professor Blumgart, the St Mungo Professor of Surgery, left to take up the prestigious chair of surgery at the Royal Postgraduate Medical School in London. The most publicised departure was that of Professor Watson Buchanan of the Centre for Rheumatic Diseases who resigned in a blaze of publicity in November 1978, condemning the NHS as a 'Holy cow' which was more responsive to acute rather than chronic illness. There were few within the NHS who would have challenged the underlying assumptions of his argument and some would have been willing to follow him to North America to make their protest. In making his allegations in the heat of the moment, Professor Buchanan overlooked the important lesson of the early years of the NHS, that everything was conditioned by the 'art of the possible', demanding great patience and tact to achieve a desired out-

246

come. By its very structure it was almost impossible for management at any level to enforce new practice and procedures without such consultations. These losses were a serious blow to the infirmary. Professor Caves was succeeded by Professor David Wheatley and Professor Blumgart by Professor D Carter.

In May 1979 the political consensus that had more or less protected the health service since its inception forty years earlier was finally shattered by the election of Mrs Thatcher's first Conservative Administration. In setting the budget for the coming financial year the new Government simply continued the restraints imposed by its Labour predecessor. There was no attempt to escape from the hand-to-mouth, year-to-year funding that characterised Treasury financing. The Eastern District faced serious difficulties in sustaining a hospital of the Royal's standing in an area with a declining, but still very disadvantaged, population. A fall in population had resulted in a confiscation under the SHARE scheme of £4.5 million from the total GGHB budget and its re-distribution to areas, mostly firmly middle class, where the population was increasing, like north Ayrshire and north Lanarkshire. At the same time, with no additional revenue, the District had to find funds to commission Phase 1 of the new infirmary. It was anticipated that the budget earmarked for development would be swallowed up in pay rises. In the new monetarist world, what the Royal wanted was a clear statement from ministers about the delivery of patient services, but this was as unlikely as had been support from Labour ministers responsible for imposing the first round of cuts. The only guidance from the Scottish Home and Health Department was the unhelpful advice that cuts should be made in administration and overheads, but not in patient services. For the Royal, the annual budget brought one piece of good news in that the deficit for the previous year was cancelled. This did not mean, however, that there would be no cuts in expenditure as there was confusion at Board level and nationally about the allocations of additional funds to cover the increase in VAT to 15 per cent announced in Sir Geoffrey Howe's budget, and over the allocation of funds for capital projects. By the end of September 1979 the Eastern District was anticipating an overspend of about £1.5 million on a budget of £33 million, due largely to the fact that the Government's projected rate for inflation was 8 per cent against an actual rate of 18 per cent.

No sooner had these gloomy forecasts become known than the

Eastern District approached the Health Board about the funding of the plan to upgrade the Royal's Accident and Emergency Service. The details had all now been worked out and beds identified in medical and surgical wards to accommodate patients while the work was in progress. Much to the annoyance of all those involved in the infirmary, the Health Board's response was that since no 'stated case' had been received for upgrading the service 'the scheme had not been given a place or priority in the Board's building programme'. Given the long running saga, this was a remarkable turn of affairs. This omission was referred to the District Planning Group chaired by the District Administrator, Ian Dorward, which had been set up in June 1978 to decide on priorities in the commissioning of Phase 1 and services to be located in Phase 2. Despite its title, or perhaps because of it, this committee had often become bogged down in the minutiae of the plans—who was to have which beds and use which corridors—rather than in a strategic overview of the demand for the services to be located in Phase 1, in the district and in the west of Scotland more generally. The Accident and Emergency Service had not been overlooked by the Group which, in January 1979, had devoted a whole meeting to reviewing the options for the future. Subsequent discussion had been prevented by the imminent commissioning of Phase 1. The oversight was quickly corrected with a strong plea to the GGHB for the urgent upgrading of the existing premises as soon as practical, hopefully with the financial support of the Scottish Home and Health Department. The Royal was not impressed by the reaction from the GGHB which, despite the much-publicised inadequacies of the service, did not seem to grasp the urgency of the situation, particularly that the accreditation of the service as a training centre was under threat. There was every danger of another fatal accident, with regular reports of fighting in the cramped waiting area.

Another reorganisation

At the end of 1979 the Conservative Government published a White Paper on the 'Structure and Management of the National Health Service in Scotland' based on the deliberations of a Royal Commission set up by Labour which called for a simplification of the administrative structure through the abolition of one tier of management, namely the district. In England and Wales it was area authorities that were to go. A cynical

observer might have concluded that the Government, like its predecessors, was simply cutting that part of the NHS which was least visible to
the patient and widely distrusted by doctors. Not surprisingly, the Eastern
District reacted badly to this proposal, but the management's criticisms
were not all self-interested. Rightly, Ian Dorward and his colleagues
pointed to flaws in the whole administrative structure, particularly the
unwieldy advisory system, which prevented articulation of clear policy by
either the Board or the Scottish Home and Health Department.
Forgetting the intense political atmosphere of the Western Regional
Hospital Board, the White Paper looked back fondly to the halcyon days
of the early years at the beginning of the NHS. For all their criticisms, the
Eastern District executives did not directly challenge the conventional
wisdom that the faults of the NHS were largely due to over-administra-
tion. What they wanted was an administration that managed the service
to deliver, at a time of rising prices, a cost-effective service to the patient.
Having failed to address head-on the whole question of management, it
seemed that the solid administrative gains secured by districts, was in danger of being swept away in further reform for its own sake. Ironically,
pressure on the GGHB budget was already beginning to result in a clearer
policy to rationalise patient care by closing a number of small inefficient
units, like the ENT and Beatson hospitals. More significantly for the
Royal, surgical beds in the Eastern District Hospital, which were to be
closed when Phase 1 was commissioned, were shut in the summer of
1980 simply to save money that was desperately needed to fund the extra
running costs associated with the scheduled demolition of the Out-
Patient Department as part 4 of the Phase 1 development. The Board,
however, was now trying to impose its authority very much on the lines
of the White Paper. Taking a wide view of patient services, the Board
wanted to extend ENT facilities at the Royal to compensate for the closure of the ENT hospital. This was not to the liking of the Eastern
District which, in the last six years, had come to enjoy a good deal of
autonomy. Having argued for strong management, the districts did not
care for it when it was the Board who did the managing.

Protest was in vain, the financial situation was deteriorating weekly.
Only two months into the financial year, the Board was forecasting a loss
of £8 million. Approval was sought from SSHD for a reduction of 1,000
in health service staff, either by natural wastage or redundancy. The first

casualty was one of the surgical registrars' posts which was abolished. In making non-paycuts, administrators had to tread carefully so as not to appear to overrule clinical judgement; for example, in the use of costly X-rays and drug therapy. One of the consequences of the cuts was the refusal of SHHD to provide any financial support for the reconstruction of the Accident and Emergency Department. The Royal and the Eastern District protested loudly at the increased hazards to seriously ill patients which would inevitably result. Nevertheless, the whole scheme had to return to the drawing board in an effort to identify a less expensive alternative. The cuts were beginning to tell on patients. Some had to wait for longer than usual in out-patient clinics at times of emergencies, while others had their operations cancelled—sometimes at short notice. During the summer the financial situation became increasingly difficult. All vacancies were frozen and overtime suspended. The Department of Medical Illustration only escaped closure after a groundswell of protest, but no amount of argument could save the surgical unit and associated operating theatres on the fifth floor of the Royal. At this juncture the Conservative Government in the Health Services Act of 1980 cancelled the withdrawal of private beds in NHS hospitals and gave boards powers to raise funds from appeals and collections—reviving the tradition of voluntary hospitals prior to 1948. This gesture was no more than a token and could do nothing to halt the rapid deterioration of the Royal's finances. By the autumn, medical beds had also to be closed and all except essential overtime banned. Waiting lists lengthened; most spectacularly the urology list climbed from 568 in June to 1,123 in July.

PHASE 1 - A THIRTY-YEAR WAIT: PHASE 2 ON THE LIST

While the Royal was grappling with the perennial problem of overspend the Eastern District was informed of the concern of obstetricians with the Victorian working conditions in the Royal Maternity Hospital. They sought assurances that the hospital would be replaced as soon as practical with an entirely new hospital on the Royal Infirmary site. There was little the District could do but refer the matter to the Board in the hope that a replacement building could be incorporated in Phase 2 of the Royal. Likewise, the Board was waiting to hear from SHHD about the funding of a revised scheme from the Accident and Emergency Department. SHHD still refused to provide any funds and the Board was compelled to make an allocation. Work was scheduled to start in the spring of 1982 by which time the process of transferring departments to the Phase 1 building—due to be handed over the previous November—would be well under way. There was still a good deal of detail to be settled even at this late stage. For example, the nursing staff pointed out that the opening of the Out-Patient Department before X-ray facilities had been commissioned would make life difficult for staff and patients. More problematic was the volume of work which would still have to be completed after the official handover—taking as long as six months to finish. For the University departments there was the added uncertainty of whether Government would make a sufficient annual running costs budget available to allow their facilities to be commissioned at all. The professorial heads of departments formed themselves into a group in an effort to find a way forward in what was recognised to be a very tight financial situation. Of concern to the nurses was the recruitment of additional staff to run Phase 1 through a promotional campaign. In commissioning Phase 1 the District was informed that the first £500,000 of running costs would have to come from existing budgets, making it hard for the Executive Group to respond to such appeals when they also had to assume responsibility for funding the running costs of the whole-body scanner now that SHHD funding had lapsed. As it was, it was only possible to make a limited number of new appointments to assist in the commissioning of Phase 1 and then only by redeploying and freezing posts in other parts of the District.

Phase 1 of the new Royal was finally handed over in mid December 1981. Ian Dorward, the District Administrator who had watched over its construction, had left the month before to take up the post of secretary to the Fife Health Board. He was succeeded by Mr T B Gibson. No sooner had the main contract been completed than the Greater Glasgow Health Board and the Eastern District put together a planning team for Phase 2, now to include a new maternity hospital. The new Administrator was soon plunged into a further financial crisis with a projected overspend by the Board in the current year of over £2 million, which would inevitably have to be carried forward for a further year. For the Eastern District these financial difficulties were exacerbated by the high cost of bringing Phase 1 into service. The Out-Patient Department alone, which opened on 5 April, was estimated to cost approximately £760,000 a year to run, and just the heating and ventilating costs of the whole new building, £1.5 million. The Eastern District reckoned the total annual running expenses would be over £5 million at 1981 prices. Such was the magnitude of the problem that there was no alternative to substantial cuts elsewhere in the District to allow Phase 1 to come into use. The GGHB could only give very limited help by permitting the recruitment of no more than a third of the staff requested for the optimum management of the new infirmary. The Royal responded by attempting to negotiate a reduction in the proposed level of service so that it could reasonably be expected 'to function within the available revenue allocation'. One proposal was to reduce the number of beds for thoracic surgery from twenty-four to twelve and the number of operating sessions from five to three. This suggestion immediately ran into opposition from thoracic surgeons throughout Glasgow who were desperately short of both beds and operating times. Given the high cost of heating and ventilation, there seemed to be no alternative to mothballing part of Phase 1 until the economic environment improved materially. There was the additional problem of an adequate budget for Professor Wheatley's cardiac surgery unit which provided a service for the whole of the west of Scotland.

After further discussions, floors 2, 3 and 4 of Phase 1 were to open in November, housing urology, surgery, medicine, peripheral vascular surgery, cardiac surgery, thoracic surgery and investigative medical cardiology. However, the bed complement in some wards was reduced because of the lack of funds. It was recognised that the consequence of this decision was that further cuts in staffing and services would have to be achieved. The medical unit at Duke Street was targeted for closure, but this was easier said than done, as many of the beds were occupied by psychogeriatric patients. The prevailing mood was for the less disabled of such patients to be relocated within the community, which was not very realistic in the deprived east end of Glasgow. With the lack of any visible means of providing care in the community, closure of medical beds might place dangerous strains on the Royal during severe winter weather. Local conditions also made it difficult to curtail services at the Royal itself. Despite the opening of health centres throughout the east end in the past eight years, many patients continued to come to the infirmary as they had always done for treatment without consulting a general practitioner and of those who attended some were suffering from a serious illness or injury that necessitated treatment. It was one thing for the Eastern District to call for the closure of the 'open door', it was another thing to try and close it, particularly on a very busy Saturday night when any bed in any department might be commandeered for acute admissions irrespective of the medical problem. All that could be done was to tell hospitals elsewhere in the west of Scotland that patients from outside the Royal's catchment area would be transferred directly the 'acute phase' of their care had been completed. For the Accident and Emergency service the chaos could be reduced if general practitioners and ambulance drivers, accustomed to sending or taking patients from the city centre eastwards straight to the Royal, checked if beds were available. This was easier said than done as the Royal's telephone system was not now equal to the demand. Another victim of the cuts was the whole-body scanner which the District was unable to maintain or staff without external support. By the end of August the situation was so desperate that the recruitment of new staff for Phase 1 was halted; nevertheless, the scheduled occupation of floors 2, 3 and 4 in November was to go ahead. It was very disappointing for all staff to have got so close to the opening of the new building, which had taken over thirty-five years to plan, to be thwarted at the eleventh hour by the shortage of funds. The only comfort was a recognition by the Board that some overspending was inevitable as services were transferred to Phase 1 and existing units closed.

The chairman of the GGHB officially opened Phase 1 on 22 March 1983. The new building boosted morale throughout the hospital. After their cramped and inadequate accommodation, the staff rejoiced in the new facilities—the clinics, the wards and the technology—and the opportunity these offered to accelerate both the pace of innovation and the scope for improving the quality of patient care. The close proximity of the University departments to the clinics and wards held out the potential for exciting collaborative research projects. In the Renal Unit the introduction of chronic ambulatory peritoneal dialysis (CAPD) allowed far more patients to be treated than ever before. In medicine better facilities allowed Dr Iain Boyle and his team to make faster progress with their investigation of metabolic bone disease in collaboration with the Departments of Biochemistry and Nuclear Medicine. Improved imaging and computer equipment gave Nuclear Medicine the opportunity to enlarge its areas of operation, notably in cardiology. Medical

Cardiology and Cardiac Surgery became much more closely integrated following the move, with a grant of £120,000 from the Fraser Foundation to enable a computer laboratory to be established in the University block. The gastroenterology unit was making significant advances in gastrointestinal biochemistry, investigative procedures and the management of long-term and complex nutritional problems; for example, in Crohn's disease, using techniques of intravenous and external nutrition. The decision to delay the opening of the Day Wards Area prevented the commissioning of the new routine endoscopy rooms. In Surgery the biggest beneficiary from Phase 1 was undoubtedly the Cardio-thoracic Unit and University Department of Cardiac Surgery. The new theatres allowed the number of open heart surgical procedures to double to almost 850 in 1982 and stimulated research in several areas, including the development of prosthetic heart valves, and the development and application of pulsatile cardiopulmonary bypass. A slight easing of the financial situation allowed the whole hospital to be opened by the end of the year, albeit with a lower than projected staffing complement. This included the transfer of the Centre for Rheumatic Diseases and the surgical beds from Duke Street Hospital into Phase 1.

TO BE JUST A UNIT

By the beginning of 1984 the role of the districts was being eclipsed as the next round of reorganisation was implemented. The districts ceased to exist in May and were replaced by a series of units. The Royal Infirmary and its associated hospitals were to be managed by East No. 1 Unit which was also responsible for Glasgow Royal Maternity Hospital and Glasgow Dental Hospital and School. The committee structure, however, remained much as before, although the Unit lacked most of the powers of the Districts. The Royal simply became a facility within the Greater Glasgow Health Board with little separate identity except for certain specialities servicing the whole area and in some cases the whole of the west of Scotland, like the new leukaemia/lymphoma/bone marrow transplant unit. Under the chairmanship of Professor Gemmell Morgan, the Unit Medical Committee did its best to defend the position of the Royal against the loss of further posts as staff retired or resigned. This was unrewarding work, entailing interminable correspondence with Board officials and the various medical divisions. Month after month the list of requests for replacements grew longer and longer with few satisfactory conclusions for the Royal. Quickly, the Unit Management Team found itself sucked into these negotiations which still seemed to lack any clear framework of policy. The Report of Wards 4 and 5 for 1983–5 epitomised the frustration of conducting such negotiations. The distinguished physician, Dr Bill Manderson, retired in August 1984 and, despite discussions that had lasted for nearly two years, no decision had been taken about the future of his post by the following summer:

> This entire saga of indecision and apparent indifference to the consequences to patients arising from these delays and obfuscations does not offer great hope for the future. Although theoretically the objective of the latest in what appears to be an endless series of reorganisation of Health Service was to devolve more decisions to hospital level, precisely the opposite seems to have occurred.

Lack of resources did not diminish the commitment of the staff to either individual patients or to pushing back the frontiers of medical knowledge through their research. Maintaining services to a growing number of patients, many with serious conditions that a generation earlier would have been considered hopeless, depended entirely on a common understanding amongst all the staff from consultants to technicians that it was always worth going the extra mile whatever the personal costs. Without such dedication it would have been impossible for the Renal Unit to cope with the rising tide of dialysis patients. Similarly, Dr A C MacCuish single-handedly shouldered the burden of the largest Diabetic Unit in the city after his senior registrar left to take up a consultancy and was not replaced. In Medical Cardiology there was a similar tale of staff shortage and a greater number of patients whose problems were now being investigated with more and more sophisticated techniques. The number of echocardiograms, a relatively new procedure allowing non-invasive examination of the heart, climbed to over two thousand a year and radionuclide studies to almost a thousand. To help interpret the results, the department developed Electro-Cardiogram computer analysis software that was marketed commercially to several other European countries. Professor Callum Macnaughton and Dr W P Black established in vitro fertilisation in the Gynaecology Department's refurbished wards 31-33, formerly occupied by the Professorial Surgical Unit. The outcome

was well worth while, with the successful establishment of several preg-
nancies. The Cardio-thoracic Unit and University Department of Cardiac
Surgery achieved a remarkable gain in productivity with an increased
workload of 43 per cent in 1984—the previous year. Altogether, 770 cardiac pulmonary bypass operations were performed. With the closure of
the Ear, Nose and Throat Hospital, the otolaryngology department was
inundated with patients. During 1983 the prestigious MRC Institute of
Hearing Research (Scottish Section) was transferred from the Southern
General to the Royal with a wide remit to conduct clinical research into
the epidemiology, aetiology and management of hearing disorders. Taken
together these were major advances for the Royal, helping it to maintain
its position as one of the country's leading teaching hospitals.

LITTLE LEFT TO CUT

The frustration caused by dwindling resources and long delays in reaching decisions about replacement of staff who left or retired became an
accepted part of life throughout the hospital service in the second half of
the 1980s. The problem was greatly acerbated by early retirement
schemes designed to cut costs by pruning the number of expensive consultancy staff with little consideration of the needs of patients. For
example, in 1986 three of the consultant staff of the Department of
Ophthalmology took early retirement, with the result that 'the workload
has increased to such an extent that there is an absurd delay between the
time patients are referred by their family doctors and when they are seen
in the outpatient department'. The long-overdue refurbishment of the
Orthopaedic and Accident Division was again postponed until 1987 at
the earliest, along with expected improvements in the Orthopaedic Out-
patient Department. Every part of the infirmary was stretched to the
limits as more patients were referred for treatment, their expectations
raised by constant press and television reporting of new life-extending
techniques and procedures. In the medical wards, it was reported in 1986:

> Efforts made to keep up a first-class geriatric service for the
> Eastern District have been swamped by, on the one hand, an
> increasing demand for their services and on the other by
> reductions and alterations of the facilities available to the
> Service. It must be appreciated that the resulting chaos pro-
> duced major effects throughout the District [Unit]. Acute

medical services are rendered less efficient by having patients admitted to inappropriate wards. Surgical activities are similarly disrupted by the necessity to admit acute medical problems to surgical wards whilst medical ward beds are occupied by patients who do not need the full panoply of services available to this major hospital. Recently one long-term resident in Ward 5 spent his 1,000th day in this acute medical ward of a major teaching hospital. The time has surely come for a radical re-appraisal of this intolerable situation which places quite absurd stresses on patients, nursing, medical and surgical staff alike.

Nevertheless the staff still in post were determined they were not going to allow the pressures to distract them from providing a quality service to a community in the east end of the city that was experiencing considerable hardship as traditional industries collapsed and efforts to replace them foundered. The Department of Gynaecology strove hard to meet the demand of the Government's programme of cervical screening, nurtured its recently launched infertility service and developed a Menopause Clinic using the newer hormone replacement therapy. An exciting advance was the development by the University Department of Cardiac Surgery, with the support of the Scottish Development Agency, the University of Glasgow, Greater Glasgow Health Board and a local company, of a pericardial heart valve which was rigorously and successfully evaluated in vitro and in vivo. Clinical trials by the infirmary had begun in February 1983 and were quickly extended to other hospitals. The valves went into commercial production in 1986.

Marriage and separation

On 25 July 1986 Queen Elizabeth named the Phase 1 block the Queen Elizabeth Building. However heartfelt the pleas made at the time for a respite in the financial restraints, there was no prospect of any relief. By the summer of 1987 the Royal was once again seriously overspent and the Unit General Manager imposed even tighter and stricter controls. This renewed restraint came at a time when further technical advances made the purchase of expensive new diagnostic equipment essential if patients' expectations were to be matched. During 1987 the Royal Infirmary and its associated hospitals were amalgamated in a Unit with Stobhill Hospital to the north of the city. The consultants at Stobhill were concerned that they would simply be swallowed up by the Royal. In shaping the management of the new Unit the Royal went out of its way to allay such fears. There was equal representation on committees and an equal division of budget. Nevertheless, agreeing the constitution of the new Unit Medical Advisory Committee chaired by Dr Ross Lorimer of the Royal required patience and tact. In the absence of clear direction from GGHB the two hospitals began discussing the rationalisation of their services, particularly laboratory services, where retiral and resignations had made this possible.

Working groups were established to review different areas and subjects. As at the Royal, the principal concern at Stobhill was the inexorable rise in Accident and Emergency cases from 29,738 in 1976 to 39,429 in 1987, representing 35 per cent of all attendances at the hospital. The bulk of these patients simply turned up with no letter of referral from their general practitioners. Ways were sought to rationalise the service at the two hospitals. It was hoped that some procedures could be concentrated at the Royal, such as orthopaedic trauma cases, with non-urgent elective orthopaedic surgery being provided at Stobhill. In many other areas exciting ideas for rationalising and improving services were being progressed, often in opposition to the strategic plans of GGHB.

As was only to be expected, achieving agreement was not easy: the future management of the whole health service was confused by a stream of Government proposals, including those for the formation of self-governing hospital trusts, and there was much mutual suspicion. However, after two years the two hospitals were beginning to coalesce into a coherent Unit with joint appointments. Staff on both sides had begun to appreciate that there was good sense in merging a large general hospital with the secondary and tertiary referral service provided by the Royal. There may have been some inconvenience to relations and friends having to travel further to visit patients and to patients in attending clinics; but these disadvantages were easily offset by the greater flexibility afforded by the larger grouping. For example, on busy nights in the Accident and Emergency Department, one hospital could call on beds in the other if there were an overwhelming number of admissions.

By the autumn 1989 relations between the Unit Medical Advisory Committee and the Greater Glasgow Health Board were badly strained. As so often in the past, but now at a time when government was encouraging consultants and other health professionals to take on a greater managerial role, the Committee could elicit no clear statement of Board strategy, or even tactics. Posts were advertised without reference to UMAC and sometimes at odds with its priorities.

The most telling example of lack of communication was the Board's response to the announcement that, under the Scottish Health Area Revenue Equalisation Scheme, GGHB would lose £2.5 million in 1990 and 1991. There was no consultation, but, instead, integration between the Royal and Stobhill and other hospitals was summarily cut short at the end of 1989, paving the way, it was hoped, for self-governing hospital trusts. There was little the Royal could do but accept the decision and plan for the development of its own site, including the construction of Phase 2 incorporating the new Royal Maternity Hospital. The Royal, like other leading hospitals in Glasgow, was very unenthusiastic about the whole concept of trusts, believing that they represented creeping privatisation and would be used to rationalise services on the basis of cost rather than need. In other words, hospitals would be forced to compete with one another irrespective of the mix of service or social background of patients. Bereft of a large general hospital with few referral services and little teaching, the Royal would find it hard to compete for routine acute or elective procedures and be left with a disparate group of expensive services. Not only do more complex procedures need to be supported by a range of other specialities, routine general medicine and surgery is a necessity for any large teaching hospital. Consequently the Royal remained lukewarm about applying for trust status, preferring to concentrate on shortening waiting lists and reducing expenditure by achieving a greater throughput of patients, and at the same time improving services to patients by introducing new techniques and research. The most spectacular of these advances was the establishment of a heart transplant unit for the west of Scotland under Professor David Wheatley. The first successful operation was carried out in January 1992. The Cardio-thoracic Unit and the University Department of Cardiac Surgery had won national acclaim three years before, when their new heart valve was awarded first prize in the Academic Enterprise Competition organised by the British Technology Group. Likewise, J G Pollock of the Peripheral Vascular Surgery Unit received a Queen's Award for Research and Development of arterial prostheses. The most visible improvement to patient services was the completion of the long-awaited refurbishment of the Accident and Emergency Unit in 1990. The most painful part of the process of reducing costs was the competitive tendering of many routine services, resulting in the placing of contracts for catering, portering and domestic services with outside contractors and the redundancy of staff.

The eighteen years from 1974 to 1992 had witnessed a sequence of bewildering changes at the Royal and in the NHS as a whole; budgets had been pruned relentlessly and new structures and management techniques introduced and often as hurriedly abandoned. At the same time, the practice of medicine had advanced at a breathtaking pace; cases that were hopeless in 1974, by 1992 were routinely manageable. These advances, due to a combination of new technology and therapeutic breakthroughs were costly, at least at the beginning, and also by their very nature resulted in more and more referrals to the Royal and other teaching hospitals. There seemed little solution to the problem. New technology, rather than cutting costs, was in fact driving them up, as it was in other areas, by holding out the potential for innovative and beneficial diagnostic and curative procedures. All the Royal could hope to do was to get better at managing its services and trusting in the loyalty of the staff always to go the extra mile. This, with few exceptions, they had consistently done over the last two decades. Junior staff were most of the time unaware of the financial problems and managerial difficulties their senior colleagues were grappling with. Consequently they had been enthusiastic supporters of new advances and determinedly sought funds, increasingly from outside the NHS, to support research and to fund equipment. The hallmark of the hospital throughout was the deep commitment to providing the best health care possible for the east end of the city.

8 TRUST IN THE FUTURE, 1992–94

The overall aim of the Glasgow Royal Infirmary group is to be through merit and within a sound financial framework, the pre-eminent provider of excellent:

  -general healthcare to the citizens of eastern Glasgow
  -specialist healthcare to a wider population
  -education, training and research facilities for University and professional bodies

  Glasgow Royal Infirmary NHS Trust Application June 1993.

The Conservative victory in 1992 meant Trust status became inevitable for Scottish hospitals. It was realised that the NHS reforms which gave rise to the Purchaser-Provider split might influence the diverse roles the Royal was expected to fill. There remained a deep-seated commitment to serve both as the general hospital for the east end of Glasgow and as a centre for secondary and tertiary referral—patients in need of specialist treatment and care, sent from hospitals in the west of Scotland and beyond. There was also a firm determination to continue as a University teaching hospital and to maintain the infirmary's reputation for academic excellence and innovative research.

Could the Royal win the resources to continue to fulfil these challenging roles in the new world of hospital trusts? One danger was that independent self-governing trusts formed on the model of pre-1948 hospitals and in the absence of an acute and maternity strategy for Glasgow might not find the playing field of 'internal market' forces to be completely level. Hospitals throughout the west of Scotland and beyond providing a standard district hospital range of services would of course continue to refer the more complicated clinical problems for assessment. However, the complexity of the clinical problem was difficult to express financially. When this was combined with the needs of teaching and training, both vital for the future of Scottish medicine, it seemed possible

261

that the Royal Infirmary might be expected to shoulder a considerable financial burden.

The Royal served a local population that was decreasing as the traditional industrial base declined and many of the most active members of the community moved away in search of work. A high proportion of those who remained were elderly, unskilled or tied to the area by loyalty to aged dependants. Long term unemployment, deteriorating housing conditions and declining state benefits had taken their toll on the community and despite initiatives such as the Glasgow Eastern Area Renewal scheme (GEAR), by the 1990s the east end had less material resources than any comparable area in western Europe. Health problems associated with multiple deprivation were aggravated by a combination of factors, among which were poor diet and above average rates of cigarette smoking, alcohol consumption and drug abuse. These factors meant that there was a higher incidence of disease in the catchment area of the Royal than in most other parts of the United Kingdom. There was a growing number of emergency referrals, including a seemingly inexorable rise in medical emergency admissions. In addition, the closure of medical and respiratory beds in Belvidere Hospital and medical beds in Duke Street Hospital, as well as the loss of convalescent beds in Canniesburn Hospital, threw an even greater workload on the acute services of the Royal. However, the NHS market structure did not easily target resources differentially to economically disadvantaged areas. The development of more sophisticated contracts will, in time, enable the Royal and those purchasing care from its hospitals to identify the added value of its complex caseload and the added costs of its deprived local population. However, the next few years, while this system is developed, will be challenging

Despite these problems, the work of the infirmary continued unabated. The application for Trust status, approved in December 1993, became fact in April 1994. The submission made it clear that the Royal will continue to be committed to provide a complete health care service for the citizens of the city's east end and continue to accept the challenge of secondary and tertiary referral of patients as requested. The provision of advanced education, training and research facilities will continue. There are considerable possibilities in further liaison with the old and new Universities and these will certainly be grasped. Further scientific co-operation with the University of Strathclyde will be actively pursued. In delivering its services the infirmary will continue to strive for excellence, introducing innovative diagnostic and curative procedures as soon as they are fully proven. There is a strong belief that quality can be enhanced through the attainment of critical mass with the expertise of every speciality available to help reinforce the others. An example is heart transplant surgery, which has been very successfully introduced to the Royal Infirmary by Professor Wheatley, Mr Richens and Mr Naik, and it has drawn on all specialities in the Royal. Indeed, even gynaecological advice has been sought. In maintaining critical mass, it is hoped that the Royal Maternity Hospital can be relocated as planned on the infirmary site in the not too distant future.

Concentration of specialities will allow centres of excellence to develop and flourish. A Trauma Centre, proposed for the infirmary site, would bring together a range of different interests to treat victims of serious accidents and would build on the Royal's reputation in this area founded on the work of Lister and Cuthbertson. Such centres of excellence, by their very nature, stimulate research and the Royal is determined to remain at the forefront of research both in the clinical and social aspects of medicine.

Even as the Trust is being planned, advances continue. Recent developments at the Royal include the founding of the chairs of Rheumatology (supported by the Arthritis and Rheumatism Council and the McLeod Bequest) and of Human Nutrition (supported by the Rank Foundation). The Chair of Geriatric Medicine has been translated from the Southern General Hospital. These chairs are filled by Professors Sturrock, Lean and Stott respectively. The work will be co-ordinated with that of the University Department of Medicine (Muirhead Professor of Medicine—Professor J H McKillop). To complement the excellent facilities in the Queen Elizabeth Building an advanced fifty-four bedded geriatric assessment unit has been created in the centre block of the main infirmary building revealing how modern facilities can be developed from old.

There are further areas of progress. Waiting lists have been reviewed and vigorously tackled in the light of the Patient's Charter. Further links with primary care are being developed with community midwifery and the women's reproductive health facilities at the Royal Maternity

Hospital. Day care and minimally invasive surgery are becoming increasingly available and there is a high focus on patient communication. Clinicians are once again being involved in management. They are making decisions and indicating their priorities.

The history of the Royal, since its foundation in 1794, presents many poignant reminders that the future is never assured. Financial constraints have always existed and there have always been difficult choices to make. However, the Royal Infirmary, with its roots deep in the city of Glasgow and west of Scotland, is alive to and welcomes its responsibilities in providing the highest qualities of health care. The future may present challenges but it will also offer opportunities to further enhance the reputation of a great Scottish Hospital.

NOTES

Where no direct reference is provided for a quotation in the text, it is taken from the Glasgow Royal Infirmary Managers' or Board of Management minutes for the relevant date

CHAPTER 1

1. *Glasgow Advertiser*, Vol.X, No.676, 14-18 May 1792, p.326 in Glasgow Collection, Mitchell Library, Glasgow
2. For example, Jardine was reappointed as secretary as late as 1803
3. James Coutts, *A History of the University of Glasgow from its Foundation in 1451 to 1909* (Glasgow, 1909), p.497
4. See John Woodward *'To do the sick no harm': A study of the British voluntary hospital system to 1875* (London, 1974), pp.1-19, *passim*
5. John D Comrie, *A History of Scottish Medicine to 1860* (London, 1927), pp.135-7
6. *A Short Account of the Town's Hospital published by order of the directors* (3rd edn, Edinburgh, 1838), p.6
7. See Town's Hospital minute book, 1 Mar. 1737 and 18 May 1738 in Rare Books and Manuscripts Collection, Mitchell Library, Glasgow
8. Town's Hospital minute book, 21 Aug. 1740
9. Town's Hospital minute book, 18 Nov. 1742
10. The provision of clinical medical teaching at the Town's Hospital has been questioned by one leading historian on Scottish medicine 'Though the Town's Hospital was largely a poorhouse, it did have some beds for the sick and had a small operating and lecture theatre, but it was run by the Town's doctors and they made few moves towards teaching.' David Hamilton, *The Healers: A History of Medicine in Scotland* (Edinburgh, 1981), p.125
11. 'No provision, however, was made here [The Town's Hospital] for clinical teaching, nor indeed was there a sufficiently large medical school in Glasgow at this time to require it', Hamilton, p.125 *op. cit.*
12. Town's Hospital minute book, 16 Nov. 1876
13. See Town's Hospital minute book 1786-98, *passim*
14. Alexander Duncan, *Memorials of the Faculty of Physicians and Surgeons of Glasgow 1599–1850* (Glasgow, 1896), p.263
15. Guenter B Risse, *Hospital Life in Enlightenment Scotland: Care and Teaching at the Royal Infirmary of Edinburgh* (Cambridge, 1986), p.28
16. Risse (1986), p.46
17. *Ibid*, p.38

18. For further information on the early industrialisation of Glasgow, see James Clelend, *The Rise and Progress of the City of Glasgow* (Glasgow, 1829); T M Devine, *The Tobacco Lords: A Study of the Tobacco Merchants of Glasgow and their Trading Activities c.1740-90* (Edinburgh, 1975); Robert Gillespie, *Glasgow and the Clyde* (Glasgow, 1876); John Strang, *Glasgow and its Clubs* (Glasgow, 1856), *passim*

19. Devine (1975), pp.93, 96

20. See Glasgow Royal Infirmary First Annual Report, list of contributors, pp.6-11, Greater Glasgow Health Board Archives, and Strang (1856), p.41 for list of leading tobacco importers

21. Extract from Robert and William Chambers, *The Gazateer for Scotland*, Vol.1 (Glasgow, 1832), pasted into Vol.19, p.28 of Glasgow Scrapbook, Glasgow Collection, Mitchell Library, Glasgow

22. *Glasgow Mercury*, Vol.X, No.492, 30 May-6 June 1786, p.182, Glasgow Collection, Mitchell Library, Glasgow

23. Alexander Chalmers, ed, *General Biographical Dictionary* (London, 1812), p.315

24. See the section on subscribers later in this chapter for details on the constitution of the Board of Managers of the Infirmary

25. *Glasgow Mercury*, Vol.XVII, No.884, 2-9 Dec. 1794, p.390

26. Strang (1856), pp.364-7; Robert Chambers, ed, revised by Thomas Thomson, *Biographical Dictionary of Eminent Scotsmen*, Vol.2 (Glasgow, 1875), pp.422-5

27. Devine (1975), pp.23-4

28. *Ibid*, p.7

29. Coutts, *op.cit.*, p.497

30. Derek Dow and Michael Moss, 'The Medical Curriculum at Glasgow in the early Nineteenth Century', *History of Universities* 7 (1988), p.227

31. Devine (1975), p.39

32. Risse (1986), pp.124, 170–71

33. A J Youngson, *The Scientific Revolution in Victorian Medicine* (London, 1979), p.90 and *passim*

34. Risse (1986), p.224

35. Hamilton (1981), p.150

36. *Chambers Biographical Dictionary of Eminent Scotsmen*, Vol.1 (1875), p.252; Duncan (1896), pp.265-6

37. *Ibid*, (1875), p.251

38. *Ibid*, p.252. See the section on students and dissection later in this chapter for more on this subject

39. *Ibid*, p.251

40. Duncan (1896), p.144

41. Risse (1896), p.245

42. Ivan Waddington, *The Medical Profession in the Industrial Revolution* (Dublin, 1984), p.27

43. Dow and Moss, *op.cit.*, (1988), p.227

44. W M Mathew, 'The Origins and Occupations of Glasgow Students, 1740-1839', *Past and Present,* 33 (1966), p.75

45. Duncan (1896), p.172

46. See for example Owen Dudley Edwards, *Burke and Hare* (Edinburgh,

1977) and Ruth Richardson, *Death, Dissection and the Destitute* (1987)

47. See Jacqueline Jenkinson, *Medical Societies in Scotland 1731-1939: Their History and Records* (Edinburgh, 1993), *passim*

48. F L M Pattison, *Granville Sharp Pattison: Anatomist and Antagonist* (Edinburgh, 1987), p.22

49. *Ibid*, p.32

50. Coutts (1909), p.518

CHAPTER 2

1. The annual report for 1823 lists separate categories for patients suffering from:

Cholera	1
Continued fever	269
Intermittent fever	12
Scarlet fever	20
Measles	8

2. Comrie (1927), p.230

3. *Ibid*, p.227

4. See *Black's Medical Dictionary* (34th edition, 1984), pp.920-22

5. In July 1828 40 people suffering from fever were turned away from the infirmary in one day due to lack of beds

6. *Black's Medical Dictionary, op.cit.*, p.329

7. See A K Chalmers, *The Health of Glasgow 1818-1925: An Outline* (Glasgow, 1930), p.153, and Glasgow Royal Infirmary annual report 1831, p.7

8. Olive Checkland and Margaret Lamb eds *Health Care as Social History: The Glasgow Case* (Aberdeen, 1982), p.214

9. R A Cage, *The Working Class in Glasgow 1750-1914* (1987), p.87

10. For more on the nature and treatment of cholera see *Black's Medical Dictionary, op.cit.*, p.192

11. Checkland and Lamb (1982), p.214

12. C M Allan, 'The Genesis of British Urban Redevelopment with Special Reference to Glasgow', *Economic History Review* 18 (1965), p.603

13. Figure taken from census returns for 1851, quoted in Cage (1987), p.18

14. T C Smout, *A Century of the Scottish People 1830-1950* (London, 1986), p.62

15. See pages 74–8 below for more on the struggle between the Faculty of Physicians and Surgeons of Glasgow and the medical School of University of Glasgow for the control of medical appointments to the infirmary

16. See *Medical Directory* (London, 1859), *passim*

17. See C J Pattison (1987), pp.66-71, *passim*

18. J B Coutts, *A History of the University of Glasgow from its foundation in 1451 to 1909* (Glasgow, 1909), p.546

19. *Ibid*, p.553

20. See Comrie (1927), pp.231-2, Hamilton (1983), p.150

21. Smout (1986), pp.22-3

CHAPTER 3

1. Monica Baly (ed), *As Miss Nightingale Said...*, London, 1991, p.49
2. *GRI Annual Report for 1861*. Significantly, medical provisions of the Poor Law (Scotland) Amendment Act of 1845 applied only to those unable to work
3. James McGhie, 'Remarks on the Construction of Hospitals, with reference to the new Surgical Hospital of Glasgow Royal Infirmary', *Glasgow Medical Journal*, 8 (1861), p.403. *Proceedings of the Opening of the New Surgical Hospital of the Glasgow Royal Infirmary* (Glasgow, 1861)
4. Sir Hector Clare Cameron, *Reminiscences of Lister and of his Work in the Wards of the Glasgow Royal Infirmary* (Glasgow, 1927), p.11
5. A K Bowman, *Sir William Macewen* (London, 1942), p.38
6. F F Cartwright, 'Antiseptic Surgery', in FNL Poynter, ed, *Medicine and Science in the 1860s* (London, 1968), pp.77-103. A J Youngson, *The Scientific Revolution in Victorian Medicine* (New York, 1979), pp.129-34
7. *Ibid*, pp.9-40
8. Richard B Fisher, *Joseph Lister, 1872-1912* (London, 1977)
9. Joseph Lister, 'On the Effects of the Antiseptic System of Treatment upon the Salubrity of a Surgical Hospital', *Lancet,* 1870, Vol. 1, pp.4-40
10. C J S Thomson, *Lord Lister: The Discoverer of Antiseptic Surgery* (London, 1934), p.37
11. HB14/5/10, Ward 24 Day Book, 1863-5. Martin Goldman, *Lister Ward* (Bristol, 1987), pp.10 and 157
12. HB14/5/10 p.263
13. HB14/5/10 p.222
14. Fisher, 1977, p.121
15. Joseph Lister, 'On a New Method of Treating Compound Fracture, Abscess, etc with Observations on the Conditions of Suppuration', *Lancet* (1867), Vols 1 and 2
16. Fisher, 1977, p.135
17. HB14/5/10, p.275
18. Lister, 'On a New Method...', (1867), p.326. Goldman, 1987, p.12, suggests that Lister was forced to amputate Kelly's leg after the failure of the antiseptic treatment.
19. HH67/56/24, Register of Admissions 1862-7
20. Lister, 'On a New Method...', p.326
21. Lister, 'On the Effects of...' (1870), Vol. 1
22. *Ibid.* See also a report in *Lancet* (1869), Vol. 2, p.450
23. *Lancet* (1870), Vol. 1, p.175, letter from Henry Lamond. According to Goldman, 1987, and others, Lister was also criticised by the authorities at the Edinburgh Royal Infirmary, for keeping many of his patients in the wards for long periods. This was due either to the nature of the cases—requiring prolonged post-operative observation—or to his desire to retain 'good clinical material' to exhibit to his students
24. For examples, see letters published in the *Lancet* (1869), Vol. 2, pp.320 and 421, and reviews published in the *Glasgow Medical Examiner*, April 1869, p.80, and February 1870, p.160
25. Letter in the *Lancet* (1870), Vol. 1, p.210

26. See Fisher, 1977, and Goldman, 1987

27. John Patrick, *A Short History of the Glasgow Royal Infirmary* (Glasgow, 1940), p.21

28. Monica E Baly, *Florence Nightingale and the Nursing Legacy* (Beckenham, 1986)

29. *Lister and the Lister Ward of the Royal Infirmary of Glasgow, A Centenary Contribution* (Glasgow, 1927), p.71

30. HB14/6/97, letter from Rebecca Strong to Mr McKindle, 3 Mar. 1930

31. HB14/9/82

32. Letter in *North British Daily Mail* (*NBDM*), 5 Oct. 1891

33. City of Glasgow Fever Hospital Annual Report, 1865-6, quoted in A K Chalmers, ed, *Public Health Administration in Glasgow: A Memorial Volume of the Writings of J B Russell* (Glasgow, 1905), p.44

34. Goldman (1987), p.71

35. Moses Thomas, *Suggestions to Improve Nursing in the Glasgow Royal Infirmary* (Glasgow, 1877)

36. A K Chalmers, *The Health of Glasgow 1818-1925: An Outline* (Glasgow 1930), p.298

37. Rona Gaffney, 'Poor Law Hospitals, 1845-1914', in Checkland and Lamb, 1982, p.44. The Poor Law (Scotland) Amendment Act of 1845 made provision for the expansion of the Poor Law hospital and out-door medical service, and some Parochial Boards were subscribers to the Royal, sending suitable cases for treatment to the infirmary

38. The story of the first years of the Dorcas Society is taken from the *GRI Annual Reports* for 1863-7, and notes supplied by Dr Abigail Reid

39. Loudon McQueen and Archibald Kerr, *The Western Infirmary, 1874-1974* (Glasgow, 1974)

40. *NBDM*, 27 Sept. 1877

41. *Ibid*, 29 Sept. 1877

42. The *GRI Annual Report for 1877* contains a transcription of the heated debate on the issue at the Annual Meeting, January 1878

43. *NBDM*, 8 Oct. 1877

44. Sectarian controversy was not confined to the west of Scotland. The *Glasgow Herald*, 26 Jan. 1909, reported that a scandal had erupted in Edinburgh over 'the attempts by the Papists to capture the [Edinburgh] Royal Infirmary for Rome'

45. The information on the Glasgow Royal Infirmary Medical School was obtained from the GRI Minute Books, 1875-89, and Moses Thomas, *The Glasgow Royal Infirmary and the Royal Infirmary School of Medicine* (Glasgow, 1888), p.13

46. Bowman, 1942

47. *Ibid*, p.1

48. *GMJ*, 1869-70, Vol.2, p.70. As a resident, Macewen apparently worked with Lister only once, in a blood transfusion case: see Macewen's 'Case of Transfusion', *GMJ* 1869-70, Vol.2, p.128

49. See Bowman, 1942; Archibald Young, 'Sir William Macewen and the Glasgow School of Surgery', in *Surgery, Gynaecology and Obstetrics*, Dec. 1926, p.823; Charles Duguid, *Macewen of Glasgow* (Edinburgh, 1957); and Hugh Allan Macewen, *The Man in the White Coat* (Glasgow, 1974)

50. Duguid, 1957, p.14
51. Susan McGann, *Battle of the Nurses: A Study of Eight Women Who Influenced the Development of Professional Nursing, 1880-1930* (Harrow, 1992), p.104. The common confusion in the identification of Macewen the surgeon and McEwen the chairman is the result of inconsistent spelling in the historical sources
52. Thomas, 1877
53. According to a report in the *NBDM*, 26 Mar. 1883, the matron had offered to resign 'four or five times, and each time she had been coaxed to withdraw the demittance, usually on an increase of salary'
54. Macewen, 1974, p.36
55. See RCSPSG 10, letters from Rebecca Strong to William Macewen, 15 Apr. and 28 Aug. 1882
56. RCSPSG 10, letter from Macewen to Strong, 28 Aug. 1884
57. *Ibid*, lettter from Strong to Macewen, 17 Nov. 1882
58. The story of the 'chloroform controversy' comes from the GRI Minute Books, and from the columns of the *Glasgow Herald*, *NBDM* and *Glasgow Weekly Mail*, March–May 1883
59. McGann, 1992, p.109
60. *NBDM*, 12 Sept. 1891
61. Wendy Alexander, *First Ladies of Medicine* (Glasgow, 1987), p.2
62. HB14/4/2, St Mungo's College Pathology Class Roll Book, 1882-1918. See D H A Boyd, *Leith Hospital, 1848-1948*, (Edinburgh, 1990), pp.27-30
63. *GMJ*, 1892, Vol.37, p.295
64. The story of medical classes at St Mungo's College and the Royal is from the GRI Minute Books, 1890-93; HB14/1/99, the Minute Book of St Mungo's College Medical Society; and *GMJ*, 1892, Vol.38, pp.205 and 275

CHAPTER 4

1. Francis H Groome, (ed), *Ordnance Gazetteer of Scotland*, Vol.3 (Edinburgh, 1886), p.92
2. James B Russell, 'Old Glasgow and Greater Glasgow', *GMJ*, 1892, Vol.37, p.45
3. For the history of the City Improvement Trust, see *Municipal Glasgow, Its Evolution and Enterprises* (Glasgow, 1915), p.48
4. For the development of Glasgow's Public Transport, see Colin Johnstone and John R Hume, *Glasgow Stations* (Newton Abbot, 1975), and Charles A Oakley, *The Last Tram* (Glasgow, 1962)
5. Dr J Barlow, 'Statistics of Surgical Operations from 1883 to 1892', *GMJ*, 1892, Vol.37, p.1
6. S D Slater and D A Dow (eds), *The Victoria Infirmary of Glasgow, 1890-1990* (Glasgow, 1990)
7. Rebecca Strong, *Introductory Remarks to Practical Classes in Ward Work, 1893. GMJ*, 1892, Vol.38, p.434
8. W J B Riddell, *The Glasgow Ophthalmic Institute, 1868-1968* (Glasgow, 1968)

9.   HB14/6/99 John Scott, 'A Great Pioneer–Dr John Macintyre'. 'John
     Macintyre - Glasgow Pioneer in Radiology', *Western Regional Hospital
     Board Regional Review*, 1969, Vol. 2.7, p30

10. John Macintyre, 'Demonstration on the Rontgen Rays', *GMJ*, 1896,
     Vol.45, p.277

11. *Proceedings of the Philosophical Society of Glasgow*, 1896, Vol.27, p.156

12. Christopher Smith, 'Medical radiology: its practical application 1895-
     1914', in Checkland and Lamb, 1982, p.111

13. *NBDM*, 23 Mar. 1896

14. The story of Schaw Home is from the GRI Minute Books, 1893-9

15. *Glasgow Herald*, 18 May and 6 June 1901

16. The acrimonious debate is recalled in *Lister and the Lister Ward*, 1927,
     and in Patrick, 1940, p.30

17. *Committee of the Managers of the Glasgow Royal Infirmary and the Governors
     of St Mungo's College*, 1905

18. McVail, 1905. HB 14/6/69, Memorial of the Joint Committee of the
     Managers of the Glasgow Royal Infirmary and the Governors of St
     Mungo's College to the Secretary of State for Scotland, 23 Apr. 1906

19. *Glasgow Herald*, 1 and 2 Apr. 1910

20. *Annual Report of Glasgow and West of Scotland Association for Promoting the
     Return of Women to Local Boards*, 1899, 1900 and 1901

21. *Glasgow Herald*, 10 Nov. 1910, 28 Jan. 1911 and 10 May 1911

22. McGann, 1992

23. For examples, see HB14/1/89, Residents' Minute Book 1894-1900,
     1 Jan. 1903. There are several references to the matron's perceived hos-
     tility to the residents in entries for the years 1904-07, in HB 14/1/90

24. *Glasgow Herald*, 25 Jan. 1909

25. *Lister and the Lister Ward*, 1927, p.61

26. The Board's response to the National Insurance Act is recorded in the
     GRI Minute Books, 1909-13

27. James Bridie, *One Way of Living* (London, 1939), p.213

28. See the *Evening News*, 24 Aug. 1898, the *Evening Times* 7 Sept. 1898,
     and the columns of all Glasgow's newspapers for accounts of the trial
     and the subsequent controversy. Cuttings are pasted in HB14/1/88, the
     Residents' Minute Book, 1894-1900

29. HB14/1/88

30. *GMJ*, 1921, Vol.95, p.202

31. Bridie, *op.cit*, p.218

32. *Glasgow Herald*, 5 Oct. 1911

33. *Ibid*, 13 Dec. 1911

34. *GMJ*, 1914, Vol.81, p.437

35. G H Edington, *The Soul of the Voluntary Hospital, Glasgow* (Glasgow,
     1931). *Glasgow Herald*, 21 June 1909

36. *Glasgow Herald*, 4 Oct. 1917

CHAPTER 5

1.   Chalmers, 1930, pp.363, 374. Sir Alexander McGregor, *Public Health in
     Glasgow, 1905–46,(* Edinburgh, 1967), p.25

2. Chalmers, 1930, p.376

3. Charles Loch Mowat, *Britain Between the Wars, 1918–40*, (London, 1962), p.27

4. Gordon McLachlan (ed), *Improving the Common Weal: Aspects of Scottish Health Services, 1900-84* (Edinburgh, 1987), p.466

5. *Lister and the Lister Ward*, 1927

6. Unpublished manuscript of Sir David Cuthbertson's autobiography, held in Glasgow University Archives. Obituary in *The Times*, 21 Apr. 1989, p.16

7. McLachlan, 1987, pp.62, 225. *Glasgow Herald*, 8 Feb. 1926

8. McGregor, 1967, p.131

9. *Glasgow News*, 27 Mar. 1983

10. See Sir James Macfarlane's speech to the annual meeting of the Court of Contributors, 13 Feb. 1933

11. Virginia Berridge, 'Health and Medicine', in F M L Thompson, (ed), *The Cambridge Social History of Britain, 1750-1950* (Cambridge, 1990), p.208

12. Dow and Slater, 1990, pp.55 and 58

13. *GMJ*, 1922, Vol.118, p.409

14. *GMJ*, 1931, Vol.116, p.142

15. HB14/9/95ii, Supplementary Charter, 1932

16. Dow and Slater, 1990, p.89

17. *Glasgow Herald*, 29 May 1935

18. Dow and Slater, 1990, p.230

19. *Glasgow Herald*, 12 Nov. 1936, 1 Jan. 1937

20. McLachlan, 1987, p.84

21. *Glasgow Herald*, 16 Jan. 1942

22. *Ibid*, 10 Oct. 1941

23. *Ibid*, 4 Apr. and 15 June 1940

24. *Ibid*, 13 Mar. 1943

25. *Report of the Committee on Scottish Health Services*, 1936, Cmd 5204, p.232

26. *Social Insurance and Allied Services*, 1942, Cmd 6404

27. *The Scottish Hospital Survey - Western Region*, HMSO, 1946, p.42, states that 'at the time of our visit the staff of the hospital was overworked'

CHAPTERS 6, 7 AND 8 are based largely on the annual reports, minutes and related papers of the Glasgow Royal Infirmary Board of Management and its successors held in the GGHB Archive and listed in A G Tough, *Medical Archives of Glasgow and Paisley - A Guide to the Greater Glasgow Health Board Archive*, Wellcome Unit for the History of Medicine, University of Glasgow, 1993. The papers from 1984 were not at the time of writing in the GGHB Archive and had to be located with the help of the Royal's administrative staff in various stores. They have now mostly been transferred and requests for access should be addressed to the GGHB Archivist at the Archives, University of Glasgow, Glasgow G12 8QQ.

Appendices

APPENDIX 1 – CHAIRMEN AND SENIOR OFFICERS 1787-1948

	Chairman or Preses of Committee of subscribers to Glasgow Royal Infirmary			**Hon Treasurer**
1787	John Riddell, Lord Provost, and Dr Alex Stevenson		1787	
1788	John Campbell, Jun, Lord Provost		1788	Archibald Grahame *(Cashier of the Thistle Bank)*
1789	do.	do.	1789	do.
1790	James McDowall	do.	1790	do.
1791	do.	do.	1791	do.

	Chairman or Preses			**Hon Treasurer**
1791	James McDowall, Lord Provost		1791	Archibald Grahame
1792-3	Gilbert Hamilton	do.	1792-3	do.
1794-5	John Dunlop	do.	1794-5	do.
1796-7	James McDowall	do.	1796-7	do.
1798-9	Laurence Craigie	do.	1798-9	do.
1800-01	John Hamilton	do.	1800-01	do.
1802-3	Laurence Craigie	do.	1802-3	do.
1804-5	John Hamilton	do.	1804-5	do.
1806	James McKenzie	do.	1806	do.
1807	do.	do.	1807	Kirkman Finlay
1808	James Black	do.	1808	Archibald Wallace
1809	do.	do.	1809	Adam Crooks
1810	John Hamilton	do.	1810	do.
1811	do.	do.	1811	William Jamieson
1812-13	Kirkman Finlay	do.	1812-13	do.
1814-15	Henry Monteith	do.	1814-15	William Glen
1816-17	James Black	do.	1816-17	James Sym
1818	Henry Monteith	do.	1818	do.
1819	do.	do.	1819	William Dalglish
1820-21	John Thomas Alston	do.	1820-21	do.
1822-3	William Smith	do.	1822-3	do.
1824	Mungo Nutter Campbell	do.	1824	do.
1825	do.	do.	1825	John Alston
1826	William Hamilton	do.	1826	do.
1827	do.	do.	1827	Robert Aitken
1828	Alexander Garden	do.	1828	Dugald McFie

	Convener of House Committee			**Hon Treasurer**
1829	William McFie		1829	William McLean
1830	Charles Hutcheson		1830	Andrew Whyte

1831-9	James Lumsden	1831-9	James Lumsden
1840	Hugh Tennent	1840	John Bain
1841-2	do.	1841-2	James Lumsden
1843-9	James Leechman	1843-9	do.
1850-51	Robert Smith	1850-51	James Leechman
1852-3	do.	1852-3	Hugh Cogan
1854	William McLean, Jun	1854	do.
1855	David Smith	1855	do.
1856-65	do.	1856-65	John Jamieson
1866	William McEwen	1866	do.
1867	do.	1867	do.
1868	do.	1868	Peter Clouston
1869	do.	1869	do.
1870	do.	1870	do.
1871	do.	1871	do.
1872	do.	1872	do.
1873	do.	1873	do.
1874	do.	1874	do.

(Supplementary Charter granted 20 August 1875)

1875	William McEwen	1875	Peter Clouston
1876	do.	1876	do.
1877	do.	1877	do.
1878	do.	1878	do.
1879	do.	1879	John McClure
1880	do.	1880	do.
1881	do.	1881	do.
1882	do.	1882	do.
1883	do.	1883	do.
1884	do.	1884	do.
1885 *(Jan)*	do.	1885	do.
1885 *(Feb)*	Hugh Brown	1886 *(Apr)*	do.
1886	do.	1886 *(May)*	David McCowan
1887	do.	1887	do.
1888	do.	1888	do.
1889	do.	1889	do.
1890	do.	1890	do.
1891	do.	1891	do.
1892	do.	1892	do.
1893	do.	1893	do.
1894	do.	1894	do.
1895	do.	1895	do.
1896	do.	1896	do.
1897	do.	1897	do.

1898	do.	1898	do.
1899	do.	1899	do.
1900	do.	1900	do.
1901 *(Jan)* do.		1901	do.

(Supplementary Charter granted 3 May 1901)

1901 *(Feb)* James David Hedderwick			
1902	do.	1902	David McGowan
1903	do.	1903	do.
1904	do	1904	do.
1905	do. *(Reconstruction commenced)*	1905	do.
1906	do.	1906	do.
1907	do.	1907	do.
1908	do.	1908 *(Apr)*	do.
		1908 *(Apr)*	Timothy Warren
1909	do.	1909	do.
1910	do.	1910	do.

(Supplementary Charter granted 5 June 1911)

Chairman of Board

1911	James David Hedderwick	1911	Timothy Warren
1912	do.	1912	do.
1913	do.	1913	do.
1914 *(Aug)* do.		1914	do.
1914	James Macfarlane *(Reconstruction completed)*		
1915	do.	1915	Timothy Warren
1916	do.	1916	do.
1917	do.	1917	do.
1918	do.	1918	do.
1919	do.	1919	do.
1920	do.	1920	do.
1921	do.	1921	do.
1922	do.	1922	do.
1923	do.	1923	do.
1924	do.	1924	do.
1925	do.	1925	James MacKenzie
1926	do.	1926	do.
1927	do.	1927	do.
1928	do.	1928	do.
1929	do.	1929	do.
1930	do.	1930	do.
1931	do.	1931	D Bruce Warren

(Supplementary Charter granted 30 Mar 1932)

1932	James Macfarlane	1932	D Bruce Warren
1933	do.	1933	do.

1934	do	1934	do.
1935	do.	1935	do.
1936	do	1936	do.
1937	do.	1937	do.
1938	do.	1938	do.
1939*(Oct)* do.		1939	do.
1939*(Oct)* Charles Glen			
1940	do.	1940*(Dec)*	do.
1941	Sir Alexander T Taylor, KBE	1941*(Apr)* Moncrieff Mitchell	
1942	do.	1942	do.
1943	do.	1943	do.
1944	do.	1944	do.
1945	do.	1945	do.
1946	do	1946	do.
1947*(Apr)* William Cross, JP		1947*(Apr)* Walter Henderson	

APPENDIX 2 – PHYSICIANS 1795-1948

Dr Robert Cleghorn	1795-96,1798-89, 1801-02, 1805-06, 1809-10
Dr Thomas C Hope	1706
Dr Richard Millar	1796-97, 1799-1800, 1802-03, 1807-08, 1811-12, 1817-26
Dr Robert Freer	1797-98, 1800-01, 1803-04, 1811, 1813-15
Dr John Balmanno	1803-04, 1807-08, 1826-35
Dr John Nimmo	1809-10
Dr Robert Graham	1812, 1813, 1816-19
Dr Robert Watt	1814-16
Dr Thomas Thomson	1820-21
Dr William Couper	1820-21
Dr John Robertson	1822, 1823, 1826
Dr Thomas Brown	1824-28, 1837-39, 1845
Dr John Couper	1827
Dr A M McLauchlin	1828
Dr William Chalmers	1829
Dr John Spittal	1830
Dr Charles Badham	1831
Dr John Burns	1833-36
Dr Robert Perry, Sen	1834-37, 1841-44, 1846-48
Dr Robert Cowan	1836-38
Dr William Young	1837
Dr Andrew Anderson	1838-40
Dr William Davidson	1838-41
Dr William Weir	1839-42, 1844-58
Dr Charles Ritchie	1840-43, 1851-57, 1859-63
Dr Thomas Watson	1842-45, 1856-60
Dr William Thomson	1843-46, 1848-51
Dr John A Easton	1847-50, 1852-55, 1857-59
Dr Robert McGregor	1848-52, 1855
Dr Joseph Bell	1853-56, 1858-62
Dr Robert T Tannahill	1856-60
Dr James Fraser	1860-64
Dr R Scott Orr	1860-68, 1870-85
Dr (afterwards Sir) William Tennent Gairdner, KCB	1862-74
Dr William Leishman	1864-69
Dr Robert Perry, Jun	1864-87 Hon Consulting Physician 1912-17
Dr J D MacLaren	1868-84 Hon Consulting Physician 1915-27
Dr T McCall Anderson	1870-74

278

Dr Matthew Charteris	1874-83	
Dr A Wood Smith	1874-91	Hon Consulting Physician 1915-21
Dr Alex Robertson	1884-99	
Dr J Wallace Anderson,	1915-24	Hon Consulting Physician 1915-24
Dr Samson Gemmell	1888-92	
Dr (afterwards Sir) David C		
McVail	1890-91	Extra Physician
	1892-1906	Physician
	1912-17	Hon Consulting Physician
Dr John Dougall	1891-1905	
Dr G S Middleton	1802-1912	Hon Consulting Physician 1913-28
Dr J Lindsay Steven	1895-1906	
Dr T K Monro	1899-1913	
Dr James W Allan	1901-06	
Dr Walter K Hunter	1906-34	Hon Consulting Physician 1934-47
Dr John M Cowan	1906-30	Hon Consulting Physician 1930-47
Dr J B MacKenzie Anderson	1907-26	Hon Consulting Physician 1926-44
Dr Alex Morton *(Skin)*	1909-14	Hon Consulting Physician 1914-37
Dr William R Jack	1913-26	Hon Consulting Physician 1926-27
Dr John Henderson	1913-37	Hon Consulting Physician 1937-
Dr George McIntyre *(Skin)*	1914-22	
Dr John F Smith *(Skin)*	1922-	
Dr John Harrington	1926-45	Hon Consulting Physician 1945-
Dr J C Middleton	1926-43	Hon Consulting Physician 1943-
Dr A M Crawford	1930-	
Dr David Smith	1934-	
Dr J M Cruickshank	1937-	
Dr J W MacFarlane	1943-	
Professor L J Davis	1945-	

APPENDIX 3 – SURGEONS 1795-1948

Mr Charles Wilsone	1795-97, 1802, 1803
Mr William Couper	1795-7, 1799, 1800, 1803
Mr Archibald Young	1795-97
Mr James Towers	1795-6,. 1798-9, 1803, 1804
Mr Robert Cowan	1796-7, 1801-2, 1806-7
Mr John Burns	1797, 1798, 1808, 1809
Mr Alexander Dunlop	1798
Mr John Grieve	1798, 1799
Mr John McNish	1798, 1799
Mr William Dunlop	1800, 1801, 1804, 1805
Mr Thomas Brown	1800, 1801, 1805, 1809, 1810
Mr John McArthur	1801, 1802, 1806, 1810, 1813-15, 1818, 1819
Mr Archibald Millar	1802, 1803
Mr William Anderson	1805, 1807, 1811, 1816
Mr George McLeod	1806, 1807, 1811, 1812
Mr John Stenhouse	1806, 1807
Dr James Corkindale	1808, 1809, 1818, 1820, 1822
Mr J McDougall	1808, 1809
Mr Hugh Miller	1810, 1812, 1813, 1817
Dr Ben Watts King	1810, 1811, 1814-16
Mr John Scruton	1812
Mr James Watson	1812, 1813
Dr G C Monteath	1813-15, 1817, 1820, 1823, 1825
Mr John Towers	1814-16
Mr G S Pattison	1816, 1817
Dr Harry Rainy	1817, 1821
Dr John Robertson	1818, 1820
Dr William Cumin	1818, 1819, 1821, 1822
Dr Robert Perry, Sen	1820, 1830, 1831
Dr William R Gibb	1821, 1824-26
Dr William Young	1821, 1822, 1826, 1827
Dr A D Anderson	1822, 1823, 1827
Dr John Couper	1823-25, 1828, 1829
Mr Robert Cowan	1824-26, 1829, 1830
Dr John MacFarlane	1826-7, 1831-2, 1835-6
Dr A McLauchlan	1827, 1828
Dr William Auchincloss	1828, 1829, 1832, 1833
Dr William Weir	1829, 1830, 1833, 1834
Dr Moses S Buchanan	1830, 1831, 1834, 1835, 1841-44, 1848-51
Mr Alexander Angus	1831, 1832

Mr John Stirling	1832–1833
Dr John M Pagan	1833, 1834, 1836–38
Dr James A Laurie	1834, 1835, 1837–41, 1844–47, 1849–53
Dr Andrew Buchanan	1835, 1836, 1838, 1843, 1845, 1848, 1851, 1854, 1856, 1862, Hon.Con.Surg. 1881–82
Dr William Davidson	1836
Dr John Spittal	1837–40
Mr William Lyon	1840–43, 1847–49, 1855–66
Dr Alex John Hannay	1844–46
Dr J G Fleming	1846–49, 1853–56
Mr George Watt	1846, 1848–52, 1856–59
Dr Robert Hunter	1852–55
Dr Robert T Corbett	1854–58
Dr Ebenezer Watson	1856–60, 1866–85
Dr James Morton	1859–67, 1870–84
Dr George Buchanan	1860–68, 1870–74
Mr (afterwards Lord) Lister	1861–69
Dr Donald Dewar	1867–76
Dr (afterwards Sir) George H B MacLeod	1869–74
Dr (afterwards Sir) Hector C Cameron	1874–81, Hon.Con.Surg. 1927–28
Dr James Dunlop	1874–92
Dr (afterwards Sir) William Macewen	1877–92
Dr James Stirton *(Diseases of Women)*	1879–96, Hon.Con.Surg. 1915–16
Dr Henry E Clark	1882–1906
Dr David Newman *(Throat)*	1886–92; Surgeon 1892–1914; Hon.Con.Surg. 1914–24; Acting Surgeon 1916, 1917
Dr D N Knox	1884–1906, Hon.Con.Surg. 1912–26
Dr William James Fleming	1886–95
Dr James Kerr Love *(Ear)*	1891–1919; Hon.Con.Surg. 1919–42
Dr John Barlow	1892–1913, Hon.Con.Surg. 1913–43
Dr James A Adams	1892–1919, Hon.Con.Surg. 1919–30
Dr John Macintyre *(Throat and Nose)*	1892–1919, Hon.Con.Surg. 1919–28
Dr Robert Fullerton	1893–1915, Hon.Con.Surg.*(Throat and Nose)* 1915–37
Dr Quintin McLennan	1895–1910, Hon.Con.Surg. 1915–24
Mr J Hogarth Pringle	1896–1923, Hon.Con.Surg. 1923–41
Dr J K Kelly *(Diseases of Women)*	1896–1907

Dr A Maitland Ramsay	1897-1920, Hon.Con.Surg. 1920-46
Mr William Taylor	Dental Surgeon 1905-19, Hon.Con.Dental Surg. 1919-37
Mr H Rutherford	1906-1921, Hon.Con.Surg. 1921-29
Mr Peter Paterson	1906-35, Hon.Con.Surg. 1935-
Dr G Balfour Marshall	1908-23, Hon.Con.Surg. *(Diseases of Women)* 1923-28
Dr Robert Kennedy	1911-24
Dr J M Munro Kerr	1911-27
Dr A N McGregor	1911-36, Hon.Con.Surg. 1926-37
Mr Thomas Kay	1914-28, Hon.Con.Surg. 1914-35
Dr David Watson *(Venereal Diseases)*	1914-25
Dr John Rowan *(Eye)*	1916-24, Hon.Con.Surg. 1927-
Dr James Adam	1919-22, Hon.Con.Surg. *(Ear, Nose and Throat)* 1922-40
Dr James Harper *(Ear, Nose and Throat)*	1919-46, Hon.Con.Surg. 1946-
Mr W Robert Taylor *(Teeth)*	1919-46, Hon.Con.Surg. 1946-
Dr W Wright Thomson *(Eye)*	1920-35, Hon.Con.Surg. 1935-43
Dr John Patrick	1921-34, Hon.Con.Surg. 1934-44
Dr John A C Macewen	1923-38, Hon.Con.Surg. 1938-44
Dr Milne McIntyre	1924-41, Hon.Con.Surg. 1941-
Dr T S Barrie *(Eye)*	1924-39, Hon.Con.Surg. 1939-
Dr A Garrow *(Eye)*	1924-39, Hon.Con.Surg. 1939-
Mr Donald Duff	1926-38, Hon.Con.Surg. 1938-45
Dr James Hendry	1927-45
Mr James Taylor	1928-34
Mr J A G Burton	1934-
Mr John Dunbar	1934-
Mr George C Swanson	1935
Dr James M Tennent *(Eye)*	1935-
Mr Arthur H Jacobs	1936
Mr George H Stevenson	1938
Mr Alfred M Clark	1938
Dr Janet F Steel *(Eye)*	1939
Dr W J B Riddell *(Eye)*	1939-41, 1941-
Mr G T Mowat	1941-
Mr I S McGregor *(Eye)*	1941-47
Mr J Patrick (Ortho)	1940
Miss A M Hunter *(Gyn)*	1946
Mr D F Anderson *(Gyn)*	1946

Mr S Young
 (Ear Nose and Throat)   1946
Mr T Walters *(Dental)*   1946

INDEX

285